Plate Tectonics and Hydrocarbon Accumulation

William R. Dickinson
Stanford University

Hunter Yarborough
Global Exploration Analysts

Acknowledgements

The AAPG Continuing Education Course Note Series
is an author-prepared publication of the
AAPG Department of Education.

Extra copies of this, and all other books in the AAPG
Education Course Note Series, are available from:

AAPG Bookstore
P.O. Box 979
Tulsa, Oklahoma 74101

Published, November 1976
Fourth Printing, May 1982
ISBN: 0-89181-150-8

PLATE TECTONIC EVOLUTION

OF SEDIMENTARY BASINS

by

William R. Dickinson

Stanford University

PLATE TECTONIC EVOLUTION OF SEDIMENTARY BASINS

by

William R. Dickinson, Geology Department
Stanford University, Stanford, California 94305

ABSTRACT

The vertical tectonics inherent in the scheme of lateral motions of plates of lithosphere affords a coherent logic for the analysis of sedimentary basins. Subsidence may stem from crustal attenuation, thermotectonics, flexure of lithosphere, or combinations of these influences in space or time. Key facets of basin evolution include geometric configuration, the nature of the stratigraphic fill, the types of structural features, and the location of fluid hydrocarbons in space and time. Critical attributes favorable to hydrocarbon occurrence include the presence of organic-rich source beds, a history of thermal flux appropriate for thermal maturation, effective migration paths to allow concentration, and adequate reservoir capacity within suitable traps.

Both divergent and convergent plate motions embody vertical tectonics within the zone of plate interaction, but pure transforms do not. At divergent plate junctures, which are associated with the generation of new oceanic lithosphere, crustal attenuation causes eventual subsidence that is delayed by thermotectonic effects but may later be enhanced by plate flexure under sedimentary loading that forces isostatic adjustment. At convergent plate junctures, which are associated with the consumption of old oceanic lithosphere, crustal thickening causes uplift of subduction complexes and of arc or collision orogens, but plate flexure associated with plate subduction and with tectonic or sedimentary loading induces subsidence in basins that lie along the flanks of orogenic belts. Most sedimentary basins can thus be grouped generally into those in rifted settings and those in orogenic settings. A given basin may occupy several settings of either kind sequentially in time, and gradational examples also occur.

Basins in rifted settings include (1) infracratonic basins and (2) marginal aulacogens where continental separation is incomplete; (3) protoceanic rifts where the initial emplacement of fresh oceanic crust occurs; (4) miogeoclinal prisms of terrace, slope, and rise assemblages that mask rifted continental margins and (5) continental embankments where sedimentary progradation of the continental edge is important; (6) nascent ocean basins in which expansion by accretion of new lithosphere at midoceanic rise crests is dominant; (7) transtensional basins along complex transform systems where pull-apart or fault-wedge features occur; and (8) interarc basins formed as marginal seas behind intra-oceanic arc-trench systems from which remnant arc structures have been calved.

Basins in orogenic settings include (9) oceanic trenches where plate consumption occurs, (10) slope basins formed above accretionary subduction complexes, and (11) forearc basins in the arc-trench gap related to subduction zones; pericratonic basins of (12) peripheral forelands adjacent to collision orogens, (13) retroarc forelands adjacent to arc orogens, and (14) broken forelands where differential basement deformation is significant; (15) transpressional basins along complex transform systems where wrench or fault-warp features occur; and (16) remnant ocean basins in which shrinkage by consumption of old lithosphere at bounding arc-trench systems is dominant.

Useful for comparative basin analysis are plots of the following parameters against time: paleolatitude, subsidence rate (maximal or volumetric), net cumulative subsidence (maximal or volumetric), heat flux, geothermal gradient, and temperature at key source horixons.

INTRODUCTION

These short-course notes are based on the proposition that plate tectonics affords a coherent logic for the analysis of basin evolution. The line of thought runs as follows:

(a) The development of a sedimentary basin, in the sense of an accumulated prism of strata, requires subsidence of the basin floor, or uplift of confining basin margins.

(b) Although the formal postulates of plate tectonic theory focus especially on the lateral motions of the plates, vertical motions of magnitudes sufficient to form sedimentary basins are equally inherent in the scheme. Plate interactions also induce the uplift of mountainous belts from which most clastic sediment is derived.

(c) Therefore, valuable insights into overall processes of basin evolution can be gained from a general consideration of various plate tectonic settings.

Of course, each individual basin has its own unique history that is dependent upon a particular sequence and combination of plate interactions and depositional conditions. The emphasis here is not upon specific histories of this kind, but rather upon general insights that can be perceived through webs of local detail.

I think of these notes, therefore, as an aid to inquiry by the reader, rather than as an exhaustive catalogue of basin types. I have prepared them in an informal style, without referencing each thought or suggestion in the formal manner. The attached bibliography is a guide to further inquiry.

In the past few years, many besides myself have taken a turn at trying to classify sedimentary basins within a plate tectonic framework. I have read all the pertinent papers and heard all the relevant talks that I could. Although I make no attempt here to follow any scheme other than the one that comes most forcefully to my own mind, the insights I have gained from the work of others are legion. In particular, I gratefully acknowledge the opportunity to peruse two unpublished manuscripts by A. W. Bally and L. L. Sloss, which I am unable to list in the bibliography. I owe many of my ideas about subduction systems and foreland systems to the fruits of extended discussions with Peter Coney and Warren Hamilton over the years. I have also been the beneficiary of many rambling discussions about the tectonic setting of sedimentary basins with Clark Burchfiel, Greg Davis, Ray Fletcher, Steve Graham, Ray Ingersoll, Dan Karig, Casey Moore, Don Seely, Eli Silver, and George Viele.

BASIN EVOLUTION

The evolution of a sedimentary basin has four interdependent facets of prime interest to petroleum geology:

1. The geometric shape and size of the basin as a whole is constrained by the evolving configuration of the bounding basement rocks that form the floor and flanks of the basin. The pattern and timing of changes in the gross shape of the basin largely control regional tilts of strata and other structural features that strongly influence migration and entrapment of fluids within the basin. In general, basin configurations directly reflect tectonic setting.

2. The nature of the stratigraphic fill of the basin is the product of the depositional systems active during basin evolution. The nature of these depositional systems is partly a resultant of the interplay between rates of subsidence and rates of sedimentation that prevail at various times during basin evolution. At one extreme, initial subsidence to form a deep hole is followed by filling that induces further isostatic subsidence under the sediment load. At the other extreme, sedimentation keeps pace with subsidence and no empty hole is ever present. Depositional systems are also influenced strongly by paleographic factors, including paleolatitude (fig. 1).

3. The types of structures that develop as folds and faults within the basin are conditioned partly by its tectonic evolution and partly by its sedimentary evolution. Extensional deformation commonly produces normal faults and tilted blocks, whereas contractional deformation commonly produces folds and thrust faults. On the other hand, the presence or absence of diapiric folds and growth faults is largely a function of the properties of the sedimentary fill.

4. The amount, nature, and location of fluid hydrocarbons within the basin is governed in part by the three previous facets of basin evolution, but perhaps most critically by the thermal history of the basin (fig. 2). Basins in different plate tectonic settings may be exposed to markedly different heat fluxes. Moreover, the same basin may experience different heat fluxes at different times during its evolution.

The diversity of styles of basin evolution that can be observed in the geologic record stems in good part from the variety of patterns through time followed by these interrelated processes of subsidence, sedimentation, structuring, and heating. In examining the plate tectonic setting of basins, we need to focus on the implications of the settings considered for each of these facets of basin evolution. The manner in which the different aspects of evolution may be combined in different instances is the key insight to seek.

HYDROCARBON OCCURRENCE

Stated most simply, the occurrence of fluid hydrocarbons depends upon four critical attributes of a sedimentary basin:

1. As an essential requirement, there must be organic-rich source beds within the sedimentary sequence. Source beds are generally fine-grained sediment deposited in black-bottom areas where clastic dilution of organic constituents is low, winnowing of fines that include organic debris is minor, and oxidation by aerobic decay during early diagenesis is limited. Rapid burial of the organic debris enhances its chances

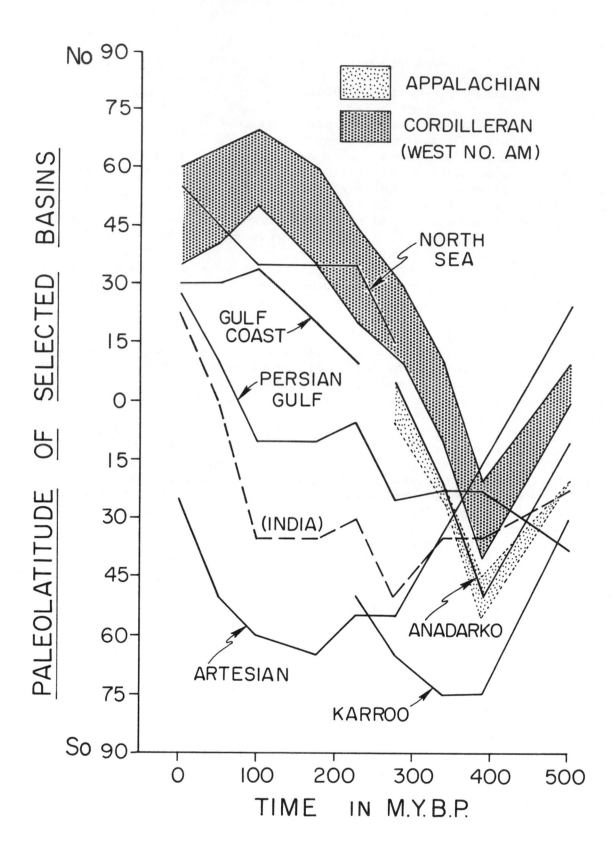

Figure 1. Approximate paleolatitudes of selected sedimentary basins through Phanerozoic time. Data from Briden, J.C., G.E. Drewry, and A.G. Smith, 1974, Phanerozoic equal-area world maps: Jour. Geology, v. 82, p. 555-574.

for preservation. Favorable sites of deposition include oxygen-minimum zones on open marine slopes, low-oxygen zones within silled marine basins, and saline non-marine or marginal-marine environments. Basins whose sedimentary fill includes widespread facies of these kinds presumably harbor the largest sources of potential hydrocarbons.

2. For generation of fluid hydrocarbons, there must be appropriate heat for thermal maturation of liquid hydrocarbons or thermal gas. Relations of time and temperature required to achieve a given degree of maturation are complex, but the guiding principles are clear. Ideally, source beds should undergo maturation during a time span in the evolution of the basin when migration of fluid hydrocarbons into traps is feasible without escape to the surface. As either underheating or overheating can spoil potential sources for liquid hydrocarbons, special attention is drawn to time-dependent variations in the heat flux experienced by a basin in relation to times of subsidence, sedimentation and structuring.

3. For concentration of fluid hydrocarbons, there must be permeable migration paths to gather any hydrocarbons produced. The most effective carriers are tilted conduit beds of well-sorted sandy strata contained beneath impermeable sealing beds of finer grained rock. Possibilities for concentration are thus enhanced where porous stratal connections are continuous laterally from source beds to reservoir beds and have an unbroken regional dip. Satisfaction of these conditions for conduit beds is more critical than simple distance alone for the migration of fluid hydrocarbons.

4. For containment of fluid hydrocarbons, there must be porous reservoir beds confined within some trapping configuration by impermeable capping beds. Reservoir beds are typically well-sorted sandy strata, whether clastic or carbonate. Favorable sites of deposition are most abundant in shallow-marine or marginal-marine environments near basin margins and within proximal turbidite assemblages along basin margins. Traps may be formed either by stratigraphic enclosure or by structural features of tectonic or sedimentary origin.

Analysis of the plate tectonics of sedimentary basins should thus seek to identify styles of basin evolution and times during basin evolution that embody favorable combinations of these four critical attributes for hydrocarbon occurrence (fig. 3). Conceivably, plate tectonics may point the way toward a comprehensive theory of hydrocarbon genesis. Understanding plate interactions fully implies understanding of the causes of subsidence, the sequencing of depositional events, the development of structural features, and the timing of thermal flux. Perhaps with adequate analysis we can now specify the most favorable combinations of subsidence, sedimentation, and deformation required to create desirable juxtapositions of sources, migration paths, and reservoirs upon which the requisite thermal flux is superimposed. If so, we can then seek these conditions in the geologic record of sedimentary basins.

PLATE INTERACTIONS

The plates of plate tectonics are spherical caps, or arcuate slabs, of the earth's lithosphere or tectosphere, which is thicker than the crust as defined by M and extends down to the so-called low-velocity zone of the upper mantle. To a surprising degree, the plates are rigid blocks. Although some internal deformation does occur, it is much less significant in terms of magnitude or rate than the relative motions of the plates. The plates apparently rest upon a mobile layer called the asthenosphere within

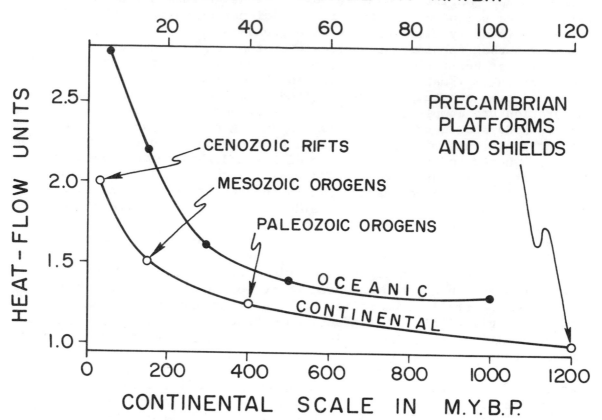

Figure 2. General logarithmic decay of heat flux. Data after Sclater, J.G. and J. Francheteau (Geophys. Jour. Roy. Astro. Soc., v. 20, p. 509-542, 1970).

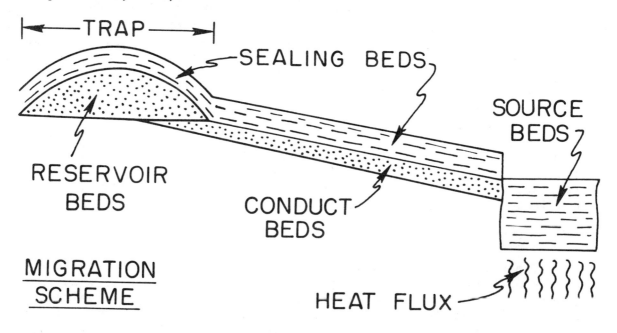

Figure 3. Idealized scheme for hydrocarbon generation, migration, and accumulation.

which the geothermal gradient is probably adiabatic. The geothermal gradient across the plates is controlled mainly by conductivity between the basal temperature, that of the asthenosphere, and the surficial temperature, that of the atmosphere and hydrosphere. In general, plate boundaries do not coincide with boundaries between continental blocks and oceanic basins. Both types of crustal elements can be joined together as parts of the same plate.

From a kinematic standpoint, there are three kinds of plate junctures (fig. 4), and these are analogous to the three classes of faults as defined by relative displacements. At divergent plate junctures, analogous to normal faults, separation of two plates occurs. At convergent plate junctures, analogous to thrust faults, one plate descends at an angle beneath the other, and dives down into the mantle. At transform plate junctures, analogous to strike-slip faults, one plate slides laterally past the other.

Incipient divergent junctures involve rupture of intact old lithosphere. Where an incipient rift crosses a continental block, intracontinental rifting occurs. If arrested at an early stage, an incipient rift may thus form a complex graben within a continental block. If allowed to proceed, the incipient rift can develop into a new oceanic basin. The oceanic lithosphere with its thin crust of mafic igneous rocks is then constructed by combined processes of magmatism from upwelling asthenosphere and chilling of depleted asthenosphere along midoceanic rise crests. The new lithosphere thus formed is emplaced incrementally between the receding pair of separating continental blocks, and is accreted to both receding plate edges. Continental separation of this kind is normally achieved by the longitudinal extension of branches of the world midoceanic rift system, rather than by random initiation of a wholly new divergent plate juncture.

Convergent plate junctures are sites of plate consumption where oceanic lithosphere formed previously at a divergent plate juncture descends into the mantle. Just as a midoceanic rise crest is the morphologic signature of a fully developed divergent plate juncture, an arc-trench system is the morphologic signature of a fully developed convergent plate juncture. The trench marks the subduction zone where oceanic lithosphere is consumed. The parallel magmatic arc, which may stand upon either oceanic or continental crustal elements, marks the line along the surface above the place where descent of lithosphere into the mantle triggers magmatism of orogenic type. Owing to the buoyancy of continental crust, continental lithosphere cannot descend into the mantle. The arrival of a continental block at a subduction zone instead causes a crustal collision between it and the arc structure. Convergent plate junctures are thus the sites of arc orogens where oceanic lithosphere may be continuously consumed or collision orgens where plate consumption is arrested by crustal collision.

Continental crust is probably built anew in two ways at convergent plate junctures: (a) by the tectonic stacking of crustal elements in subduction zones where sedimentary layers are scraped off the top of descending slabs of oceanic lithosphere, and (b) by the magmatic emplacement of igneous crustal elements added as plutons and volcanogenic piles to the arc structures associated with trenches. Some ancient continental crust may also be inherited from unfamiliar processes operative deep in the Precambrian. In any case, continental crust and lithosphere

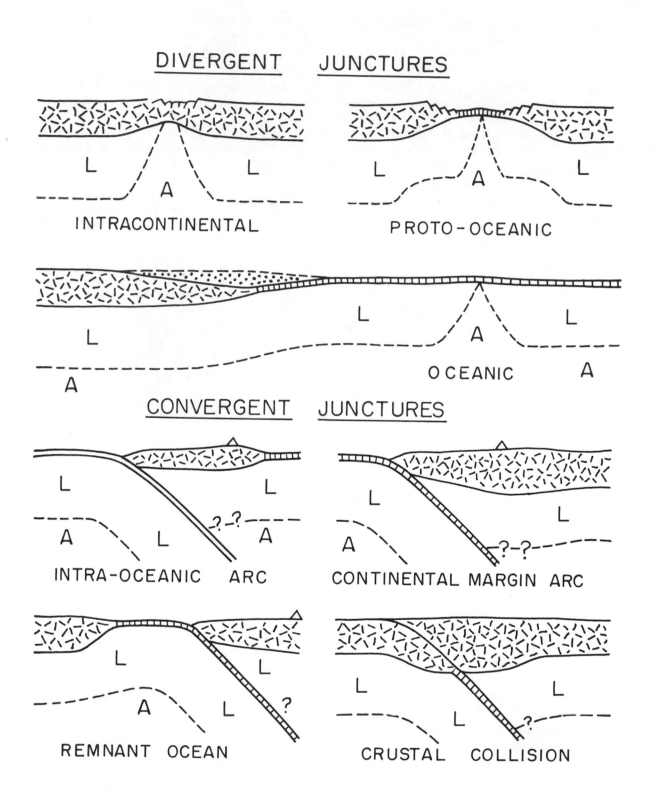

Figure 4. Principal kinds of plate interactions at divergent (above) and convergent (below) plate junctures showing relations of lithosphere (L) and asthenosphere (A) as well as crust (ornamented).

apparently conserved while oceanic crust and lithosphere are continually recycled.

A grand scheme of crustal development is thus involved in the functioning of divergent and convergent plate junctures. Conceptually, rupture of continent at incipient rift leads to genesis of nascent ocean at midoceanic rise; consumption of such ocean at arc-trench system leads first to building of new continent in arc orogen, and finally to rewelding of continents together at collision orogen as intervening ocean is destroyed.

By contrast, transform plate junctures are neutral with respect to the mass balance of crust and lithosphere. Ideally, plates slide laterally past one another without accretion or consumption. However, just as oblique-slip faults occur, hybrid plate boundaries also occur in some areas. Where some component of extensional or contractional motion occurs along a transform, the terms *transtension* and *transpression* are convenient to describe the interaction.

VERTICAL TECTONICS

All plate interactions that involve construction of new lithosphere or consumption of old lithosphere as a result of large horizontal motions of plates also involve significant vertical motions of lithosphere. Vertical tectonics of the general sort needed to explain the origin of sedimentary basins are thus inherent in the basic concepts of plate tectonics. There are three root causes of subsidence or uplift as a result of plate interactions: changes in crustal thickness, thermal expansion or contraction of lithosphere, and broad flexure of plates of lithosphere in response to local tectonic or sedimentary loading.

Crustal Thickness (fig. 5).

The contrasting elevations of the surfaces of the continental blocks and the ocean floors are well known. The rupture of a continental block and subsequent development of a new oceanic basin along a divergent plate juncture thus forms a fresh receptacle for sediment between the two separating continental fragments. The great contrasts in thickness and composition between continental and standard oceanic crust also imply that belts of transitional crust with some intermediate thickness will form along the edges of rifted continental blocks. The region of the continent-ocean interface along rifted continental margins will thus stand, in the absence of sedimentation, at elevations intermediate between those of continental blocks and ocean floors.

The transitional crust that bridges between the two domains may have either of two characters, depending on details of the process of continental separation. On the one hand, it may be attenuated continental crust, with the same composition but with lesser net thickness than continental basement. On the other hand, it may be composed of oceanic mafic igneous rocks mixed as flows, dikes, and sills with sediments of continental derivation. Complex mixtures of the quasicontinental and quasioceanic types of transitional crust also seem likely to form from calving of microcontinental fragments off the edges of rifted continental margins.

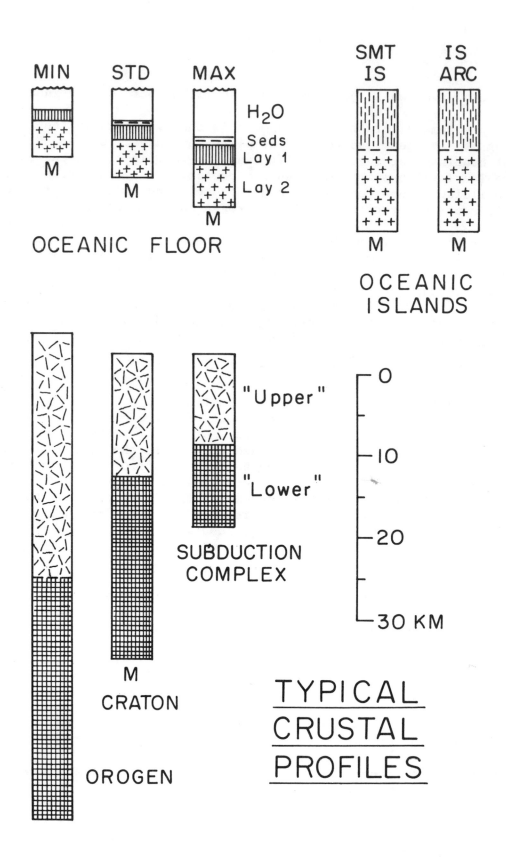

Figure 5. Representative crustal profiles in oceanic (above) and continental (below) regions.

The construction of new lithosphere at divergent plate junctures thus forms crustal profiles that are thinner than those present locally before, and thereby induces wholesale subsidence in belts along continental margins. On the other hand, processes related to plate consumption at arc-trench systems along convergent plate junctures construct crustal profiles that are thicker than those present locally before, and thereby induce uplift within arc and collision orogens. Such uplifts commonly form new sediment sources and locally form the sills or flanks of adjacent residual sedimentary basins.

The processes that form crust of anomalous thickness at convergent plate junctures may serve to thicken profiles that were previously either oceanic or continental. Thickening processes include (a) the addition of tectonic increments of oceanic elements to growing subduction complexes, (b) the addition of magmatic increments to either oceanic or continental profiles of magmatic arcs, which occur in both intra-oceanic and continental-margin settings, and (c) the tectonic overlapping or telescoping of continental elements along the sture belts of collision orogens. Where the resulting thickness of paraoceanic or paracontinental crust initially exceeds that of normal continental crust, isostatic uplift and accompanying erosion will tend to reduce it to normal values with the passage of time.

Thermal Effects (fig. 6)

Thermotectonic uplift and erosion are displayed most clearly in oceanic basins where new lithosphere is formed. Near midoceanic rise crests, the lithosphere is thin, heat flux is high, the geothermal gradient near the surface is steep, and water depths are comparatively shallow. As lithosphere passes farther away from the rises, it first thickens rapidly and then contracts slowly as it cools. As several have noted, the net effect at the surface is gradual subsidence of the ocean floor at a rate that is remarkably regular on a logarithmic time scale. A simple linear equation can be written relating depth of water to the square root of the age of the igneous oceanic substratum. The equation holds to an age between 75 and 100 million years, beyond which a steady-state heat flux and stable geothermal gradient are apparently attained.

Where continental separations occur at divergent plate junctures, analogous thermotectonic uplift and subsidence can be expected to occur. Uplifts along incipient and juvenile rifts occur prior to and during separation events when the effects of high local heat flux can offset the opposing effects of crustal thinning. Erosional truncation of uplifted domes and arches at this time may contribute to crustal thinning during rifting. Following completion of rift separation, subsidence occurs as the distance between midoceanic rise crest and rifted continental margin increases. Although the isostatic subsidence of transitional crust in response to crustal thinning may cause an appropriate amount of rapid subsidence, further slow subsidence in response to thermal decay of previously heated lithosphere will be prolonged for perhaps 100 million years if the behavior in oceanic regions affords a proper analogy.

The high heat flux in magmatic arcs can also be expected to induce thermotectonic uplift of parts of orogenic belts. Behavior of this kind is not well documented and full understanding will not come easily, for the governing conditions are much more complex. Also clearly related in some manner to the arc heat flux are the marginal seas in which some form

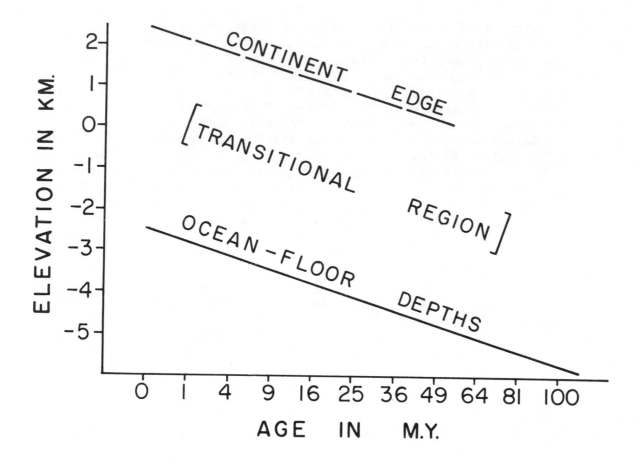

Figure 6. Subsidence of rifted lithosphere; plot of oceanic depths vs. square root of age after A.M. Tréhu (Earth and Planetary Science Letters, v. 27, p. 287-304, 1975).

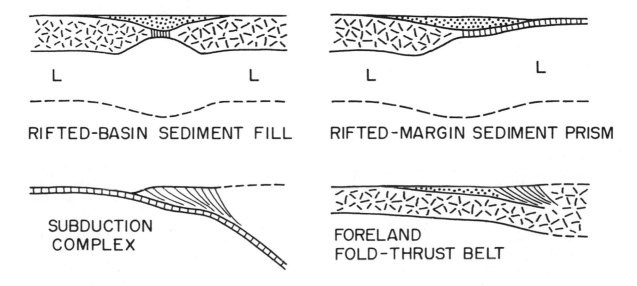

RIFTED-BASIN SEDIMENT FILL   RIFTED-MARGIN SEDIMENT PRISM

SUBDUCTION
COMPLEX

FORELAND
FOLD-THRUST BELT

Figure 7. Schematic diagrams depicting concept of broad flexure of lithosphere downward under local sedimentary (above) or tectonic (below) loads.

of spreading occurs. Although this type of oceanic basin develops in the main behind magmatic arcs, the earliest step in its evolution is the splitting of an arc structure along a rift belt in a manner that can be viewed as a special case of crustal separation.

Flexural Bending (fig. 7)

The presence of hot and relatively weak asthenosphere beneath the plates of cooler and stronger lithosphere makes the flexure of lithosphere an important phenomenon. The mobile asthenosphere is readily able to mold its upper surface to the shape adopted by the base of the lithosphere. Because of broad flexures of the lithosphere, deformations associated with vertical tectonics can exert effects for large lateral distances.

The most apparent loci of bending of slabs of lithosphere are the flexures where consumed plates turn downward at an angle to begin their descent into the mantle. The great depths of oceanic trenches, whose floors stand well below the ordinary level of the open ocean floor, are not reached by crustal thinning or by thermal decay, but as the result of plate flexure. Crustal profiles and heat flow in trenches are similar to those of the ocean floors except for the influence of ponded trench sediment.

Other important flexures of plates are caused by the imposition of local loads that induce broad downbowing as a means to balance the load. Classic examples are the annular isostatic moats that surround some volcanic islands and their archipelagic aprons of sediment far out in the oceans. More significant cases of local loads are the vast sediment prisms that are dumped into the edges of oceanic basins as continental rises along rifted continental margins. As this sediment displaces water, its load can induce isostatic subsidence beyond that resulting from crustal thinning and thermotectonics. By flexuring rather than failing through local fracture, the lithosphere is able to deform into a broad regional downwarp. Not only does the basement beneath the continental rise subside, but the edge of the nearby continental block may also tilt downward as well.

Tectonic loads formed by the structural stacking of thrust sheets or nappes can induce similar downwarps. Wherever deformation involves décollement that peels cover rocks off basement and mounds them into a telescoped welt, the resulting load can depress the underthrust slab of lithosphere over broad areas beyond the structurally disturbed belt. Settings where this mechanism can operate include subduction complexes that pile up above moving slabs of oceanic lithosphere, and fold-thrust belts that pile up above foreland slabs of continental lithosphere.

BASIN TYPES

Consideration of the causes of subsidence indicates that sedimentary basins can occur in two general kinds of geodynamic settings:
1. Rifted settings where divergent plate motions and extensional structures are dominant; subsidence occurs initially in response to attenuational thinning of crust, is later enhanced by thermal decay as time passes, and may be augmented eventually by flexure in response to sedimentary loading.

TERMINATION BASIN : - a zone of minor structures at the end of a fault

ROTATED BLOCK :
BASIN - converging faults in major transpressional areas.
- blocks rotate c̄ some vertical and horizontal component.

Table 1: Types of Rifted Settings

EXTENTIONAL Plate motions and crustal Rifting

-incomplete rupture of cont. blocks along incipient divergent plate junctures.

INFRACRATONIC BASIN	Intracontinental rift basin floored by attenuated continental basement
MARGINAL AULACOGEN	Rift trough elongate inward toward continental interior from re-entrant in adjacent continental margin

-complete rupture of continental blocks along divergent plate junctures.
-produces true oceanic crust.

PROTOCEANIC RIFT	Incipient oceanic basin flanked by uplifts along nearby rifted continental margins
MIOGEOCLINAL PRISM	Continental terrace, slope, and rise association developed along continent-ocean interface
CONTINENTAL EMBANKMENT	Progradational sediment pile constructed off the edge of a rifted continental margin
NASCENT OCEAN	Growing oceanic basin with a midoceanic rise system building new lithosphere

-rifting occurs in association with transform or convergent plate junctures.

TRANSTENSIONAL BASIN	Local pull-apart and fault-wedge features along a complex transform system
INTERARC BASIN	Oceanic basin formed by backarc spreading behind a migratory intra-oceanic island arc

Table 2: Types of Orogenic Settings

Contractional Plate motions + orogenic Deformation.

-related to development of subduction complexes along the trench flank of arc orogens.

OCEANIC TRENCH	Deep trough formed by plate descent at a subduction zone related to plate consumption
SLOPE BASIN	Local structural depression developed between trench axis and trench slope break
FOREARC BASIN	Basin located within arc-trench gap between trench slope break and magmatic or volcanic front

-formed in pericratonic foreland settings adjacent to the deforming flanks of orogenic belts.

PERIPHERAL BASIN	Foreland basin adjacent to fold-thrust belt associated with suture belt of collision orogen
RETROARC BASIN	Foreland basin adjacent to fold-thrust belt associated with infrastructure of arc orogen
BROKEN FORELAND	Local structural depressions isolated by basement deformation within orogenic foreland region

-contractional effects central basinal evolution outside arc or collision orogens.

TRANSPRESSIONAL BASIN	Local wrench and fault-warp features along a complex transform system
REMNANT OCEAN	Shrinking oceanic basin undergoing plate consumption along flanking arc-trench systems

2.   Orogenic settings where convergent plate motions and contractional structures are dominant; subsidence occurs initially by plate flexure related either to plate consumption or to local tectonic thickening of crustal profiles, may also be augmented by sedimentary loading, and is subject to influence by more varied thermotectonic effects.

Grouping sedimentary basins into two such gross categories represents a deliberate attempt to seek the broadest possible common ground and masks a great deal of variability. My purpose in doing so is to focus attention on certain key themes of basin evolution. Any grouping of sedimentary basins risks the unwarranted assumption that the different types are wholly distinct entities in space as well as in time. In truth, however, the same piece of lithosphere may at one time be located in a rifted setting and at a later time in an orogenic setting, or vice versa. Thus, different kinds of sedimentary basins may be superimposed, one atop the other. To use a better emphasis, individual sedimentary basins may be and commonly are composite basins in terms of plate tectonic setting. The pace of plate interactions is rapid in geologic terms and the nature of the interactions that affect the evolution of a given basin may change several times during its life.

Rifted Settings (Table 1)

Basins whose tectonic evolution is dominated by extensional plate motions and crustal rifting include three idealized subgroups (gradational examples also exist):

A.   Basins where rupture of continental blocks along incipient divergent plate junctures is incomplete; these include two related types:

(1)   Infracratonic basins where clearcut structural connections to ocean basins are doubtful; the substratum is attenuated transitional crust but is not truly oceanic in nature.

(2)   Marginal aulacogens formed at re-entrants in the trends of continental margins as elongate or wedge-shaped gashes floored by oceanic or transitional crust; the aulacogen represents the failed arm of a triple junction.

B.   Basins where rupture of continental blocks is complete along divergent plate junctures, hence continental separation is achieved and true oceanic crust is formed in the intervening area; these include four types which can be formed in sequence by the operation of the same plate juncture:

(3)   Protoceanic rifts where a narrow belt of initially hot oceanic lithosphere forms between two continental fragments; sedimentation across the rift can still be influenced by both flanking continental blocks.

(4)   Miogeoclinal prisms deposited along rifted continental margins beside open oceanic basins; these include continental terrace deposits along the edge of the continental block and continental rise deposits along the edge of the oceanic basin with the starved continental slope between.

(5)   Continental embankments where sedimentary accretion to the edge of a rifted continental margin has prograded the continental slope out into the adjacent oceanic basin; as the toe of the embankment advances, the slope break can reach a point that was initially within the oceanic basin.

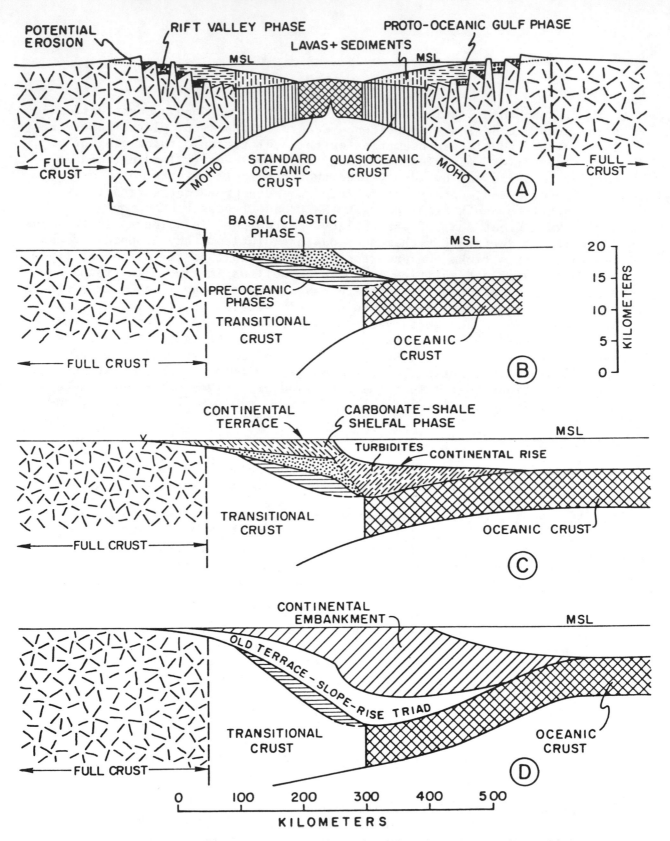

Figure 8. Schematic diagrams (vertical exaggeration 10X) to illustrate general evolution of rifted-margin prism along rifted continental margin: (A) incipient oceanic stage showing pre-oceanic depositional phases; (B) end of narrow-ocean stage when thermal subsidence is complete; (C) continental terrace-slope-rise configuration during open ocean stage; (D) prograding continental embankment at a later state of growth not reached unless sediment delivery is ultimately voluminous enough.

(6)   Nascent oceanic basins where gradual subsidence
of the oceanic lithosphere between a midoceanic rise crest
and the trailing edge of a continental block forms a broad,
elongate depression in which abyssal plains of turbidites
can form above oceanic crust; seamounts and archipelagic
aprons may occupy parts of such a basin.

C.   Basins where rifting occurs in association with transform or
convergent plate junctures; examples of each case can be identified:

(7)   Pull-apart and fault-wedge basins along transtensional fault systems where local attenuation of crust occurs
to form depressions between subparallel branches of a transform system; such basins may be associated with yoked uplifts.

(8)   Interarc basins where splitting apart of a magmatic
arc leads to development of oceanic crust between an inactive
remnant arc and a frontal arc where active magmatism continues;
interarc basins may have their inception as downdropped graben
within arc structures.

Orogenic Settings (Table 2)

Basins whose tectonic evolution is dominated by contractional plate
motions and orogenic deformation include three idealized subgroups (gradational examples also exist):

A.   Basins related to the development of subduction complexes along
the trench flank of arc orogens; these are the three main sedimentary
components of arc-trench systems:

(9)   Oceanic trenches whose substratum is the descending
oceanic lithosphere of a plate being consumed; the inner flank
of the trench is marked by the deformation front of the subduction complex.

(10) Slope basins formed as fault-bounded depressions on
the deforming submarine slopes between trench axes and trench
slope breaks; sediments of these basins are eventually incorporated into subduction complexes along with trench sediments.

(11) Forearc basins formed within the arc-trench gap between the trench slope break and the magmatic arc; the trench
slope break marking the edge of the active subduction zone
serves as the sill for such a basin.

B.   Basins formed in pericratonic foreland settings adjacent to the
deforming flanks of orogenic belts; these basins are systematically asymmetric, with their deepest keels adjacent to fold-thrust belts at the
flanks of the adjacent orogens, but three distinct types occur:

(12) Peripheral basins formed where the surface of a
continental block is drawn downward against the suture belt
of a collision orogen; the polarity of the adjacent orogen
faces this type of foreland basin, hence the ophiolitic
suture belt lies closer to the basin than the magmatic
belt of batholiths and volcanogenic rocks.

(13) Retroarc basins formed where the surface of a
continental block is drawn downward against the rear flank
of an arc orogen; the polarity of the adjacent orogen faces
away from this type of foreland basin (really a hinterland
basin!), hence the ophiolitic subduction complex lies farther from the basin than the magmatic belt of batholiths
and volcanogenic rocks.

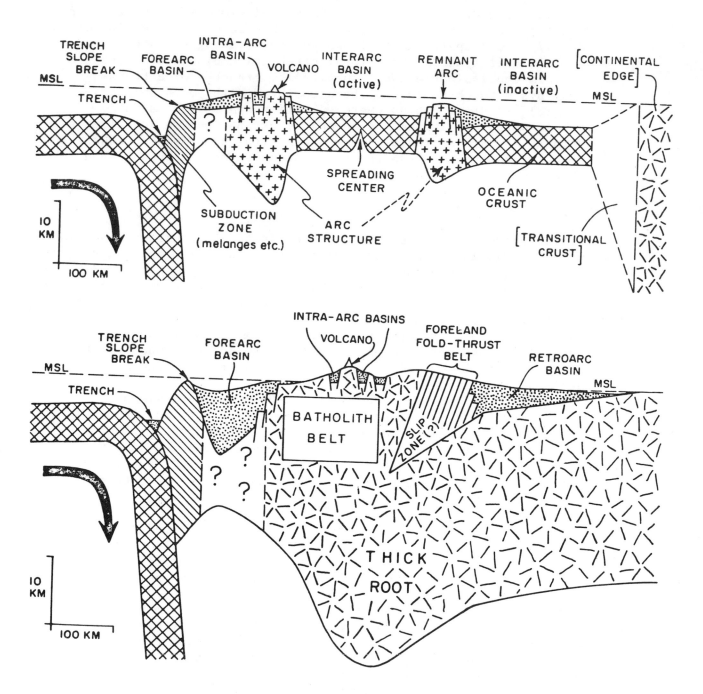

Figure 9. Schematic diagrams (vertical exaggeration 10X) to illustrate
sedimentary basins associated with intraoceanic (above) and continental margin (below) magmatic arcs.

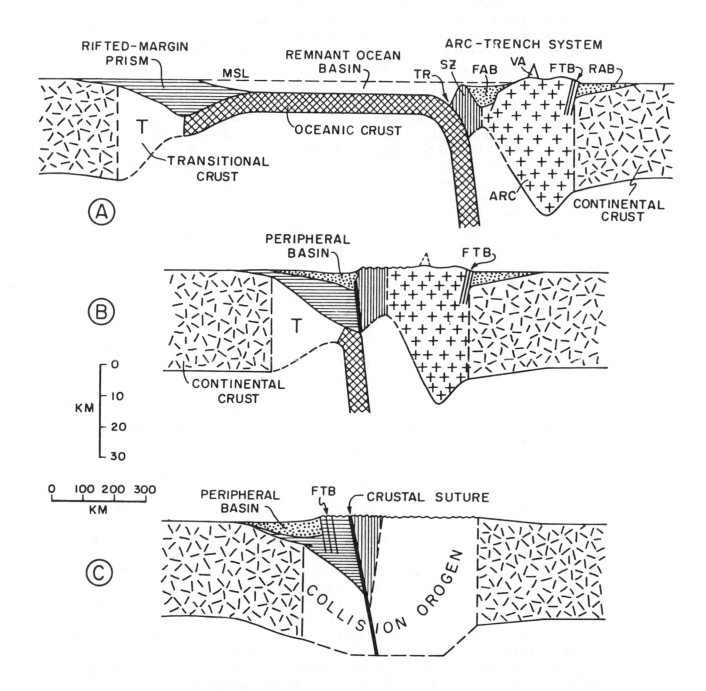

Figure 10. Schematic diagrams (vertical exaggeration 10X) to illustrate sedimentary basins associated with crustal collision to form intercontinental suture belt with collision orogen. Symbols: TR, trench; SZ, subduction zone; FAB, forearc basin: RAB, retroarc basin; FTB, foreland fold-thrust belt. Diagrams A-B-C represent a sequence of events in time at one place along a collision orogen marked by diachronous closure; hence, erosion in one segment (C) of the orogen where the sutured intercontinental join is complete could disperse sediment longitudinally past a migrating tectonic transition point (B) to feed subsea turbidite fans of flysch in a remnant ocean basin (A) along tectonic strike.

(14) Broken-foreland basins formed where basement is
involved in foreland deformation to cause block uplifts
and basement-cored folds separating isolated basinal depressions; this style of deformation may occur in either
peripheral or retroarc settings.
C. Basins where contractional effects control basinal evolution
outside arc or collision orogens:
(15) Downwarped basins along transpressional fault
systems where wrench folds and other fault-warp structures
cause tectonic thickening and regional flexure; features
of this kind may occur as evidence of incipient deformation in the absence of fully developed transform faults.
(16) Remnant ocean basins into which clastics shed
longitudinally from the ends of propagating collision
orogens may build subsea fans and deltas; these deposits
are probably the typical flysch and molasse of classic
terminology.

BASIN COMPARISONS

The logic of plate tectonics indicates that certain sequences of
basinal settings should recur frequently in the geologic record. In the
simplest case, the governing cycle of opening and closing oceans dictates
that oceanic basins must evolve regularly from nascent phases dominated
by extensional tectonics to remnant phases dominated by contractional
tectonics. Similarly, the sedimentary assemblages along rifted continental margins (fig. 8) must include phases deposited within protoceanic
rifts underlying the younger miogeoclinal prism, which may in turn be
covered and flanked by the deposits of a progradational continental embankment. These rifted-margin sedimentary associations may later be
covered in part, with the onset of orogeny, by the foreland deposits of
retroarc or peripheral basins as arc (fig. 9) or collision (fig. 10)
orogens develop along the deformed continental margin. Special variants
of the guiding plate interactions can lead to other successions of
basinal development.
The inference that different mechanisms of subsidence must operate
in the various rifted and orogenic settings suggests that the pattern of
subsidence may vary in different types of basins. One difference in
pattern is apparent in the contrasting cross-sectional shapes of the
various types of basins. Differences may also exist in the timing of
subsidence during the history of the basins. For basins where water
depths are consistently shallow throughout the depositional history,
subsidence rates and net subsidence can be estimated closely on either
a maximal or volumetric basis from columnar sections or isopach maps.
For basins where water depths vary greatly during the depositional history, estimates of changing bathymetry must be incorporated into an
analysis of subsidence. Maximum subsidence rates (fig. 11) and net
maximum subsidence integrated through time (fig. 12) have been plotted
for a number of basins representing many of the types distinguished here.
A clearcut difference is suggested between rifted basins, where rapid
early subsidence rates decline with time, and orogenic basins, where
subsidence rates tend to build toward a final climax. The former pattern
probably reflects the dominance of thermotectonic effects following initial crustal attenuation, whereas the latter may reflect progressively
more intense flexuring until contractional movements cease.

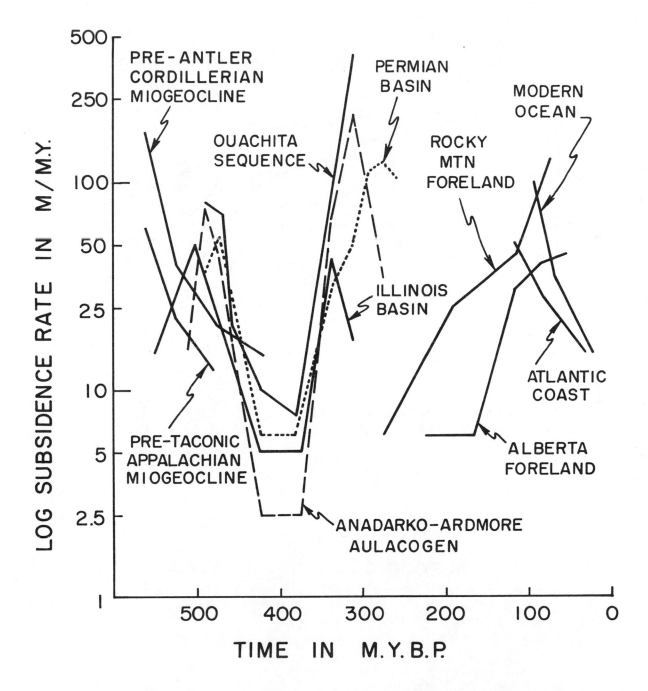

Figure 11. Estimated subsidence rates for selected sedimentary basins through Phanerozoic time; note negative slopes for rifted basins, positive slopes for orogenic basins, and trough shape for full history of aulacogens and oceanic Ouachita sequence.

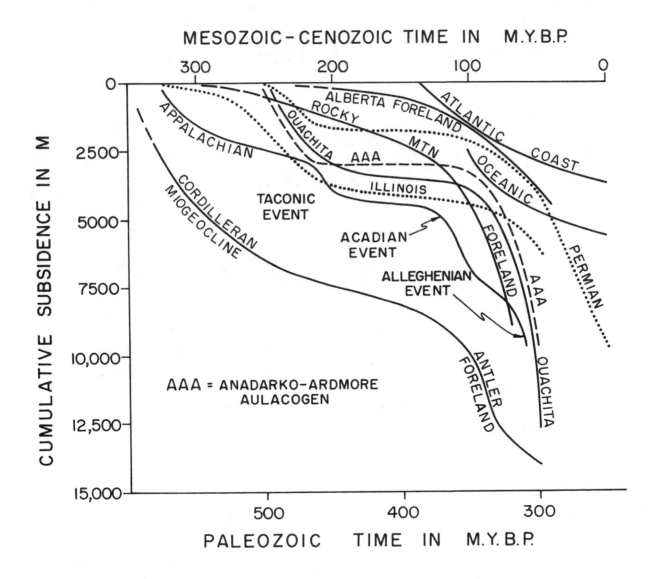

Figure 12. Approximate cumulative subsidence in selected sedimentary
basins through Phanerozoic time; note concave-up shape for rifted
basins, convex-up shape for orogenic basins, and S-shape for full
history of aulacogens and oceanic Ouachita sequence.

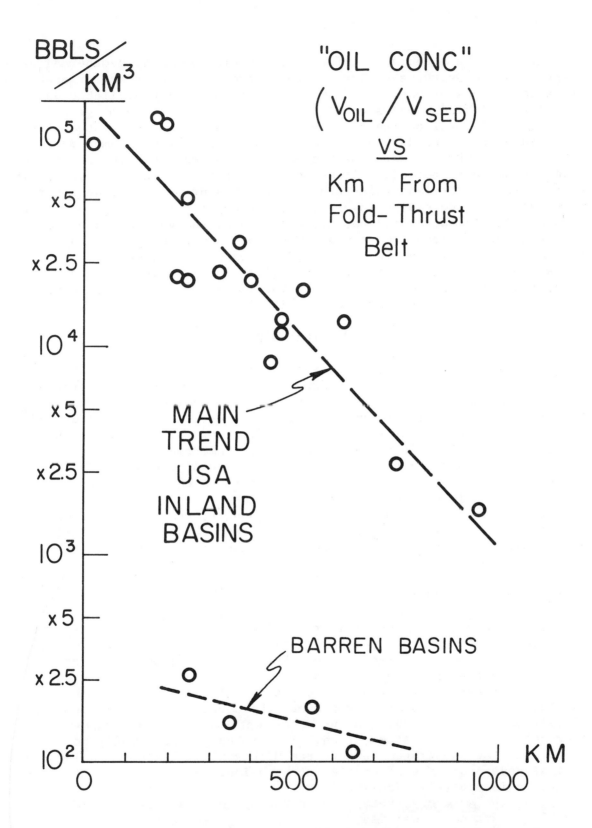

Figure 13. Plot of "Oil Concentration," expressed as oil volume in barrels per cubic kilometer of total sediment, as a function of distance inward from craton margin as defined by distance from nearest fold-thrust belt (Appalachian, Ouachitan, or Cordilleran). Data from estimates of ultimate potential for 20 U.S. interior basins from AAPG Memoir 15 (I.H. Cram, editor).

It would be especially informative to plot changing geothermal gradients and temperatures at key source horizons against time for examples of various types of basins. I am unable to do so with available data.

I have included one special plot (fig. 13) of volume of petroleum per volume of total sediment for various basins in the present continental interior. The data are taken from the AAPG Cram Volumes on Future U.S. Petroleum Provinces. The basins are arranged according to distance from the nearest orogenic belt as measured from the center of the basin to the closest foreland fold-thrust belt. Measurements are necessarily rough values. The basins involved include supracratonic sags of uncertain origin, infracratonic basins, aulacogens, and various foreland basins, some of composite origin. The plot is interpreted to support the concept that migration of oil updip toward the craton from the depressed orogenic flanks of foreland regions is an important phenomenon. As distance from the orogenic fronts increases, the overall concentration of petroleum appears to decline logarithmically.

INCIPIENT RIFTS

Basins related to incipient rifting of continental blocks have several aspects in common: (a) crustal attenuation of the substratum is characteristic and is the prime trigger of subsidence; (b) high heat flux is associated with thermotectonic doming prior to subsidence and continues during the early stages of subsidence; (c) the overall transverse profiles of the basins are generally symmetric; and (d) orogenic deformation is not intense. Two major features of the basins are inherently difficult to evaluate: (a) the attenuated crustal profile of the substratum is entirely covered by sediment, hence its nature can be established only by geophysical methods; and (b) the geothermal gradients that prevailed early in basin evolution must be hindcast from inferences of the magnitude of the initial heat flux and of the influence of the growing sedimentary blanket during thermal decay.

Infracratonic Basins (fig. 14)

The inference that major intracontinental basins represent infracratonic structures where partial continental separation occurred prior to subsidence remains largely an unsubstantiated hypothesis. Perhaps the best documentation pertains to the North Sea basin, where geophysical studies have established that the crust is thinner than normal beneath the major graben trends that represent the deeper portions of the basin. Similar patterns of basal grabens in the West Siberian basin suggest similar belts of crustal attenuation. The presence of unusually dense rocks locally in the substratum beneath the Michigan and Illinois basins hints at analogous processes of crustal attenuation, but direct structural confirmation is generally lacking.

From the surface, typical infracratonic basins appear to be broad, roughly equant downbows; flanks are typically gentle and merge with surrounding platforms without sharp structural margins. In the subsurface, abrupt changes in the stratal thickness of lower horizons may reflect graben structures controlled by normal faulting during the early stages of subsidence. Buried graben trends commonly display branching trilete patterns that suggest initiation as branching rifts on thermotectonic domes that developed in association with the processes responsible for crustal attenuation. The importance of thermal gas in the North Sea and

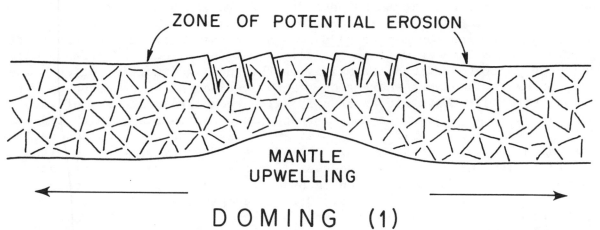

ZONE OF POTENTIAL EROSION

MANTLE
UPWELLING

DOMING (1)

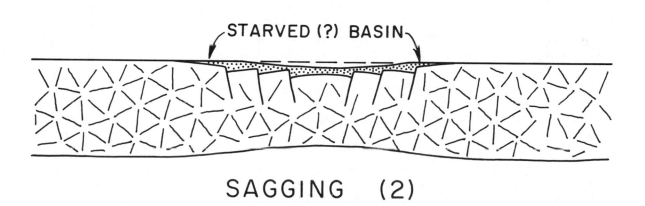

STARVED (?) BASIN

SAGGING (2)

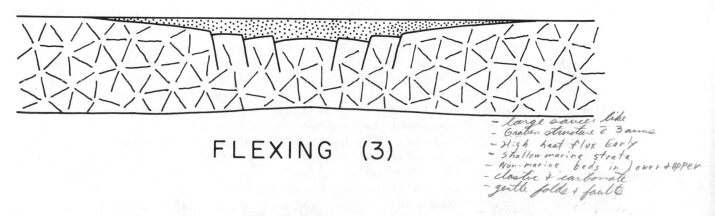

FILLED BASIN

FLEXING (3)

- large saucer like
- Graben structure ē 3 arms
- High heat flux Early
- Shallow marine strata
- Non-marine beds in lower + upper
- clastic + carbonate
- gentle folds + faults

Figure 14. Schematic diagrams to illustrate development of rifted
infracratonic basin in profile view. Time runs top to bottom.

West Siberian basins may reflect a corresponding high heat flux early in basin evolution. Later tectonic structures tend to be gentle folds and faults with modest offset that probably reflect either minor contractional deformation or isostatic adjustments to the growing sedimentary load.

The sediment fills of infracratonic basins are typically shallow-marine strata with non-marine beds present in the lowermost and uppermost parts of the column as well as locally in marginal areas. Contrasts with adjacent platform regions are mainly in thickness and not in facies. The easy access to sediment sources on nearby continental blocks coupled with modest rates of subsidence apparently allow combined processes of clastic and carbonate deposition to keep infracratonic basins filled with sediment during subsidence. Shelf deposits of well sorted mature sands and various carbonate types are thus common. Periods of temporary starvation with silled conditions also allow, however, for the development of stagnant basins in which organic-rich source beds can accumulate in the basin interior or within local grabens. Deltaic complexes or carbonate buildups may form on adjacent shelves or horst blocks. Attractive reservoirs and traps of combined structural and stratigraphic origin thus tend to cluster around basin margins or along internal tectonic trends. Geometric patterns of subsidence controlled by irregular amounts of crustal attenuation may be complex, but the subsequent sediment load tends to induce centripetal downflexure of the lithosphere beneath the basin as a whole. Updip migration paths thus tend to be centrifugal toward marginal parts of the basins.

Marginal Aulacogens (fig. 15)

The term aulacogen originated in the Soviet literature to describe long-lived, fault-bounded troughs disposed in a generally radial pattern as wedge-shaped flaws in the marginal areas of cratons. The features differ from geosynclines in lacking ophiolitic sequences or orogenic magmatism, and do not experience ordinary orogenesis of the same style. Plate tectonic interpretations view aulacogens as aborted oceans; that is, as the failed arms of branching rift systems whose other members continued to evolve into full-fledged oceanic basins. The margins of those ocean basins then define the edges of the cratons into which the aulacogens extend. The craton margins to either side of the mouth of an aulacogen are thus rifted continental margins early in their history, and eventually become orogenic belts when the adjacent oceanic lithosphere is later consumed. The Benue trough of Nigeria is a Mesozoic aulacogen related to the Atlantic Ocean, and the Anadarko-Ardmore basin of Oklahoma is a Paleozoic aulacogen related to the Ouachita orogenic belt.

The structure of aulacogens is intermediate between those of infracratonic basins and oceanic basins, to each of which aulacogens are gradational at their continental and oceanic ends, respectively. The nature of the crust beneath the floor of aulacogens is transitional to oceanic, and may include several kilometers of igneous rocks emplaced at the time the aulacogen first developed. Unlike typical infracratonic basins, aulacogens are markedly elongate, although roughly symmetrical in transverse profile. Their flanks commonly are prominent fault-controlled hinge lines where intermittently active fault scarps serve as local sediment sources. Activity on these bounding fault trends is most significant early in the history of the aulacogen when rapid subsidence of the floor accmpanies initial thermotectonic subsidence. A second period of major activity may occur late in the history of the aulacogen when deformation related to orogenesis along the associated geosynclinal trend causes reactivation of the fracture

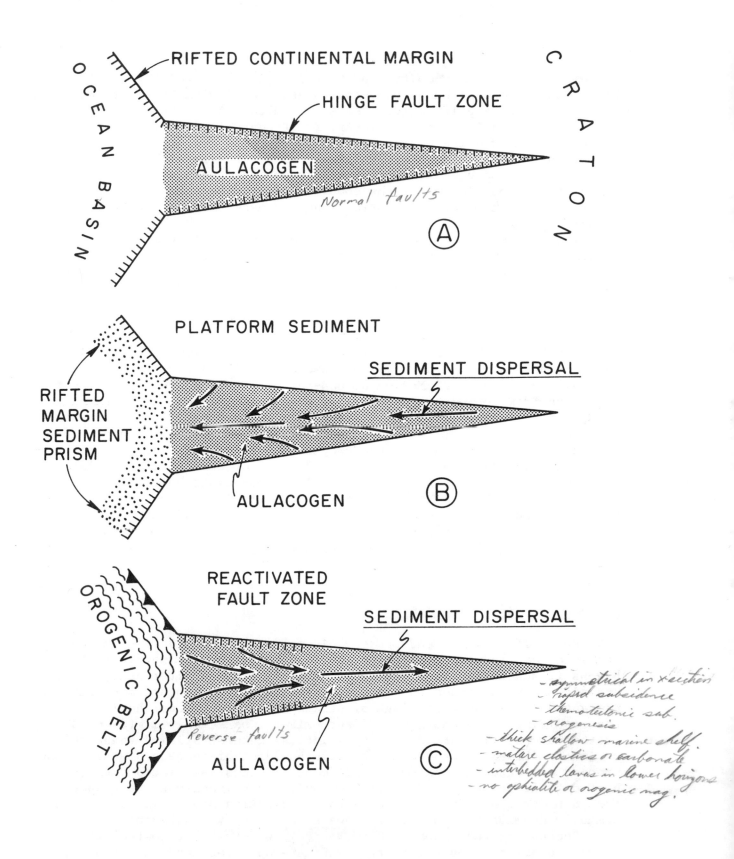

Figure 15. Schematic diagrams to illustrate development of aulacogen
in plan view. Transverse profile of cratonic end of aulacogen is
similar to infracratonic basin (fig. 14), and transverse profile of
oceanic end of aulacogen is similar to protoceanic rift (fig. 16).
Time runs top to bottom.

systems. The earlier faults tend to be normal block-faults, whereas the later faults tend to be reverse faults associated with basement-cored folds and block-uplifts. Both sets of faults tend to break the aulaco- gen into subparallel sets of linear, fault-controlled structural elements. During the intervening middle period of aulacogen evolution, thick sedi- mentation forms an elongate downflexure with its axis along the keel of the aulacogen where crust is thin. This enhanced subsidence tilts the edges of the bounding platforms downward toward the aulacogen structure. Under these conditions, deposition tends to mask the structural margins of the aulacogen.

The sediment fills of aulacogens are mainly shallow-marine shelf strata similar to but several times thicker than the nearby platform sequences. Prominent sedimentary components may include mature clastic sediment drawn preferentially into the aulacogen, which acts as a drain for the adjacent continental block, or carbonate sediment deposited during gradual subsidence. Additional components are also important. Lavas associated with the extensive rifting that establishes the struc- ture may be interbedded at lower horizons. Coarse, immature clastics that are non-marine in part may be associated with activity on local marginal fault scarps. Marine or non-marine clastics may be shed up the aulacogen from the orogenic belt that eventually closes its mouth. This direction of sediment delivery is opposite to that prevalent during the time that the mouth of the aulacogen is open to an oceanic basin. Con- current with the arrival of such orogenic clastics, the seaward tilt of the aulacogen axis may be enhanced by flexure of the continental margin downward beneath the flank of the developing orogenic belt.

Updip migration paths from source beds within an aulacogen or beyond its mouth lie along the trend of the feature and outward toward its flanks. Reservoirs in suitable traps may be associated either with the structurally defined hinges along the margins of the aulacogen, or within the aulacogen where tectonic crumpling may occur toward the close of its evolution.

Protoceanic Rifts (fig. 16)

Deep rift valleys and protoceanic gulfs that form during the early stages of continental separation may form persistent symmetric rift basins if separation is arrested at an early stage. Alternately, if the oceanic basin continues to broaden, deposits of the protoceanic stage are present as a unique assemblage of strata forming the lower horizons of the resulting rifted-margin sediment prism. Characteristic features of protoceanic sedimentary assemblages include interstratified lavas and sediments formed as deposition and the building of igneous oceanic crust proceed concurrently, extensive piedmont clastics associated with large buried fault scarps bounding tilted fault blocks, and massive evaporites formed under conditions of restricted circulation and desiccation that commonly develop in the narrow seaways that occupy the basins.

Because of the intense thermotectonic effects that control the elevation of the substratum, true sabkha evaporites may rest directly on strongly attenuated or even truly oceanic crust that later undergoes dramatic subsidence capable of carrying the evaporites downward beneath great depths of water or immense thicknesses of younger sediment. Ther- motectonic uplift of the edges of the continental blocks bordering a protoceanic rift forms bounding uplands that act as protective shoulders to screen major rivers away from the crustal cleft, and thus to help

-28-

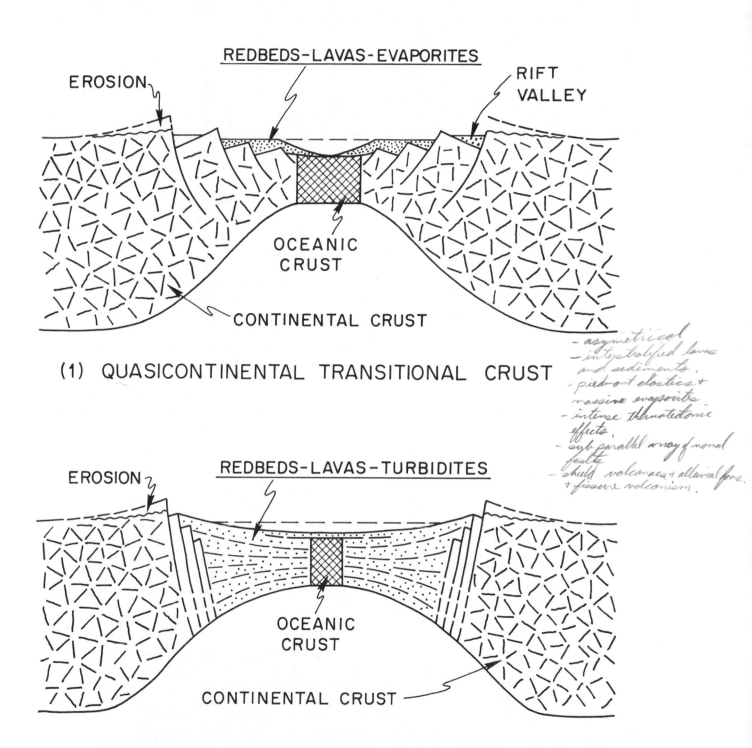

EROSION

REDBEDS-LAVAS-EVAPORITES

RIFT VALLEY

OCEANIC CRUST

CONTINENTAL CRUST

(1) QUASICONTINENTAL TRANSITIONAL CRUST

- asymetrical
- interstratified lavas and sediments.
- piedmont clastics + massive evaporites
- intense thermotectonic effects.
- sub parallel array of normal faults
- shield volcanoes + alluvial fans + fissure volcanism.

EROSION

REDBEDS-LAVAS-TURBIDITES

OCEANIC CRUST

CONTINENTAL CRUST

(2) QUASIOCEANIC TRANSITIONAL CRUST

Figure 16. Schematic diagrams to illustrate protoceanic rifts with quasicontinental (above) and quasioceanic (below) floors.

-29-

promote conditions suitable for evaporite depositon. Such conditions appear to reach ideal expresion in the modern Red Sea where thick Neogene evaporites were laid down essentially at sea level upon thin crust. Where protoceanic evaporites are thick along the flanks of major ocean basins, they may cause attractive diapiric structuring within subsequent continental terraces or embankments.

In a case like the Gulf of California, however, the Colorado River is able to enter a protoceanic rift through a breach in the bounding highlands near one end of the structure. Major evaporite deposits are lacking. A progradational deltaic complex has advanced longitudinally down the protoceanic rift and clastic sediments shed off the front of the delta have travelled even farther as turbidity currents into deep water. Within the reach of this clastic dispersal system, spreading centers where igneous oceanic crust is forming are covered with a blanket of sediment. A transitional crust of mingled lavas, dikes, sills, and sediments is thus being formed beneath the protoceanic rift.

Other transitional crust in protoceanic rifts is composed of greatly attenuated and fault-fragmented continental basement rocks. Subparallel arrays of normal faults scallop both flanks of the rift, stepping down the broken flanks of adjacent uplifted platforms and calving horst blocks away into the growing cleft. Fissure volcanism, local shield volcanoes, and broad alluvial fan complexes are associated with the deformation. As thermal decay causes foundering of the transitional crust, carbonate buildups may develop on horst blocks or on the high shoulders of tilted fault blocks. In time, this structurally complex terrane with varied local sediment types is buried by transgressive marine deposits. Sedimentary loading of the deep rift, or of the edges of the ocean basin that develops from it, eventually tilts the edges of the adjacent continental platforms downward toward the rift belt. The structurally broken terrane is then masked beneath a smoothly draped sediment cover.

Protoceanic source beds may include organic-rich algal sabkha sediments, but the likelihood is uncertain. Carbonate buildups and local shoreline sand facies may form suitable reservoirs, but the great depths to which they are ordinarily buried beneath younger marine sediments makes them unattractive targets in many instances. Subordinate redbed basins that occur as elongate grabens and tilted fault blocks in the outer parts of protoceanic rift belts are less deeply buried but are unlikely to harbor important hydrocarbon occurrences. The Triassic and Jurassic redbed basins of eastern North America are apt examples.

CONTINENTAL SEPARATIONS

Basins formed by continental separation that fragments continental blocks include those developed along the margins of the continental fragments and those within the adjacent ocean basin itself. Basins in both areas have several aspects in common: (a) initial subsidence of thin crust stems from thermal decay of heated lithosphere; (b) additional flexural subsidence is caused by the accumulation of thick sediment loads; (c) the depositional systems are asymmetric or one-sided; and (d) orogenic deformation can ultimately disrupt gross stratal continuity to a remarkable degree. Two major features of the basins are inherently difficult to evaluate; (a) the transitional crust along the continent-ocean interface is masked by thick sediment cover, hence its nature can be established only by geophysical methods; and (b) after orogenesis has occurred, the original facies relationships of the strata must be hindcast by palinspastic reconstructions for which adequate constraints must be inferred from limited control.

Miogeoclinal Prisms (fig. 17)

The classic miogeosynclinal sequences of past usage are regarded now as miogeoclinal prisms deposited along rifted continental margins in settings open to a neighboring ocean. Modern analogues include the Mesozoic and Cenozoic sequences along the eastern edge of the Americas, where the upper part of the sediment pile is well understood but the details of the lower parts are obscure. Paleozoic analogues include the Appalachian and Cordilleran miogeoclines as developed prior to the Taconic and Antler orogenies, respectively. Within these successions, local sequences can be observed in detail throughout, but facies relations on a large scale are structurally disrupted by major thrusts, hence the initial overall configurations of both are known by inference only.

Miogeoclinal prisms extend as continuous elongate belts for long distances along rifted continental margins, although cross-sectional volumes may vary markedly from place to place with the vagaries of sediment delivery and bypass. Their continuity may be broken at intervals by the presence of marginal offsets in the edge of the continent, where an early history of transform rather than rift separation leads to a different subsequent history of sedimentation. Along marginal offsets, crustal attenuation is suppressed to some degree, and volcanogenic marginal fracture ridges may form. These long-lived positive features thereafter deflect clastic sediment to deeper sites elsewhere and may serve instead as loci of organogenic carbonate deposition.

In transverse section, miogeoclinal prisms have an overall lensoid form, but the depositional relief spans the difference in elevation between the continental surface and the ocean floor. The ourter part of the lens is composed of turbidites beneath the continental rise. The coalesced subsea fans of this region grade to the abyssal plains of the oceanic basin beyond. The inner part of the lens is composed of shelf and paralic deposits of the continental terrace. These strata grade laterally to non-marine deposits of the coastal plain. Between continental rise and continental terrace is the continental slope, located roughly along the continent-ocean interface. Reduced sedimentation on typical starved, shaly slopes lends an hourglass shape to the prism as a whole. Terrace and rise deposits form the bulk of the prism.

The continental terrace has two major components. The lower part is commonly a rapidly deposited basal clastic phase whose accumulation probably reflects the initial quick subsidence of attenuated basement along the rifted continental margin during the early period of development when thermal decay was a dominant influence. During this phase, the stripping of residual highlands along the edge of the continental block may contribute to high sedimentation rates. This phase is brought to a close when local isostatic balance of the transitional crust and its overlying continental terrace is achieved.

Subsequent slower deposition of shelf sediments that may include abundant carbonates as well as clastics probably only proceeds as flexural downwarping of the continental block occurs in response to the sedimentary load of the continental rise offshore. Wedge-shaped bodies of sediment deposited as part of the continental terrace during this time may include successively prograded regressive cycles of deltaic clastics or algal-bank carbonates as well as marine shelf deposits. Disconformities may separate successive wedges of sediment.

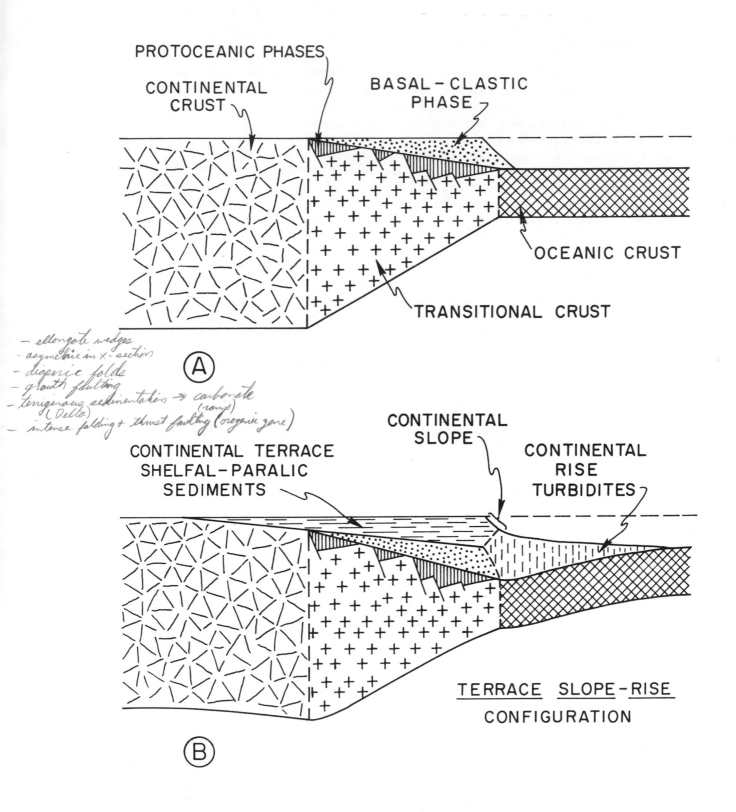

PROTOCEANIC PHASES

CONTINENTAL CRUST

BASAL–CLASTIC PHASE

OCEANIC CRUST

TRANSITIONAL CRUST

(A)

– elongate wedges
– asymetric in x-section
– diapiric folds
– growth faulting
– teriginous sedimentaries → carbonate
  (Delta)   (ramp)
– intense folding + thrust faulting (orogenic zone)

CONTINENTAL TERRACE
SHELFAL–PARALIC
SEDIMENTS

CONTINENTAL SLOPE

CONTINENTAL RISE TURBIDITES

TERRACE SLOPE-RISE
CONFIGURATION

(B)

Figure 17. Schematic diagrams to illustrate development of miogeoclinal
prism from basal clastic phase (above) during early thermotectonic
subsidence of transitional crust to mature phase (below) when flexural
subsidence is dominant.

Carbonate buildups may form near the shelf break. The inner limit of the downwarped continental terrace may come to stand well within the continental block where no crustal attenuation occurred during continental separation.

Structural features of miogeoclinal prisms include diapiric folds whose development depends upon the presence of underlying protoceanic evaporites. Faults that cut the protoceanic facies should be overlapped by overlying miogeoclinal strata, but some growth faulting may continue, especially during rapid deposition of the basal clastic phase. Moreover, if structural coupling across the continent-ocean interface is imperfect, the sedimentary load of the continental rise may cause reactivation of older fractures, including those of marginal offsets, as well as simple flexure of lithosphere. Continental terraces underlain by protoceanic horst-and-graben structures at depth may even develop constituent basins and arches with structural closure at higher stratigraphic horizons as well. Orogenesis brings miogeoclinal evolution to a close by forming major fold-thrust belts composed of crumpled and imbricated miogeoclinal strata.

Several kinds of organic-rich source beds might occur within miogeoclinal prisms: (a) shaly continental slope deposits laid down within the oxygen minimum zone, (b) carbonate or shale beds of the continental terrace deposited in silled depressions on the shelf; and (c) phosphorites deposited on shelves where upwelling of nutrient-rich water is strong. Reservoirs may be abundant in both stratigraphic and gentle structural traps within the continental terrace. However, the total volume of source beds may be low, and effective migration paths updip from slope sources to terrace reservoirs may be rare owing to the lack of continuous stratal connections through starved facies.

Continental Embankments (Fig. 18)

In areas where massive sedimentary progradation of the edge of the continent occurs, the configuration of the rifted-margin sediment prism changes from that of the continental terrace-slope-rise triad to that of a continental embankment. The shelf break advances from the original continent-ocean interface until it reaches a position above oceanic basement. The latter is then buried, of course, beneath an immense sediment pile, probably the thickest kind of stratal succession possible. The embankment is an immense unstable lens, extending from sea level to oceanic depths and having a deep keel made possible by isostatic down-flexure of the lithosphere. The Gulf Coast and the Niger Delta are outstanding modern examples. Both have restricted extent along their respective continental margins.

Internal structuring of an embankment is intricate and related mainly to loading processes. Overall gravitational failure may produce pseudotectonic folds and thrusts near the toe. Listric growth faults and associated folds may scar many parts of the pile but commonly are concentrated near prominent delta lobes. Salt diapirs fed by underlying protoceanic facies are also common.

Sediment associations within an embankment consist of a series of overlapping lenses, each with stratal continuity laterally from shallowest to deepest facies. Fluvio-deltaic and shoreline assemblages with numerous potential reservoir sand bodies grade offshore to organic-rich prodelta and slope facies that in turn grade to turbidite associations. As progradational growth of the embankment occurs, each successive

-33-

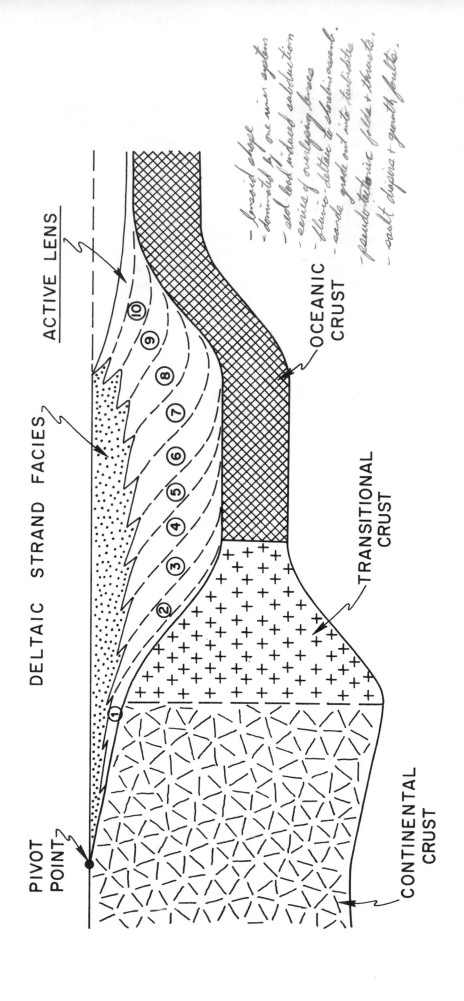

Figure 18. Schematic diagram to illustrate growing continental embankment in profile view.

increment of strata is progressively loaded by more and more overlying
beds and progressively tilted to higher and higher dips by the flexure
of lithosphere associated with sedimentary loading farther offshore.
These actions combine to pump any hydrocarbons generated continually
updip toward favorable reservoirs in shoreline associations, which form
a diachronous stratigraphic lid across the top of the embankment. Diapiric and growth structures combine to produce abundant attractive traps.
Stratigraphic traps are also common in fluvio-deltaic and shoreline
assemblages where sand bodies have limited individual extent.

During the later phases of growth of rifted-margin sediment prisms,
heat flux is low to normal. In continental embankments, adequate maturation can still be achieved because of the great depths involved. Fluid
overpressures are characteristic because of the rapid sedimentation.

- Deep water basins. — ocean crust formed at ridges ophiolite
Nascent Oceans
- Pillows → met. lavas → dolerite dikes + sills → massive Gabbros + Amphib. → cumulus gabbros + perid.
PROTO - OCEANIC BASIN — carbonate sed above CCD, silicious oozes + terriginous seds, metelliferous muds.
— seamounts, volcanic islands, reef carbonates.

The sediment cover in nascent oceanic basins with midoceanic rises
varies in nature and thickness for different elevations of the ocean
floor corresponding to different ages. The characteristic oceanic layers
build diachronous facies added successively to each increment of oceanic
lithosphere as it is formed and moves away from the rise crest.

The igneous oceanic crust forms at the rise crest as an ophiolite
sequence. Pillow lavas near the top pass downward into altered and metamorphosed lavas cut by swarms of dolerite dikes and sills. The latter
are fed from underlying crustal magma chambers that solidify to form
bodies of massive gabbro, locally converted to amphibolite. Igneous
deposition within the magma chambers forms cumulus gabbros and perido-
tites near their base. Underneath are ultramafic tectonites of the
mantle. The emplacement of all these rocks obviously takes place in an
environment of high heat flux and pervasive hydrothermal activity.

Sediment cover at the rise crest is sparse, but on the upper flanks
of the rise, accumulation of carbonate sediment, mainly pelagites, can
be rapid above the CCD. Farther down the flanks of the rise, siliceous
pelagites and argillaceous hemipelagites are added to the growing succession. Finally, the terrigenous turbidites of abyssal plains may cover
or interfinger with pelagic and hemipelagic sediment in the broad oceanic
basins between midoceanic rises and continental margins. Special facies
developed locally include lavas of seamounts and volcanic islands, together with the reef carbonates that may surmount them and the archipelagic aprons of turbidites that may surround them.

During orogenesis, scraps or slices of the ophiolitic assemblage
of the ocean floor may be carried by thrusts across the contrasting facies
of rifted-margin sediment prisms. In favorable instances, as in Oman,
an intact ophiolitic slab may be thrust across slope assemblages that
in turn are thrust across shelf assemblages. Where orogenic disruption
of a continental margin is severe, care must be taken with detailed
interpretations of the nature of basement beneath various successions,
for even the thick continental rise sequences rest on an oceanic and
presumably ophiolitic basement.

HYBRID RIFTS

Local plate divergence along or near complex plate junctures where
transform motions or convergence are dominant regionally also give rise
locally to rifted basins. Transtensional basins along complex transforms

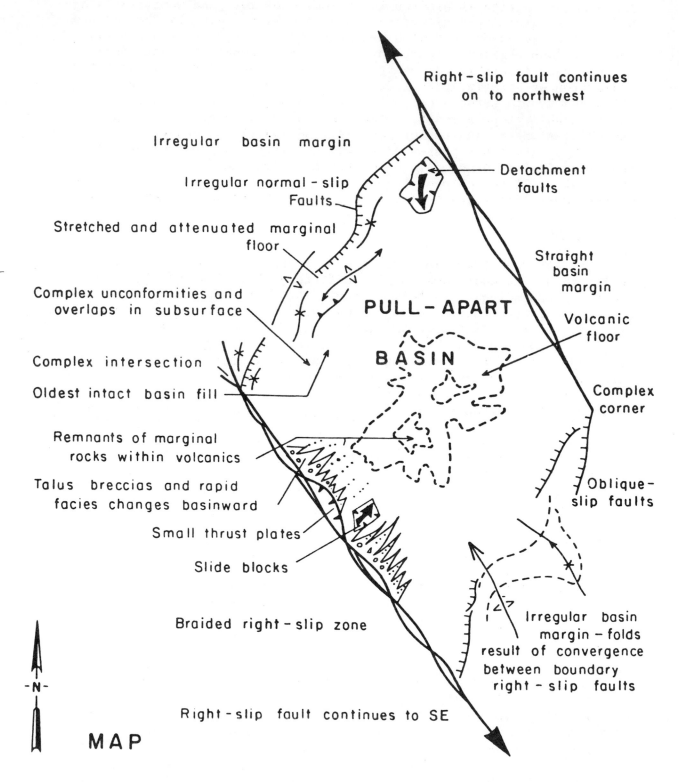

Figure 19. Sketch map of idealized transtensional pull-apart basin
(from J.C. Crowell, 1974, Origin of late Cenozoic basins in southern
California: Soc. Econ. Paleontologists and Mineralogists Special
Pub. No. 22, p. 190-204).

are a variety of incipient rift, whereas interarc basins formed near convergent plate junctures are a variety of truly oceanic basin where crustal separation is complete.

Transtensional Basins (fig. 19)

Transtensional basins may occur along the trend of transform systems wherever en echelon fault segments, curving faults, or branching faults are arranged in a releasing, rather than a constraining, orientation with respect to the direction of relative plate motion. Approximately equant pull-apart basins between en echelon transform segments are perhaps most typical. More elongate fault-wedge basins between branching faults or beside curving faults are variants of the same essential behavior.

Pull apart basins may occur in a variety of overall tectonic settings. Some depressions along intra-oceanic rise-to-rise transforms probably have this basic origin. Spreading centers along the Cayman trend in the Caribbean also apparently lie between en echelon transform segments. Where continental collisions occur, continued lateral slippage after subduction has stopped may form local post-orogenic pull-apart basins, as was apparently the case for Carboniferous redbed basins in the maritime Appalachians. Perhaps the most-discussed transtensional basins, however, are the Tertiary basins of California related to development of both Paleogene and Neogene continental borderlands. The deep basins within the Gulf of California and the fully filled basin of the Salton Depression at its northern end are modern members of the same group of basins.

Miocene transtensional basins related to the inception of the late Cenozoic San Andreas system subsided rapidly to form deep water into which turbidites were shed from nearby basement uplifts to form coarse subsea fan complexes. Contemporaneous volcanism formed partly volcanic floors within some basins. Shallow sills marked by starved, abbreviated stratigraphic sections led to stagnant conditions and organogenic deposits over large parts of some basins. High heat flux that favored rapid maturation was probably characteristic. Such conditions seem especially conducive to the concentration of hydrocarbons within proximal turbidite reservoirs in traps delineated by stratigraphic pinchouts or local structures near basin margins. Later deformation of the whole basin interior by wrench structures related to continued transform motions can also be expected.

Interarc Basins (fig. 20)

Interarc basins are one of the most puzzling types because they represent clearly extensional tectonics related to arc-trench systems where the dominant plate motion is convergent. The key to understanding their origin is to appreciate that the high heat flux in magmatic arcs spoils the integrity of the lithosphere across arc structures. High temperature at shallow depths below the magmatic arc softens the rigid lithosphere and allows lithosphere in the region behind the arc to move independently of lithosphere in the arc-trench gap. In effect, a thermal curtain along the belt of magmatism saws the lithosphere into two separate slabs. Once this detachment is achieved, various relative motions are possible. In Sumatra, for example, transform-like strike-slip motion occurs along the Semangko fault system that extends right down the length of the Barisan volcanic chain. Even local pull-apart structures occur as unusually large volcano-tectonic depressions along the trend of the magmatic arc.

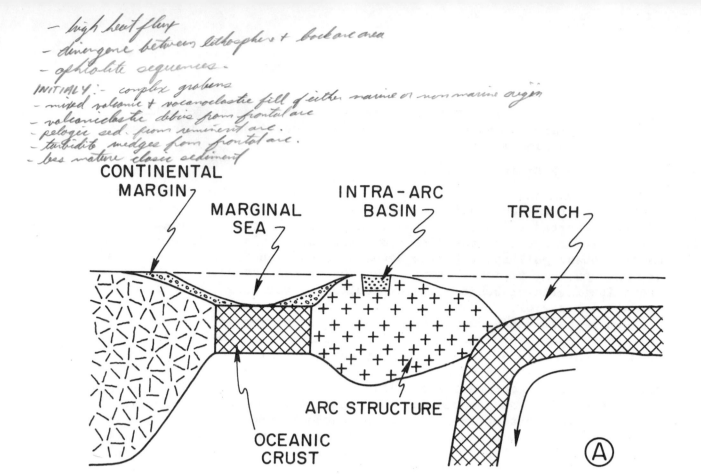

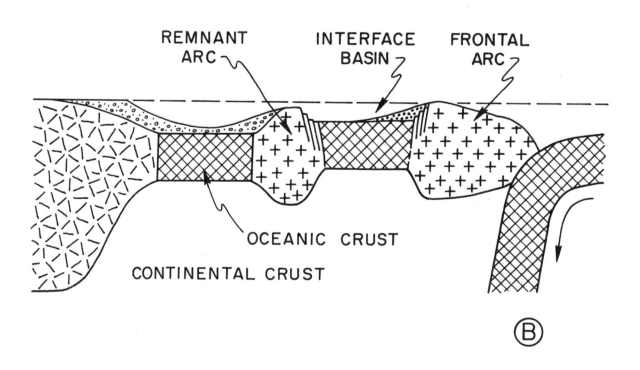

Figure 20. Schematic diagrams to illustrate incipient (above) and fully developed (below) interarc basins in profile view.

Elsewhere, divergence occurs between lithosphere in the backarc area and that in the arc-trench gap. The geodynamic forces involved are not well understood, but the kinematics are clear. Young, bare oceanic crust occurs in the Lau Basin west of Tonga, and also west of the active Marianas arc. The Sea of Japan contains two main rift structures with the microcontinental block of the Yamato Bank sandwiched between. The style of sea-floor spreading in these interarc basins seems less regular than at midoceanic rise crests, for magnetic anomalies caused by magnetic reversals cannot be identified clearly. Still, the structure of the oceanic crust seems from present data to be the same as that in the open oceans, and is thus presumed to be an ophiolite sequence.

Interarc basins probably begin their evolution as complex grabens along the volcanic chain, and may at that intra-arc stage resemble the Nicaraguan depression along the arc trend in Central America. Mixed volcanic and volcaniclastic fill of either non-marine or marine origin would be expected initially. A later phase of separation may be represented in the New Hebrides where a deep marine trough has developed from which large volcanoes emerge as islands locally. When the frontal arc and remnant arc have separated fully, the flanks of each face the interarc basin as compound normal fault scarps. Volcaniclastic debris shed backward from the frontal arc where magmatism continues will in time mask one flank of the basin with a thick sediment cover, but in general only pelagic sediment can be draped over the remnant arc. The interior of the interarc basin will undergo pelagic sedimentation similar to that of the open ocean unless turbidite wedges extending backward from the active frontal arc eventually cross it.

Special conditions exist where one side of an interarc basin is a continental margin, as is the case along the Sikhote-Alin coast of the Sea of Japan. The evolution of such a basin margin should resemble that of a more normal rifted continental margin. One significant detail of geologic history should differ; namely, orogenic arc magmatism should prevail along the site of the continental margin until just before its formation. Such is the case for Sikhote-Alin.

Even the eastern flank of the Sea of Japan bears some resemblance to a rifted continental margin because the Japanese arc is such a massive crustal element. Faulted Neogene basins of considerable extent are developed there on crust of continental or transitional thickness. Unlike those along rifted continental margins, however, these basins have undergone pronounced local contractional deformation quite early in their history.

In summary, the interior parts of interarc basins are similar to other nascent oceanic basins, except perhaps for relative proximity to sources of airborne ash. The flanks are structurally similar to rifted continental margins but commonly receive much less sediment except in special cases. The clastic sediment ordinarily is markedly less mature. There is probably a higher heat flux initially, as the arc splits, and a likelihood of prolonged high heat flux along the rear flank of the frontal arc where continued deformation may also occur. The full implications of these conditions for hydrocarbon genesis are not clear, but rapid maturation might be expected. However, widespread source beds and adequate reservoirs seem unlikely in most cases. During orogenesis that results in oceanic closure, interarc basins and intra-oceanic arcs are severely deformed and metamorphosed together as integral parts of so-called eugeosynclinal terranes, and thereby become wholly unattractive for exploration.

Where island arcs are initiated across oceanic areas, as in the Aleutians, the oceanic basin behind the arc is a marginal sea but not an interarc basin. Volcaniclastic turbidites shed from the new arc may cover older oceanic sediment within the basin much as archipelagic aprons are spread from basaltic seamount chains.

SUBDUCTION PRISMS (fig. 21)

Depositional settings related to the accretion of subduction complexes have several aspects in common: (a) crustal thickening from tectonic telescoping tends to counteract subsidence related to plate consumption and sedimentary loading; (b) low heat flux that is associated with subduction of cool lithosphere prevails during basin evolution; (c) the overall transverse profiles of the basins are asymmetric; and (d) flexural subsidence of lithosphere is significant. Two major features of the basin are inherently difficult to evaluate: (a) the nature of the substratum in the belt between trenches and magmatic arcs is hidden beneath thick sedimentary and tectonic loads, and is constantly changing in part while active subduction continues; and (b) the original geometry of the basins is continually modified during their evolution by concurrent tectonism, and is further modified before their exposure to view on land by additional deformation associated with uplift after subduction has ceased.

Oceanic Trenches

The sedimentary fills of trenches where plate consumption occurs are not preserved intact, but instead are incorporated as severely deformed strata within subduction complexes. The morphologic crest of the tectonically thickened and isostatically uplifted subduction complex is located at the trench slope break. The steep inner slope of the trench thus represents the active subduction zone and the trench axis is the deformation front. Sediment ponded along the trench floor at any given time is a steady-state volume that represents a dynamic balance between rate of sedimentation and rate of subduction.

The deep water of the trench is formed primarily by flexure associated with plate consumption. A compensatory broad upbow of the ocean floor occurs as an outer arch or outer swell in front of the trench. Normal faulting associated with this feature commonly offsets oceanic sediment layers and the underlying surface of mafic igneous crust just prior to insertion of lithosphere into the subduction zone. Fault scarps present locally on the gentle outer slope of the trench reflect this deformation. Along the floor of the trench, turbidites dispersed longitudinally down the axis of the trench are deposited on top of oceanic pelagites or other sediments of the oceanic crust that is carried into the trench by plate motion. As oceanic lithosphere passes beneath the inner slope of the trench, the sediment layers that have accumulated on it tend to be underthrust beneath older components of the subduction complex, and simultaneously to be scraped off the descending slab of lithosphere.

The subduction complex is thus an accretionary tectonic feature of immense structural complexity. Revealing reflection profiles of the Lesser Antilles, Middle America, Aleutian, Japanese, and Sunda trenches have been published. The gross internal geometry appears to be dominated by a series of underlapping wedges of intensely deformed strata separated by imbricate thrust zones that merge downward into a surface of décollement at the top of the descending slab of lithosphere. The décollement surface is apparently near the interface between igneous

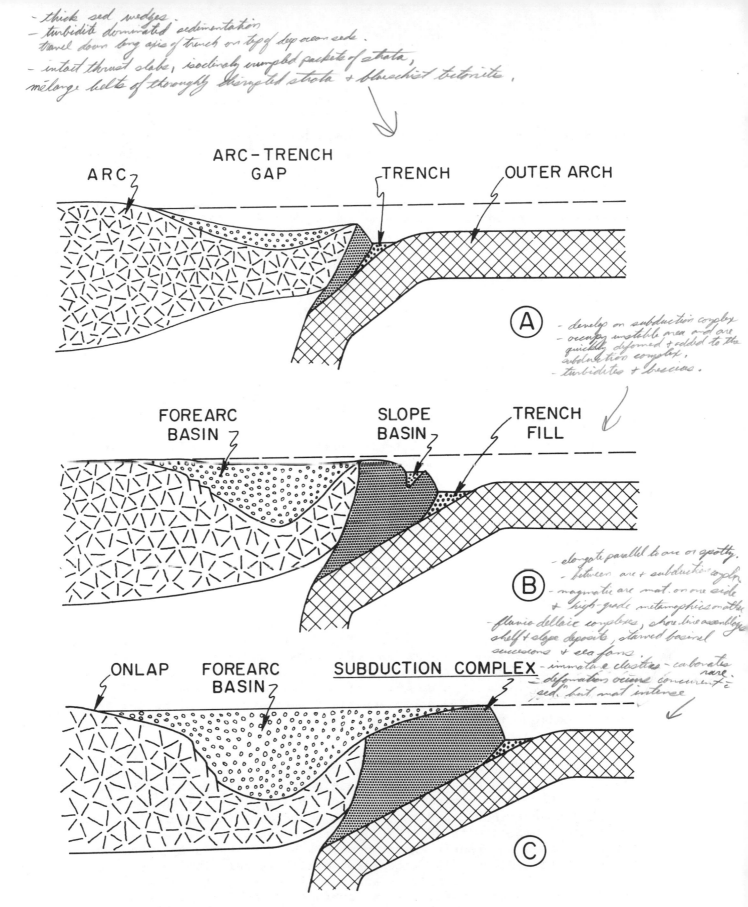

handwritten annotations (top):
- thick sed wedges.
- turbidite dominated sedimentation
travel down long axis of trench on top of deep ocean sed.
- intact thrust slabs, isoclinally crumpled packets of strata,
mélange belts of thoroughly disrupted strata & blueschist tectonite.

ARC-TRENCH GAP

ARC   TRENCH   OUTER ARCH

Ⓐ

handwritten annotations (A):
- develop on subduction complex
- occupy unstable area and are quickly deformed & added to the subduction complex.
- turbidites & breccias.

FOREARC BASIN   SLOPE BASIN   TRENCH FILL

Ⓑ

handwritten annotations (B):
- elongate parallel to arc or spotty.
- between arc + subduction complex
- magmatic arc mat. on one side & high-grade metamorphics on other
- fluvio deltaic complexes, shore line assemblages, shelf & slope deposits, starved basinal successions & sea fans.
- immature clastics - carbonate rare
- deformation occurs concurrent = sed. but mat intense

ONLAP   FOREARC BASIN   SUBDUCTION COMPLEX

Ⓒ

Figure 21. Schematic diagrams to illustrate association of oceanic
trench, slope basin, and forearc basin with growing subduction
complex. Time runs top to bottom.

and sedimentary components of the ophiolite sequence at the top of oceanic lithosphere. Locally, however, it may form between pelagites and overlying clastics, or may penetrate the igneous layering. The internal imbrication of the subduction complex is partly inherited from tectonic boundaries initially established between successively underthrust components of the subduction complex. Also in part, however, the internal imbrication is generated by later structural failure of the growing mass by gravitational spreading. As tectonic thickening uplifts deformed materials beneath the inner slope of the trench, the drag of the descending lithosphere at the toe of the slope tends to oversteepen the slope. The elevation of the trench slope break and the angle of the inner slope of the trench are controlled, therefore, by internal imbrication that adjusts the overall geometry to a gravitationally stable configuration. The tectonic load of the subduction complex may also tend to deepen the trench by plate flexure.

The materials of the subduction complex can be varied. In structural style, they may include intact thrust slabs, isoclinally crumpled packets of strata, mélange belts of thoroughly disrupted strata, and metamorphosed blueschist tectonites. Protoliths of these units include not only trench sediments, but also oceanic pelagites, abyssal turbidites, and pieces of ophiolite sequences. The subduction complex is most massive and the trench slope break stands highest where the most sediment is present on the oceanic plate being consumed. Thus, paradoxically, the subduction complex is most prominent where the trench is topographically most subdued. The oceanic plate must carry thick turbidite sequences or sedimentation rates must keep the trench full if the geologic record of the subduction zone as preserved in the subduction complex is to be impressive. Empty trenches leave little record.

Slope Basins

Within the active subduction zone along the inner slope of a trench, the presence of outcropping thrust faults or growing folds may give rise to small depressions where modest thicknesses of slope strata can accumulate locally. The substratum is deformed subduction complex rather than the ophiolite sequence upon which trench sediments are deposited. If the trench slope is regarded as an imperfect escalator trying to uplift deformed sediment from the trench axis to the trench slope break, then the slope basins can be viewed as sediment added part way up.

The history of slope basins is not well understood, but continued deformation probably deforms them quickly and adds them to the subduction complex. Although bounded by tectonic contacts within the complex, they may well show less internal deformation by isoclinal folding or mélange shearing than trench deposits that are added more incrementally to the subduction complex with accordingly more opportunity for pervasive deformation. Cases apparently exist, however, as off the Pacific Northwest today, where sedimentation rates are so high in relation to subduction rates that subsea fan complexes and associated slope deposits can build steadily across the surface of the subduction complex and extend right across the subduction zone. The trench does not then exist or, if you will, the trench is then overfilled. In such cases, any distinction between trench fill and slope deposits within the resulting subduction complex would be almost meaningless. The overall degree of structural dislocation presumably would be less than in more ordinary instances.

Regardless of details of evolution, subduction complexes would appear to be unattractive basins for hydrocarbon exploration. Although organic-rich source beds may occur within slope deposits, the combination of intense deformation, poor reservoir conditions, disruption of migration paths by structural dislocation, and low heat flux are discouraging factors.

Forearc Basins

Forearc basins can be regarded as a variety of slope basin, but are treated separately here because they occur within the arc-trench gap between the trench slope break and the magmatic front of the arc. They are thus deposited outside the active subduction zone and do not undergo the intensive and pervasive deformation characteristic of the subduction complex. Nor do they experience the magmatism and metamorphism characteristic of the magmatic arc terrane. The late Mesozoic Great Valley Sequence, deposited in California between the coeval Franciscan subduction complex and the Sierra Nevada batholith belt, is a good example.

On the arc side of a forearc basin, sediments lap depositionally upon eroded igneous and metamorphic rocks along the flank of the magmatic arc. During the evolution of a forearc basin, there is commonly a progressive transgressive enroachment of deposition across the eroded arc terrane because the site of the magmatic belt tends to reatreat with time. This effect is partly counteracted, however, by movements on a fault system that commonly lies along the flank of the arc structure and sets the basin side down.

On the trench side of a forearc basin, the edge of the basin also tends to shift gradually away from its center as the accretionary subduction complex broadens, and the position of the trench slope break accordingly migrates. The flank of the basin at the trench slope break is essentially defined tectonically as the edge of the active subduction zone. Sediment deposited beyond the trench slope break is incorporated within the subduction complex by deformation that is essentially concurrent with sedimentation. As the flank of the forearc basin transgresses across the growing subduction complex, the basal contact of the undeformed sequence with the subduction complex thus may not develop as a simple unconformity, but rather as a time-transgressive zone of tectonic dislocation mappable as a thrust zone at any given place on the outcrop.

The substratum beneath the center of a forearc basin is composed of rock older than either the subduction complex or the magmatic arc. In typical cases, the floor of the forearc basin spans a continent-ocean interface and hence masks the transition from continental to oceanic basement inherited from a time prior to establishment of the arc-trench system. Where forearc basins are thickest, the substratum is probably oceanic crust. A Paleozoic forearc basin in New Zealand, a Mesozoic forearc basin in California, and a Cenozoic forearc basin in Burma are known to rest depositionally on ophiolite sequences along their oceanic flanks.

Forearc basins are commonly elongate parallel to the trend of the arc-trench system, but may occur as thick features only at intervals along the length of an arc-trench gap. In effect, the sediment in a forearc basin is ponded behind the threshold formed by the trench slope break. The amount that can accumulate is probably controlled largely by the local thickness of crust from place to place within the arc-trench gap. The progressive expansion of a forearc basin across the flanks of the adjacent arc terrane and subduction complex may be facilitated by

broad downflexure of lithosphere in response to the sediment load
of the forearc basin.

Sedimentary facies within forearc basins are highly variable,
dependent in part upon the elevation of the basin threshold at the
trench slope break and in part upon the sedimentation rate within the
basin in relation to the rate of tectonic uplift of the trench slope
break. Configurations of the ground within arc-trench gaps include
uplifted mountainous tracts, terrestrial lowlands, shelf seas, deep-
marine terraces, and deep-marine troughs. Sediments of forearc basins
thus include fluvio-deltaic complexes and shoreline assemblages, shelf
and slope deposits, starved basin plains, and subsea fan associations in
widely varying proportions. Clastic sediment is commonly immature and
carbonates are rare.

Although there are clear opportunities for deposition of organic-
rich source beds on marine slopes and in silled marine depressions, heat
flux is abnormally low and maturation processes should be slow. The
high heat flux associated with magmatic arcs is apparently not present
far from the magmatic front. Diagenetic mineral assemblages and reflectivities of organic debris in ancient forearc basins of New Zealand and
California imply geothermal gradients as low as those for adjacent subduction complexes.

Structures within forearc basins include some folds and faults
that apparently reflect deformation concurrent with sedimentation.
These are related both to contractional deformation near the disloca-
tional contact with the subduction complex, and to extensional deformation near the fault system marking the flank of the arc structure.
Progressive regional tilt, downward away from the uplifted subduction
complex and toward the downfaulted zone of the magmatic arc, is also
common in many forearc basins. Major structures are associated, however, with later uplift of the subduction complex, perhaps by isostatic
rebound when the geodynamic effects of plate consumption end. At that
time, the flank of the forearc basin structurally above the subduction
complex is tilted steeply upward and eroded. The remaining part of the
forearc basin then lies within a strongly asymmetric regional syncline
with its gentle limb draped across the flank of the arc. Regional
migration paths are thus partly toward the trench side of the basin
during sedimentation, but persistent updip migration paths are later
mainly toward the arc side of the basin.

FORELAND BASINS

Depositional basins along continental flanks of orogenic belts have
several aspects in common: (a) the tectonic load of fold-thrust belts
that lie adjacent to the basins contributes to flexural subsidence of
the basins; (b) the transverse profiles of the basins are strongly asymmetric; (c) the orogenic flanks of the basins undergo deformation during
their evolution; and (d) the cratonic flanks of the basins merge gradually with platform sequences. Two major features of the basins are
inherently difficult to evaluate: (a) the relative importance of different mechanisms of subsidence; and (b) the geothermal gradients that
prevail in different parts of the basins during evolution.

Isopachs indicate that the substratum beneath all pericratonic
foreland basins is tilted downward toward the orogenic belt during deposition, but structure contours indicate that later structural development
may tilt the substratum away from the orogenic belt. Underlying tectonic

elements commonly include the margin of the craton and part of a
miogeoclinal prism older than the foreland basin. Composite foreland
basins may reflect the net effects of successive orogenic episodes
along a continental margin. For example, the Appalachian basin contains
separate clastic wedges from the Taconic, Acadian, and Alleghenian
orogenies in the adjacent orogenic belt. In such cases, both peripheral
and retroarc components as described here may be present in the same
composite foreland basin. Distinction between those two kinds of
settings depends upon knowledge of the relative positions of batholith
belts and ophiolite belts of various ages in the nearby orogen.

Peripheral Basins (fig. 22)

Peripheral foreland basins are the classic foreland basins developed
adjacent to crustal suture belts where continental margins have been
drawn against subduction complexes after the intervening oceanic crust
has been consumed. The foreland basin is formed on the continental block
as it tilts downward toward the subduction zone. The Arkoma and Fort
Worth basins adjacent to the Ouachita orogenic belt are examples.

Flexural subsidence in peripheral basins may have two causes whose
relative importance is unclear. First, flexure associated directly with
plate consumption is possible, and may be illustrated where the northern
edge of the Australian continental platform is now tilted downward into
deep water near Timor along the Sunda arc-trench system. Second, where
the edge of the continent is underthrust beneath the imbricated fold-
thrust belt of a subduction complex, the tectonic load of the latter
may induce additional flexure. A tectonic load of that kind may have
been responsible for subsidence in the Arkoma basin when the Ouachita
overthrust sequence to the south was carried northward over the edge of
the Oklahoma platform.

Folds and thrusts along the orogenic margin of peripheral basins
define an evolving structural margin on one side. Normal faults analogous in position to those on the outer slopes of trenches may form
on the cratonic side. Clastic sediment may enter the basin from either
side, although prominent clastic wedges are most commonly associated
with the orogenic side. Although turbidites may occur in some instances,
fluvio-deltaic complexes are more typical. Sediment transport may be
either transverse or longitudinal locally. The proportion of marine
and non-marine beds is dependent on relations between subsidence rate
and sedimentation rate. Source beds may be abundant where silled marine
depressions occur or may be nearly absent where the section is entirely
terrestrial clastics.

The fate of older miogeoclinal prisms buried beneath foreland
sediment is a critical facet of the development of peripheral basins.
Miogeoclinal prisms ride the edges of continental blocks like bumpers
on cars. Where a crustal collision occurs, the marginal sediment prism
is drawn first into the subduction zone. Strata of the prism are tilted
downward strongly beneath the flank of the subduction complex and
covered by the peripheral basin. Within such a tilted miogeoclinal prism,
as well as in the overlying asymmetric foreland basin, migration paths
are dominantly updip away from the flank of the orogenic belt. The
inducement for migration is strong, for tectonic and sedimentary loading
both increase downdip. I have argued elsewhere that the remarkable productivity of the Persian Gulf peripheral foreland may reflect such conditions. In that region, an immense rifted-margin sediment prism of

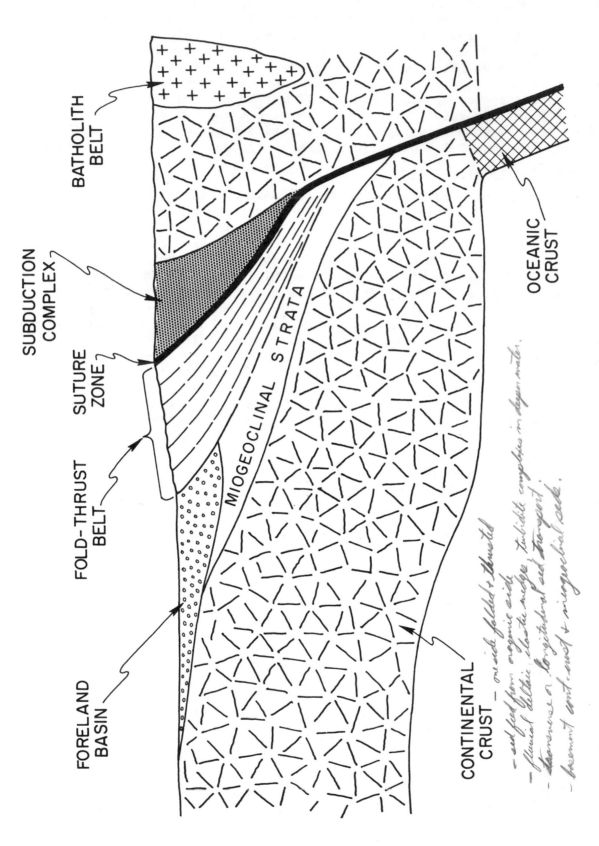

Figure 22. Schematic diagram to illustrate peripheral foreland basin adjacent to collision orogen.

Mesozoic age along the edge of the Arabian platform has been drawn against the Zagros suture belt and covered by a Tertiary foreland basin. Both Mesozoic and Tertiary rocks are richly productive in traps along the gentle foreland limb of the basin as well as in folds along the orogenic flank. Deformation is just sufficient, however, to impose attractive structuring and has not crumpled all the marine strata. If suturing proceeds too far along a collision orogen, the favorable conditions for hydrocarbon concentration are destroyed by deformation and metamorphism. Conditions are optimal while continuous migration paths still exist updip away from subduction zones.

Retroarc Basins (fig. 23)

Retroarc foreland basins occur behind continental-margin magmatic arcs. Their clear relationship to arc-trench systems is shown by the general parallelism maintained by trench or subduction complex, volcanic chain or batholith belt, and foreland basin for long distances. The Cenozoic Subandean basins east of the Andes and the marine Cretaceous of the Rocky Mountains east of the Mesozoic batholith belt are salient examples of retroarc foreland basins. The wide extent of major subsidence in the Cretaceous basin indicates that roughly half a continental block can be affected directly by plate interactions in a continental-margin arc-trench system.

Flexural subsidence in retroarc foreland basins is probably mainly the result of tectonic loading in a backarc fold-thrust belt, although a limited amount of partial subduction occurs there. Backarc fold-thrust belts apparently develop when thermally softened lithosphere along the trend of the arc accommodates contractional motion as lithosphere behind the arc crowds toward lithosphere in the arc-trench gap. Retroarc basins and backarc fold-thrust belts thus reflect overall kinematics across the arc structure opposite to that responsible for interarc basins and back-arc rifts. The foreland fold-thrust belt presumably develops where the edge of the still-rigid craton underthrusts the rear flank of the arc structure. Décollement peels off strata of an older miogeoclinal prism along the continental margin and stacks them into a telescoped pile of thrust sheets. Parts of the flank of the retroarc basin are eventually involved in the deformation as well.

Fluvio-deltaic complexes shed mainly from the orogenic flank but partly from the cratonic flank are perhaps the most characteristic strata of retroarc basins. Shallow-marine deposits are also common but deeper marine strata are rare. Source beds may be common where silled marine depressions occur or may be nearly absent where the section is entirely terrestial clastics. Effective stratigraphic traps as well as structural traps in gentle tectonic flexures can be expected within retroarc basins.

The tilting of older miogeoclinal prisms beneath retroarc basins may have as strong an influence on hydrocarbon concentration as do similar conditions beneath peripheral basins. Migration may not be so forceful, because the amounts of tilting and loading may not be as dramatic. However, increased heat flux along the rear flank of the arc orogen may promote thermal maturation. Metamorphic mineral assemblages in the so-called infrastructural belt between batholith belt and fold-thrust belt, as well as reflectivities of organic debris within retroarc basins, suggest a high heat flux within the arc orogen and inclined isotherms across the region of the fold-thrust belt. Conceivably, a moving thermal front as well as growing load and increasing tilt could contribute to updip migration within the retroarc basin and portions of the older miogeoclinal prism below it.

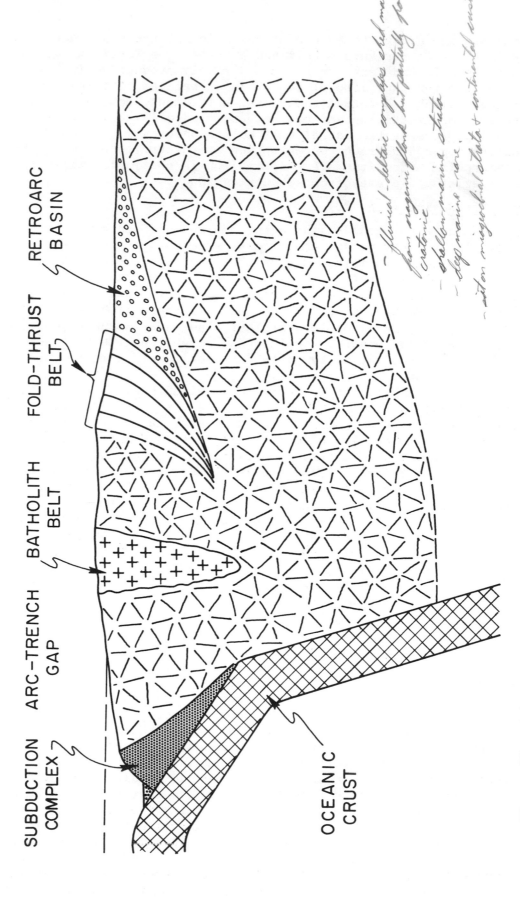

Figure 23. Schematic diagram to illustrate retroarc foreland basin in profile view.

SUBDUCTION COMPLEX

ARC—TRENCH GAP

BATHOLITH BELT

FOLD—THRUST BELT

RETROARC BASIN

OCEANIC CRUST

- fluvial-deltaic complexes shed mainly from orogenic flank but partially from craton
- shallow-marine strata
- magmatic arc
- sits on miogeoclinal strata + continental crust

BROKEN FORELANDS

Both peripheral and retroarc foreland basins have been discussed in terms of coherent asymmetric downbows with broad and generally smooth floors. Such features are common, with only gentle undulations to break their continuity and attest to the overall integrity of plates of lithosphere. However, in some foreland settings, like the Laramide belt, basement-cored uplifts and local fault-bounded basins reflect involvement of basement in foreland deformation. The conditions that promote this kind of behavior are not fully understood. Where thin platform sequences rather than thick miogeoclinal successions occupy the fold-thrust belt, the tendency for décollement may be suppressed and the possibility of basement deformation may be enhanced. Where major pre-existing crustal features like aulacogens exist in the foreland region, reactivation of older fault trends may also favor the development of block uplifts and local depressions rather than broad, continuous basins.

Within broken foreland regions, quite heterogeneous conditions prevail and few generalizations are possible with present data. Source beds may occur in local silled marine basins or even as non-marine sabkha deposits in terrestrial basins. Local pull-apart or wrench structures or both may occur if transform-like motions develop within the region. The character of individual basins within the same general foreland region may well differ greatly.

OTHER BASINS

Two other kinds of basins are related to plate convergence, but not in strictly orogenic settings. Transpressional basins occur along complex transform systems and remnant ocean basins lie along tectonic strike from the closing suture belts of collision orogens.

Transpressional Basins (fig. 24)

Where a component of plate motion in a convergent sense is present along a transform, wrench folds may develop as en echelon features along the margins of the plates involved. The late Cenozoic folds of the central California Coast Ranges beside the San Andreas fault are examples. Major synclines form local terrestrial basins. More significant, perhaps, is the tectonic thickening achieved by the formation of the en echelon fold belt as a whole. Especially where contraction is sufficient to generate marginal thrusts, the fold belt represents a tectonic load that may be sufficient to downwarp a foreland-like basin along the flank of the fold belt away from the transform.

Remnant Oceans (fig. 25)

During sequential development of a collision orogen, sediment from the highlands is shed not only into adjacent foreland basins, but also longitudinally into remnant ocean basins. The immense volumes of the Ganges delta and the Bengal fan in the Bay of Bengal along tectonic strike from the Himalayan Ranges are modern examples of this phenomenon. Turbidites with this origin may account for much of the so-called pre-orogenic flysch in classic orogenic belts. Such flysch is dumped on older oceanic sediments in a previously starved oceanic basin just prior to the crustal collision that sutures each successive segment of the remnant ocean closed. Orogeny accompanies closure as the thick flysch is deformed into a massive subduction complex. Subsequent post-orogenic

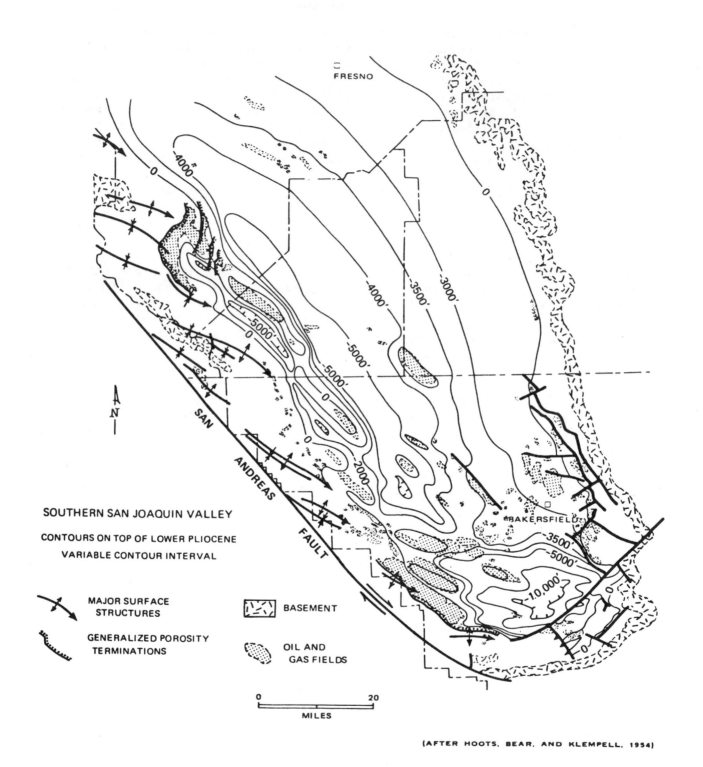

Figure 24. Sketch map of generalized transpressional wrench features (from Wilcox, R.E., T.P. Harding, and D.R. Seeley, 1973, Basic wrench tectonics: Am. Assoc. Petroleum Geologists Bull., v. 57, p. 74-96).

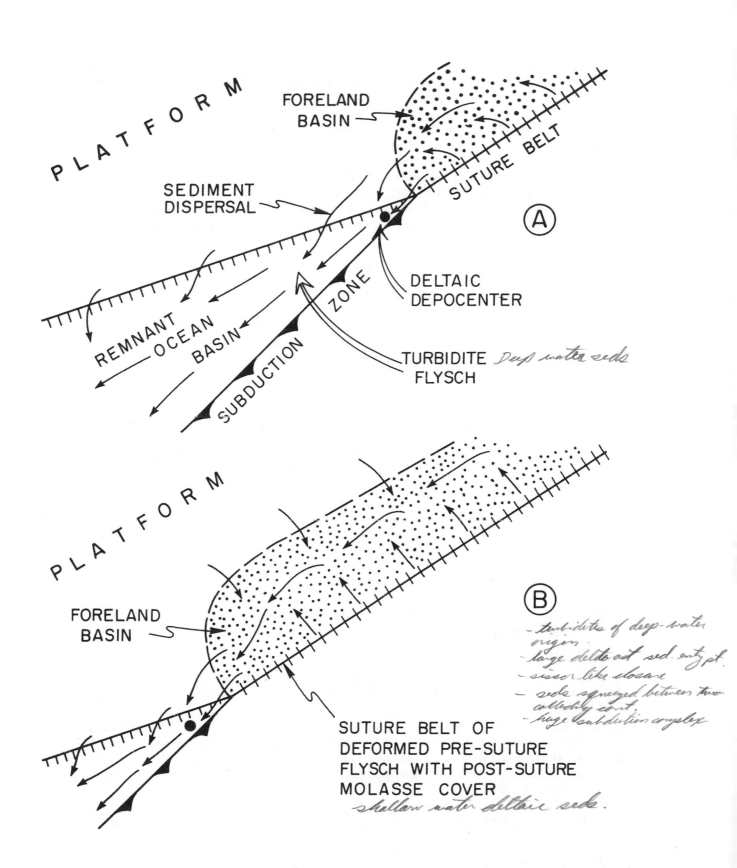

Figure 25. Schematic diagrams to illustrate progressive closure of remnant ocean basin by development of suture belt along collision orogen seen in map view. Time runs from top to bottom.

molasse is represented by fluvio-deltaic complexes that form a time-transgressive facies most extensively developed in the region marking the transition from fully closed collision orogen to remnant ocean basin.

Both flysch and molasse are thus seen as time-transgressive facies whose age varies sequentially along strike within the completed orogenic belt. At any one place, however, molasse succeeds flysch, and orogenic events are sandwiched between their respective times of deposition. Settings transitional between pre-collision remnant ocean basins and post-collision peripheral foreland basins clearly should exist during early stages of collision as subduction of a continental margin has just begun.

SELECTED BIBLIOGRAPHY

General

Mitchell, A.H. and H.G. Reading, 1969, Continental margins, geosynclines, and ocean-floor spreading: Jour. Geology, v. 77, p. 629-646.

Dewey, J.F. and J.M. Bird, 1970, Plate tectonics and geosynclines: Tectonophysics, v. 10, p. 625-638.

Dickinson, W.R., 1971, Plate tectonic models of geosynclines: Earth and Planet. Sci. Lettrs., v. 10, p. 165-174.

Halbouty, M.T., R.E. King, H.D. Klemme, R.H. Dott, Sr., and A.A. Meyerhoff, 1970, Factors affecting formation of giant oil and gas fields, and basin classification, in Halbouty, M.T. (ed.), Geology of giant petroleum fields: Am. Assoc. Petroleum Geologists Mem. 14, p. 528-540.

North, F.K., 1971, Characteristics of oil provinces; a study for students: Bull. Can. Petroleum Geology, v. 19, p. 601-658.

Dickinson, W.R., 1974, Plate tectonics and sedimentation, in Dickinson, W.R. (ed.), Tectonics and sedimentation: Soc. Econ. Paleontologists and Mineralogists Special Pub. No. 22, p. 1-27.

Klemme, H.D., 1975, Giant oil fields related to their geologic setting; a possible guide to exploration: Bull. Can. Petroleum Geology, v. 23, p. 30-66.

Dickinson, W.R., 1974, Subduction and oil migration: Geology, v. 2, p. 421-424.

Rift Valleys

Klein, G. deV., 1969, Deposition of Triassic sedimentary rocks in separate basins, eastern North America: Geol. Soc. America Bull., v. 80, p. 1825-1832.

Baker, B.H., P.A. Mohr, and L.A.J. Williams, 1972, Geology of the eastern rift system of Africa: Geol. Soc. America Special Paper 136, 67 p.

Bishop, W.W. and M.H.L. Pickford, 1975, Geology, fauna, and palaeo-environments of the Ngorora Formation, Kenya rift valley: Nature, v. 254, p. 185.

Chapin, C.E. and W.R. Seager, 1975, Evolution of the Rio Grande rift in the Socorro and Las Cruces areas: N. Mex. Geol. Soc. 26th Field Guidebook, p. 297-321.

Rifted Basins

Brink, A.H., 1974, Petroleum geology of Gabon Basin: Am. Assoc. Petroleum Geologists Bull., v. 58, p. 216-235.

Whiteman, A., D. Naylor, R. Pegrum, and G. Rees, 1975, North Sea troughs and plate tectonics: Tectonophysics, v. 26, p. 39-54.

Ziegler, P.A., 1975, Geologic evolution of North Sea and its tectonic
    framework: Am. Assoc. Petroleum Geologists Bull., v. 59, p. 1073-1097.
Ballard, R.D. and E. Uchupi, 1975, Triassic rift structure in Gulf of
    Maine: Am. Assoc. Petroleum Geologists Bull., v. 59, p. 1041-1072.

Rifted Margins

Sleep, N.H., 1971, Thermal effects of the formation of Atlantic continental
    margins by continental breakup: Geophys. Jour. Roy. Astronom. Soc.,
    v. 25, p. 325-350.
Schneider, E.D., 1972, Sedimentary evolution of rifted continental margins:
    Geol. Soc. America Mem. 132, p. 109-118.
Falvey, D.A., 1974, The development of continental margins in plate tec-
    tonic theory: Austral. Petroleum Exploration Assoc. Jour., p. 95-106.
Rona, P.A., 1974, Subsidence of Atlantic continental margins: Tectono-
    physics, v. 22, p. 283-299.

Continental Separations

Scrutton, R.A., 1973, The age relationship of igneous activity and
    continental break up: Geol. Mag., v. 110, p. 227-234.
Hutchinson, R.W. and G.G. Engels, 1972, Tectonic evolution in the southern
    Red Sea and its possible significance to older rifted continental
    margins: Geol. Soc. America Bull., v. 83, p. 2989-3002.
Talwani, M. and O. Eldholm, 1973, Boundary between continental and oceanic
    crust at the margin of rifted continents: Nature, v. 241, p. 325-330.
Barberi, F. E, Bonatti, G. Marinelli, and J. Varet, 1974, Transverse
    tectonics during the split of a continent; data from the Afar rift:
    Tectonophysics, v. 23, p. 17-29.

Protoceanic Gulfs

Lowell, J.D. and G.J. Genik, 1972, Sea-floor spreading and structural
    evolution of southern Red Sea: Am. Assoc. Petroleum Geologists Bull.,
    v. 56, p. 247-259.
Pautot, G., J.M. Auzende, and X. le Pichon, 1970, Continuous deep sea
    salt layer along North Atlantic margins related to early phase of
    rifting: Nature, v. 227, p. 351-354.
Pautot, G., V. Renard, J. Daniel, and J. Dupont, 1973, Morphology, limits,
    origin, and age of salt layer along South Atlantic African margin:
    Am. Assoc. Petroleum Geologists, v. 57, p. 1658-1671.
Kinsman, D.J.J., 1975, Salt floors to geosynclines: Nature, v. 255,
    p. 375-378.
Elders, W.A., R.W. Rex, T. Meidav, P.T. Robinson, and S. Biehler, 1972,
    Crustal spreading in southern California: Science, v. 178, p. 15-24.
Moore, D.G., 1973, Plate-edge deformation and crustal growth, Gulf of
    California structural province: Geol. Soc. America Bull., v. 84,
    p. 1883-1906.
Meckel, L.D., 1973, Recent sediment distribution in the Colorado delta
    area, northern Gulf of California: Gulf Coast Assoc. Geol. Soc.,
    v. 23, p. 27-29.
Van Andel, Tj.H., 1964, Recent marine sediments of Gulf of California,
    p. 216-310 in Van Andel, Tj.H. and G.G. Shor, Jr., Marine Geology of
    the Gulf of California: Am. Assoc. Petroleum Geologists Mem. 3, 408 p.

Marginal Prisms

Dietz, R.S., 1963, Wave-base, marine profile of equilibrium, and wave-built terraces: a critical appraisal: Geol. Soc. America Bull., v. 74, p. 971-990.

Walcott, R.E., 1972, Gravity, flexure, and the growth of sedimentary basins at a continental edge: Geol. Soc. America Bull., v. 83, p. 1845-1848.

Rona, P.A., 1970, Comparison of continental margins of eastern North America at Cape Hatteras and northwestern Africa at Cap Blanc: Am. Assoc. Petroleum Geologists Bull., v. 54, p. 129-157. (See also discussions, v. 54, p. 2214-2218, 1970).

Stewart, T.H. and Poole, F.G., 1974, lower Paleozoic and uppermost Precambrian Cordilleran miogeocline, Great Basin, western United States; in Dickinson, W.R. (ed.), Tectonics and sedimentation: Soc. Econ. Paleontologists and Mineralogists Special Pub. No. 22, p. 28-57.

Kraft, J.C., R.E. Sheridan, and M. Maisano, 1971, Time-stratigraphic units and petroleum entrapment models in Baltimore Canyon basin of Atlantic continental margin geosyncline: Am. Assoc. Petroleum Geologists Bull., v. 55, p. 658-679.

Emery, K.O., E. Uchupi, J.D. Phillips, C.O. Bowin, E.T. Bunce, and S.T. Knott, 1970, Continental rise off eastern North America: Am. Assoc. Petroleum Geologists Bull., v. 54, p. 44-108.

Worzel, J.L. and J.S. Watkins, 1973, Evolution of the northern Gulf Coast deduced from geophysical data: Gulf Coast Assoc. Geol. Soc., v. 23, p. 84-91.

Jones, P.H. and R.H. Wallace, Jr., 1974, Hydrogeologic aspects of structural deformation in the northern Gulf of Mexico basin: U.S. Geol. Survey Jour. Research, v. 2, p. 511-518.

Marginal Aulacogens

Burke, K., T.F.J. Dessauvagie, and A.J. Whiteman, 1971, Opening of the Gulf of Guinea and geological history of the Benue Depression and Niger Delta: Nature Phys. Sci., v. 233, p. 51-55.

Francheteau, J. and X. Le Pichon, 1972, Marginal fracture zones as structural framework of continental margins in South Atlantic Ocean: Am. Assoc. Petroleum Geologists Bull., v. 56, p. 991-1007.

Hoffman, P., J.F. Dewey, and K. Burke, 1974, Aulacogens and their genetic relation to geosynclines, with a Proterozoic example from Great Slave Lake, Canada, in Dott, R.H., Jr., (ed.), Modern and ancient geosynclinal sedimentation: Soc. Econ. Paleontologists and Mineralogists Spec. Pub. No. 19, p. 38-55.

Ham, W.E., 1969, Regional geology of the Arbuckle Mountains: Okla. Geol. Survey Guidebook XVII, 52 p.

Transformal Basins

Lowell, J.D., 1972, Spitsbergen Tertiary orogenic belt and the Spitzbergen fracture zone: Geol. Soc. America Bull., v. 83, p. 3091-3102.

Wilcox, R.E., T.P. Harding, and D.R. Seely, 1973, Basic wrench tectonics: Am. Assoc. Petroleum Geologists Bull., v. 57, p. 74-96.

Crowell, J.C., 1974, origin of late Cenozoic basins in California, in Dickinson, W.R. (ed.), Tectonics and sedimentation: Soc. Econ. Paleontologists and Mineralogists Special Pub. No. 22, p. 190-204.

Kellogg, H.E., 1975, Tertiary stratigraphy and tectonism in Svalbard and
    continental drift: Am. Assoc, Petroleum Geologists Bull., v. 59,
    p. 465-485.

Arc Orogens

Oxburgh, E.R. and D.L. Turcotte, 1970, Thermal structure of island arcs:
    Geol. Soc. America Bull., v. 81, p. 1655-1688.
Dickinson, W.R., 1970, Relations of andesites, granites, and derivative
    sandstones to arc-trench tectonics: Rev. Geophysics and Space
    Physics, v. 8, p. 813-862.
Plafker, George, 1972, Alaskan earthquake of 1964 and Chilean earthquake
    of 1960; implications for arc tectonics: Jour. Geophys. Res., v. 77,
    p. 901-925.
Uyeda, S. and A. Miyashiro, 1974, Plate tectonics and the Japanese
    Islands: Geol. Soc. America Bull., v. 85, p. 1159-1170.

Subduction Complexes

Ross, D.A., 1971, Sediments of the northern Middle America trench: Geol.
    Soc. America, v. 82, p. 303-322.
Moore, J.C., 1973, Cretaceous continental margin sedimentation, south-
    western Alaska: Geol. Soc. America Bull., v. 84, p. 595-614.
Ernst, W.G., 1975, Systematics of large-scale tectonics and age progres-
    sions in Alpine and circum-Pacific blueschist belts: Tectonophysics,
    v. 26, p. 229-246.
Karig, D.E. and G.F. Sharman III, 1975, subduction and accretion in
    trenches: Geol. Soc. America Bull., v. 86, p. 377-389.

Forearc Basins

Dickinson, W.R., 1971, Clastic sedimentary sequences deposited in shelf,
    slope, and trough settings between magmatic arcs and associated
    trenches: Pacific Geology, v. 3, p. 15-30.
Dickinson, W.R., 1973, Widths of modern arc-trench gaps proportional to
    past duration of igneous activity in associated magmatic arcs: Jour.
    Geophys. Res., v. 78, p. 3376-3389.
Marlow, M.S., D.W. Scholl, E.D. Buffington, and T.R. Alpha, 1973,
    Tectonic history of the central Aleutian arc: Geol. Soc. America
    Bull., v. 84, p. 1555-1574.
Grow, J.A., 1973, Crustal and upper mantle structure of the central
    Aleutian arc: Geol. Soc. America Bull., v. 84, p. 2169-2192.

Interarc Basins

Karig, D.E., 1970, Ridges and basins of the Tonga-Kermadec island arc
    system: Jour. Geophys. Res., v. 75, p. 239-254.
Karig, D.E., 1971, Structural history of the Mariana island arc system:
    Geol. Soc. America, v. 82, p. 323-344.
Ballance, P.F., 1974, An inter-arc flysch basin in northern New Zealand;
    Waitemata Group (upper Oligocene to lower Miocene): Jour. Geology,
    v. 82, p. 439-471.
Scholl, D.W., M.S. Marlow and E.C. Buffington, 1975, Summit basins of
    Aleutian Ridge: Am, Assoc. Petroleum Geologists Bull., v. 59,
    p. 799-816.

Foreland Basins

Meckel, L.D., 1970, Paleozoic alluvial deposition in the central Appalachians, p. 49-67 in Fisher, G.W., F.J. Pettijohn, and J.C. Reed (eds.), Studies of Appalachian Geology; Central and Southern: Wiley Interscience, N.Y., 460 p.

Weimer, R.J., 1970, Rates of deltaic sedimentation and intrabasin deformation, Upper Cretaceous of Rocky Mountain region: Soc. Econ. Paleontologists and Mineralogists Special Paper No. 15, p. 270-292.

Poole, F.G., 1974, Flysch deposits of Antler foreland basin, western United States, in Dickinson, W.R. (ed,), Tectonics and sedimentation: Soc. Econ. Paleontologists and Mineralogists Special Pub. No. 22, p. 58-82.

Eisbacher, G.H., M.A. Carrigy and R.B. Campbell, 1974, Paleodrainage pattern and late-orogenic basins of the Canadian Cordillera, in Dickinson, W.R. (ed.), Tectonics and sedimentation: Soc. Econ. Paleontologists and Mineralogists Special Pub. No. 22, p. 143-166.

Remnant Oceans

Curray, J.R. and D.G. Moore, 1971, Growth of the Bengal deep-sea fan and denudation in the Himalayas: Geol. Soc. America Bull., v. 82, p. 563-572.

Morris, R.C., 1974, Carboniferous rocks of the Ouachita Mountains, Arkansas; a study of facies patterns along the unstable slope and axis of a flysch trough: Geol. Soc. America Special Paper 148, p. 241-279.

Mitchell, A.H.G., 1974, Flysch-ophiolite successions, polarity indicators in arc and collision-type orogens: Nature, v. 248, p. 747-749.

Gansser, A., 1974, The ophiolitic melange, a world-wide problem on Tethyan examples: Eclog. Geolog. Helvet., v. 67, p. 479-507.

Collision Orogens

Graham, S.A., W.R. Dickinson, and R.V. Ingersoll, 1975, Himalayan-Bengal model for flysch dispersal in Appalachian-Ouachita system: Geol. Soc. America Bull., v. 86, p. 273-286.

Powell, C.McA. and J.J. Conaghan, 1973, Plate tectonics and the Himalayas: Earth Planet. Sci. Lettrs., v. 20, p. 1-12.

Boccaletti, M., P. Elter, and G. Guazzone, 1971, Plate tectonic models for the development of the western Alps and northern Apennines: Nature Phys. Sci., v. 234, p. 108-111.

Alvarez, W., T. Cocozza, and F.C. Wezel, 1974, Fragmentation of the Alpine orogenic belt by microplate dispersal: Nature, v. 248, p. 309-314.

TRUE-SCALE DIAGRAMS OF OROGENIC BASINS

(Supplement to Plate Tectonic Evolution of Sedimentary Basins)

by

William R. Dickinson, Geology Department

Stanford University, Stanford, California   94305

The geometric configuration and setting of orogenic sedimentary basins is varied (fig. 26). Figures 27-30 are an attempt to depict the geometry of key types of orogenic basins at true scale without vertical exaggeration. Overall relationships to crust and lithosphere are best seen on such diagrams. Each sketch necessarily represents a generalization and idealization. In the spirit of the text, they are intended here as a stimulus to thinking. Although each is thought to be valid in concept, none should be taken as a direct analogue of any particular basin, whose history and geometry may deviate in important ways from any general model.

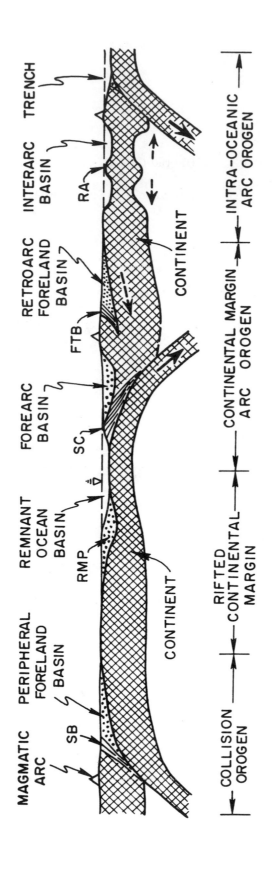

Fig. 26. Sketch to illustrate plate-tectonic settings of different types of orogenic basins. Ornament denotes lithosphere. Not to scale: SB, suture belt; RMP, rifted-margin sediment prism: SC, subduction complex, FTB, backarc fold-thrust belt; RA, remnant arc.

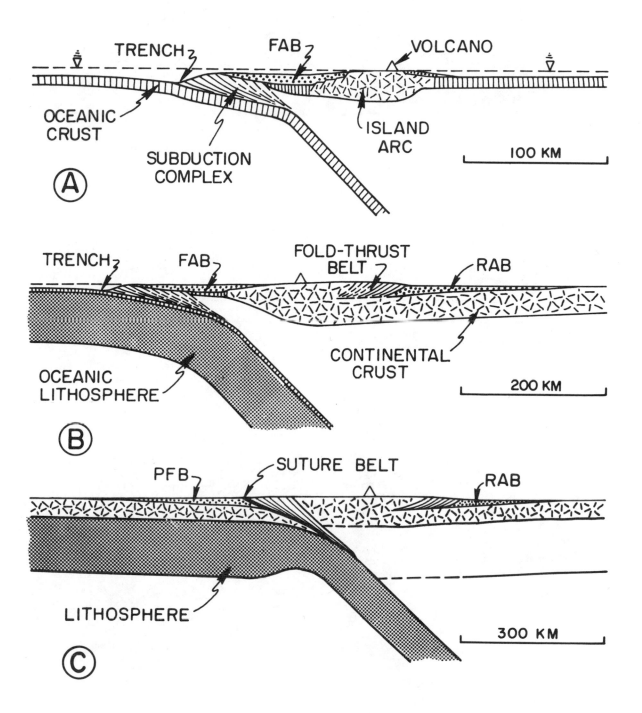

Fig. 27. Schematic diagrams of orogen types: (A) intra-oceanic arc orogen,
(B) continental-margin arc orogen, (C) intercontinental collision orogen.
Horizontal and vertical scales are the same but differ for each diagram
(see legend). Types of orogenic basins shown by stipples include:
    FAB, forearc basin; RAB, retroarc foreland basin;
    PFB, peripheral foreland basin.

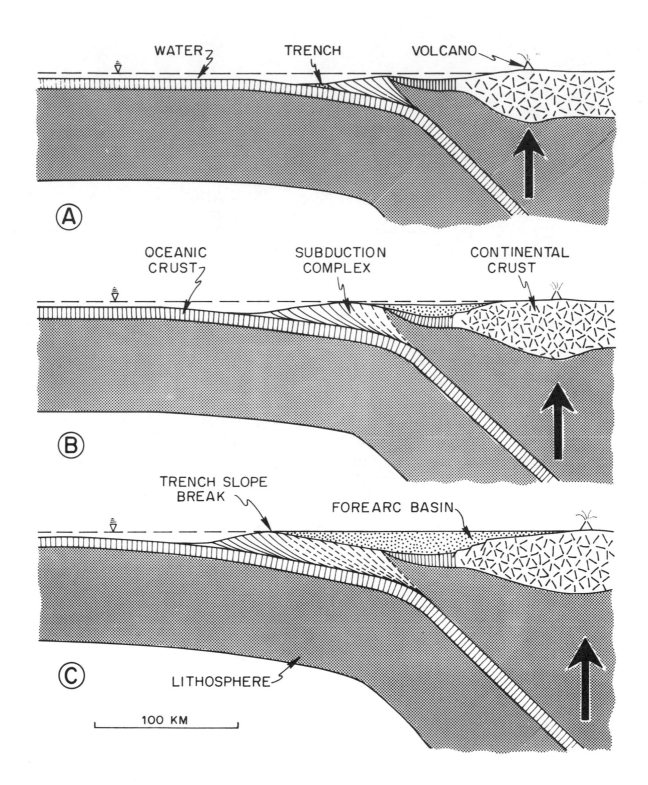

Fig. 28. Idealized diagrams showing inferred evolution (A to B to C) of the accretionary prism (Karig and Sharman, 1975) of an arc-trench system: A, incipient stage; B, starved forearc basin; C, full forearc basin. Solid lines within subduction complex denote active imbricate thrusts, whereas dashed lines denote inactive structures. Large arrows show path of magma transit from seismic zone to magmatic arc. Vertical scale equals horizontal scale.

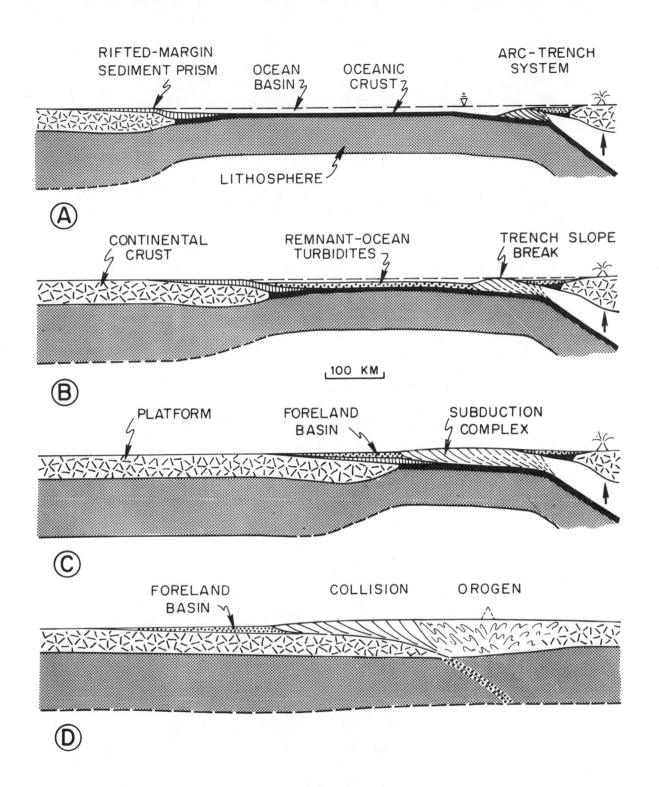

Fig. 29. Idealized diagrams showing inferred evolution (A to B to C to D) of
sedimentary basins associated with crustal collision to form cryptic intercontinental suture belt within collision orogen (sketch D highly stylized).
Diagrams represent a sequence of events in time at one place along a developing collision orogen or coeval events at different places along a suture
belt marked by diachronous closure. Hence, erosion in one segment (D) of
the orogen where the sutured intercontinental join was complete could
disperse sediment longitudinally past a migrating tectonic transition
point (C) to feed subsea turbide fans in a remnant ocean basin (B) along
tectonic strike. Vertical scale equals horizontal scale.

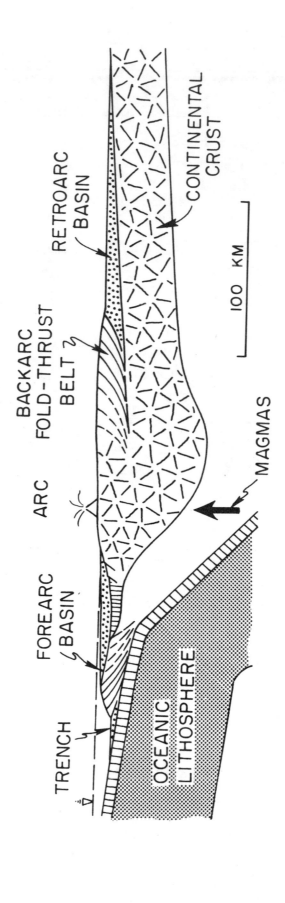

Fig. 30. Idealized diagram showing tectonic relations of retroarc foreland basin associated with continental margin arc-trench system. Vertical scale equals horizontal scale.

--Notes--

TERMINATION BASIN :-
  - a zone of minor structures at the end of a fault
  - same size as a pull apart basin.
  - high areas erode into basins.

ROTATED BLOCK BASIN :- in major transpressional areas you get faults covering a very wide zone. The blocks have a tendency to rotate with some vertical component and some horizontal component.
  - Get large areas between two fault blocks (hundred of km's in size)

-- Notes --

--Notes--

-- Notes --

HYDROCARBON ACCUMULATION

by

Hunter Yarborough

Global Exploration Analysts, Inc.

and Associates

BASIN ASSESSMENT:	A.	ORIGIN, MIGRATION & ACCUMULATION OF OIL & GAS;
	B.	SEDIMENTARY ENVIRONMENTS & THE OCCURRENCE OF HYDROCARBONS: SOURCE ROCKS, RESERVOIR ROCKS, AND SEALING ROCKS;
	C.	THE APPLICATION OF PLATE TECTONICS TO THE EXPLORATION FOR HYDROCARBONS & METALLIFEROUS DEPOSITS;
	D.	TECTONIC SETTINGS & MAJOR HYDROCARBON ACCUMULATIONS

Critical to exploration success is the recognition of the types of data that we utilize, their utility and their limitations. Geological, geophysical and geochemical data may be classifed as: "hard", "soft", and "contaminated".

We utilize hypotheses which are nothing more than suppositions put forward as a starting point for further investigations by which they may be either proved or disproved. Many of these hypotheses may ultimately be proved valid; however, others may be barren, and cannot be tested or proved. There are many of us who have beliefs that we may consider to be evident truths; others however may rate our beliefs as merely barren hypotheses.

We are constantly reminded to think optimistically. And frequently when the investment is minor and the potential rewards are great, purely optimistic thinking is justified, for so often serendipity plays a significant part in exploration. However, many of our exploration ventures of today involve huge sums of invested capital. Thus we must now be very realistic in our thinking. We must "attack" our exploration programs with the most modern scientific techniques. More than ever before, exploration today is a joint effort of geologists, geophysicists and geochemists. Finally, we must never forget how inexact our "science" is! Only by the drilling of many rank wildcats can the "odds of serendipity" act in our favor.

Today's exploration in the cratonic basins of the U.S. is primarily a "house-cleaning" operations. We are "sweeping-up" the bits and pieces of hydrocarbon accumulations that have been overlooked in the past either because they were difficult to find or because their economics were questionable. We are exploring our more "difficult" basins with renewed vigor and with a better understanding of those geological and geochemical factors that seem to control the occurrence of hydrocarbons.

Specifically, around the world, we are hunting for the "sweet spots" either within large basins or isolated as small basins. We recognize that many of our most significant accumulations are found in "kettles with a lid-on-the-top"; a "kettle" filled with source and reservoir sediments that has been "cooked" just the right amount ("Not too hot and not too cold...."), and always with the "lid" on top to prevent the escape of the hydrocarbons. Many of these "pots" are very small and have been easily overlooked, but they may be incredibly "rich".

In exploring for the "sweet spots" we must recognize the difficulty in seeing through the "lid". Thick evaporites and shales which usually are the "lids" on the "kettle" are frequently very difficult to "see through". But in many cases random wildcatting "through the lid" may be very rewarding.

Today we are entering the initial stages of exploring and developing the outer continental shelves, the continental slopes and the abyssal plains of the ocean basins. The continually rising world prices of oil and gas responding to the normal laws of supply and demand will offer economic incentives for the capital investments required for Submerged Production Systems (S.P.S.). Those of us who will lead and direct the exploration of the sediments beneath the deep waters will be severly challenged by these new frontiers.

Finally, as scientists, we must be aware that the published or "printed word" (whether a product of the news media or members of our own professions) is generally accepted by many and most as factual. More than ever before, we are being "bombarded" by irrationalism (not a single fact) and the specious argument (which is seemingly true but actually false).

HUNTER YARBOROUGH
4550 Post Oak Place
Suite 141
Houston, Texas 77027
(713) 965-9674
      686-7881
CABLE: Globex-Houston

BASIN ASSESSMENT:

A. Sediment Thickness

    Magnetic data (depth to a magnetic basement),
    refraction seismic and CDP reflection seismic.
    Critical thickness of sediment needed for
    liquid hydrocarbon generation is function of
    paleo and present geothermal gradients.

B. Structure

    No major oil producing basins in which regional
    or local structural trapping is not the
    dominant trapping mechanism.

C. Source Rocks

D. Reservoir Rocks   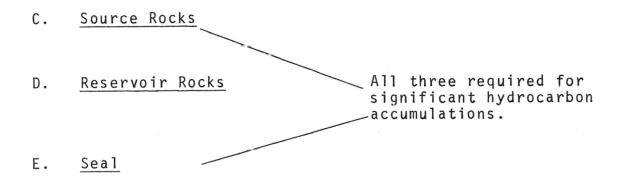 All three required for
                             significant hydrocarbon
                             accumulations.

E. Seal

F. Hydrocarbon Maturation

    The modern hypotheses utilized in reconstructing
    the biogenic, thermal, and chemical processes
    acting upon organic debris deposited in a
    sedimentary sequence.

I. ORIGIN, MIGRATION & ACCUMULATION OF HYDROCARBONS -
    INTRODUCTION

    In recent years, geochemistry has contributed many new
    fundamental concepts concerning the origin and migration
    of hydrocarbons. As a result, many explorationists have
    been forced to reject (and revise) many old hypotheses
    and beliefs, some of which are so "entrenched" in explora-
    tion thinking that they are "sacred cows" to many. This
    is particularly true for many geologists whose experience
    has been limited to the basins (and oil and gas fields)
    of the United States.

    To many explorationists, source rocks are marine sedi-
    ments. While it is probably true that most of the oil
    and gas produced from U.S. basins is sourced in marine
    clastics and carbonates, this is not true in many other
    petroliferous basins of the earth. Lacustrine and/or
    continental sediments are the only source rocks for
    many major oil and gas accumulations. Also it is only
    in the last decade that many geologists have finally
    accepted the fact that plants (marine waters, brackish
    waters, fresh waters, and land) contribute most of the
    organic debris (to the sediments) which is finally
    converted to hydrocarbons in the subsurface.

    Early migration out of source rocks into reservoir
    rocks has been required by many geologists as a fundamental
    for accumulation. As a result of this belief, structural

and/or stratigraphic traps were required soon after the source (and reservoir) rocks were deposited. Today we recognize many examples of major accumulations where the traps were formed tens and even hundreds of million years after the source rocks were deposited. "Late migration" is the rule rather than the exception in many basins.

Lateral and some vertical migration has always been accepted. Today the evidence is quite convincing that vertical migration contributes far more to migration patterns in many basins than many of us had suspected. There are many major hydrocarbon accumulations that require vertical migration of thousands of feet.

The "sealing" function of evaporites, shales, and other impermeable "lids" are now being recognized as a very fundamental and significant part of basin assessment.

As a result of geochemistry, "we have come a long way in a short time". For example, we no longer assume (without question) that the marine shale overlying (and sealing) underlying non-marine oil and gas sands is also the source rock. In fact (as a worldwide statistic) it most likely is not the source. It may be merely the "lid" that prevented further vertical migration.

I. ORIGIN, MIGRATION & ACCUMULATION OF HYDROCARBONS

    A. Source and Reservoir Beds of Petroleum and Basin Environments (Figure 1)

    B. Basic Requirements for Origin and Entrapment of Hydrocarbons (Figure 1-A)

        1. Abundant organic life - (plant)

        2. Rapid burial and/or reducing environment to organic debris

    C. Biomass of Land and Sea

        Plant debris both autochthonous and allochthonous, (continental, lacustrine, marine) principal source of organic matter (algae, phytoplankton, etc.)

    D. Geochemical Aspects of the Origin of Oil and Gas

        Lipids and lignins most important fractions of organic compounds.

    E. Deposition of Organic Matter in a Basin

    F. Formation of Oil from Organic Debris

        1. Near surface biogenic alteration of organic debris yields kerogen, biogenic methane ("marsh gas"), nitrogen, hydrogen sulphide, carbon dioxide.

        2. Thermal maturation of kerogen yields "heavy oil" and NSO compounds.

        3. "Higher" thermal maturation of "heavy oil" and kerogen yields lighter oils and wet gases.

        4. "Higher" thermal maturation of "lighter oils" and kerogen yields methane, carbon dioxide, hydrogen sulphide.

5. The concept of thermo-chemical basement: the total "destruction" of liquid and gaseous hydrocarbons by thermo-chemical reactions (involving sulphur and oxygen).

6. Evolution Organic Matter, Douala Basin, Cameroon

7. Zone of Intense Oil Generation (Figure 2)

8. Types of kerogen and evolution "paths" (Figure 2-A)

9. Evolution of coal macerals (Figure 2-B)

10. Kerogen evolution and hydrocarbon formation

G. The "Temperature Windows" of Thermal Maturation in an Average Mesozoic-Cenozoic Petroliferous Basin. Vertical "Leakage" Anomalies. (Figure 3)

H. Oil Degradation (Figure 4)

Fresh water migrating through reservoir dissolves and washes away most soluble (light) oils, reduces salinity and brings bacteria. Tar belts, heavy oils and "tar mats" at oil-water contacts may be a result of this degradation. Tar belts also due to inspissation and oxidation.

Deasphalting: methane migrating (from deeper in basin?) into pre-existing oil accumulations precipitates asphaltenes (in colloidal suspension) creating "heavy oil" at base of oil column and lighter oil above. Methane may be a result of increased thermal maturation of liquid hydrocarbons within pre-existing accumulation.

Iron in clastic reservoirs combines with sulphur to clean "oils" (pyrite).

I. Hydrocarbon and Source Sediments (Figure 5)

Basins may be continental, lacustrine, brackish and marine. Organic debris deposited in basins may be autochthonous and/or allochthonous. All that is needed for source rocks is the basic requirements. Many huge oil accumulations have as their only source "lacustrine" sediments. Most basins have complex mixtures of continental, lacustrine, and marine organic debris. Geochemical clues ("finger-prints") as to the source debris are C13/C12 ratios, molecular structure, and trace elements.

J. An Average Oil

Elemental composition, compound types, molecular size

K. Similarity of Lipids and Oil Components

L. Sedimentary Organic Matter

Bitumens, kerogen, NSO's (nitrogen, sulphur and oxygen compounds)

M. Dispersed Organic Debris in Sediments

Primary: terrestrial and marine

Modified: sapropelic, etc.

Thermal "blackened"

N. Metamorphism of Organic Debris (Figure 6)

1. Coal (Rank, BTU, %VM)

2. Spore carbonization

3. Thermal alteration index (kerogen)

4. Vitrinite reflectance

5. Level of organic metamorphism

O. Thermal Alteration Index and Associated Hydrocarbons

P. Maturation, Heat Flow and "Kerogen" Color

Q.   Lateral and Vertical Migration of Hydrocarbons

Hypotheses requiring extensive vertical migration
(leakage) are becoming attractive, i.e. Persian
Gulf, Mexico Mesozoic; Pleistocene oil from Pre-
Pleistocene source rocks.

   1.   Primary petroleum migration hypotheses

   2.   Lateral, vertical and late migration (Figure 7)

   3.   Hydrostatic entrapment of oil and gas

   4.   Hydrodynamic entrapment of oil and gas

   5.   Up-dip migration patterns

   6.   Saturation pressures: hypothesis

   7.   East Texas Field: "Re-migration" accumulation.

   8.   Original accumulation vs. uplift and burial

   9.   Vertical migration

   10. Ventura Avenue Field, California (Figure 8)

   11. South Mountain Field, California

   12. North Rankin Field, Australia

   13   Kirkuk Field, Iraq (Figure 9)

   14. Agha Jari Field, Iran

   15. Sumatra Basins (Figure 9-A)

   16. Northern Gulf Basin

   17. "Vertical migration" - Louisiana Continental
        Shelf

   18. Age of oil vs. age of reservoir

        (Young, et al., A.A.P.G 4-1977)

R.   Time of Maximum Migration is a Function of Viscosity

   1.   Darst Creek, Luling and Salt Flat Fields, Texas

One-half billion bbls. of Lower Cretaceous,
shallow, light oil trapped by a "Miocene"
fault.

2. Cross Section: South Texas Shelf: End
    Cretaceous Time 60 MY

3. Cross Section: South Texas Lower Cretaceous
    Fields and Tertiary Migration

4. Migration Curve for Lower Cretaceous Source
    and Reservoir Rocks of South Texas (Figure 10)

5. Phosphoria fm., Wyoming

    a. Northern Rocky Mountain Basins
        Southern Rocky Mountain Basins

    b. Permian Structure, Wyoming

    C. Permian Facies

    d. Sedimentary Environments Phosphoria
        Formation

    e. Burial History and Migration
        End Triassic Period
        End Cretaceous Period

    f. Elk Basin Field; Garland Field

    g. Migration History Curve (Figure 11)

6. Gronigen Gas Field, Netherlands (Figure 11-A)

    a. Migration History Curve

7. Oklahoma City Field

    a. Migration History Curve (Figure 12)

S. Algerian Sahara Basins - "Late" Migration

    Silurian source rocks have been "buried" and
    "heated-up" by Mesozoic and Cenozoic sediments
    causing late migration of oil and gas

T. Hassi Messaoud Field - "Late" Migration

U.   Potential Hydrocarbon Source Rocks

    1.   Richness: Total organic carbon content
                       Insoluble organic matter (kerogen)
                       Soluble organic matter (bitumen)

    2.   Type: oil, condensate; or gas precursor

    3.   Thermal Maturity

V.   Hydrocarbon Geochemistry

    1.   Source Rock Evaluation

    2.   Crude Oil Source and Character

    3.   Geochemical Prospecting

W.   Hydrocarbon Geochemistry of Basin

    1.   Location, areal extent, depth, thickness
        and richness of potential source sediments

    2.   Type and volume of hydrocarbons predicted
        (if any).

X.   Geochemical Exploration

The Baltimore Canyon basin - U.S. Atlantic Shelf
(Figure 13)

Y.   Source Rock: Organic Productivity of Basin

Nutrient supply (proximity to land, water circulation, temperature, illumination, salinity, pollution,
organic evolution). (Figure 1-A)

The "Green River" oil shale basins of Colorado,
Wyoming, and Utah contain some of the earth's
richest source rocks. These lacustrine sediments
possibly owe their unique organic richness to
frequent "fertilizing" of the lake waters with
phosphorous derived from the Permian Phosphoria

fm. which cropped-out around the margins of
these large lake basins. (Figure 13-A)

Source Rocks: Late Jurassic-Early Cretaceous Times

Persian gulf, Gulf basin, Viking graben, N.W.
India?, Eastern Pakistan?, Eastern shelf U.S.?,
E. New Guinea?, Wyoming "Disturbed Belt" (back-
arc basins?), Prudhoe Bay. (Figure 14)

Z.   Vertical Migration: Louisiana Continental Shelf

Suggested Literature:

1.   Petroleum Transformations In Reservoirs; C. W. D.
      Milner, M.A. Rogers and C. R. Evans, Jour. Geochemical
      Exploration 7 (1977) 101-153.

2.   Applied Petroleum Geochemistry To Search For Oil:
      Examples From Western Canada Basin, M. J. L. Bailey,
      C. R. Evans and C. W. D. Milner, A.A.P.G. 11 (1974)
      2284-2295.

II. <u>SEDIMENTARY ENVIRONMENTS & THE OCCURRENCE OF HYDROCARBON</u>
<u>ACCUMULATIONS:</u> <u>SOURCE ROCKS, RESERVOIR ROCKS & SEALING</u>
<u>ROCKS:</u>

A. <u>Source Beds vs. Reservoir Rocks of Typical Basin</u>

1. Most Favorable Reservoirs for Entrapment of
Hydrocarbons.

a. Rapidly "Subsiding" Deltaic Complexes

b. Rapidly Subsiding Carbonate Lagoons
and Shelves

c. Reef Complexes Related to Rapidly
Subsiding Lagoons and Shelves

d. Turbidites - "Sands" and "Carbonates"

B. <u>Deltaic Complexes</u> (Fluvial, Delta Margin, etc.)
(Figure 15)

Seal and reservoir beds interfinger. Excellent

stratigraphic trapping of liquids and gases.

1. Numerous types of excellent reservoir sands.

2. Numerous types of excellent seal rocks in
"contact" with reservoir rocks.

3. Modern Mississippi Delta

30,000 square miles in 5,000 years

C_{14} dates document shifting depocenters;
"pile of leaves".

4. Typical Deltaic Complex: Barrier Island
(Beach?)

Galveston Island - Recent

San Jaun Basin, N.W. New Mexico - Cretaceous
"still-stand" beach ridges and barrier islands.

Horshoe Gallup Field

Muddy ss. Paleoenvironments: Montana and
Wyoming (Figure 16)

Bell Creek Field

5. "Classic" Seismic Profile Delta Margin Complex
(Figures 17 & 18)

6.   Examples of Major Productive Deltaic Complexes

C.   <u>Rapidly Subsiding Carbonate Shelves and "Lagoons"</u>

Abundant plant life

Rapid subsidence plus fast sedimentation preserves organic debris.

Porous reservoir facies: skeletal debris, reef detritus, oolitic ls., patch reefs, dolomites and sands.

Evaporites and "muds" cause mass mortalities of organisms, capping and "burial" of organic debris. "Evaporites" contribute to dolomitization. Evaporites are excellent "seals".

Occasional very rich source rock along continental margins due to upwelling currents supplying nutrients for organisms (i.e. Phosphoria fm.)

1.   Generalized Framework of Carbonate Environments (Figure 19)

2.   Acetate Peels of Carbonate Rocks

3.   Recent Carbonates of Bahamas

4.   Belton Quarry, Texas

5.   Delaware Basin - Permian Reef Complex

6.   Comparison of Modern vs. Ancient Carbonate-Evaporite Facies

7.   Diagenetic Changes of Carbonate Rocks

Solution, mineralogical changes, lithification, dolomitization, etc.

8.   Examples of Major Productive Carbonate Provinces

<u>Note significance of "burial" (seal)</u>

9.   Theories of Evaporite Formation

Shallow and "deep" waters (Figure 20)

D. <u>Reef Complexes Related to Rapidly Subsiding
   "Lagoons" and Shelves</u>

   Warm clear water. Abundant plant (and animal)
   life.

   Rapid subsidence plus fast sedimentation.

   Porous reservoir rocks: reef, fore reef detritus,
   back reef carbonates, dolomites and sands.

   Reef "death", burial, and sealing by muds,
   evaporites, marls and chalks.

   1.   Typical Carbonate "Build-ups". (Figure 21)

   2.   Silurian Atoll - Midland Basin

   3.   "Transgressive" vs. "Regressive" Reef
        Growth

   4.   Middle Cretaceous Paleogeography Northern
        Gulf Basin

   5.   Carbonate Environments

   6.   Environment Interpretation and Explora-
        tion

   7.   Seismic Examples of "Reefs"

   8.   Examples of Major Productive "Reefs"

        <u>Note significance of proper "burial" (seal)</u>

E. <u>Turbidites ("Pro-Delta", "Marine")</u> - Gravity-induced
   flows; below wave base (shallow to very deep waters)

   Originally accumulated at delta and shelf margins

   Displaced from shallow into deeper water environment

   Deeper waters' reducing environments more favorable
   for preservation of organic debris (excellent source
   rocks)

   Mesozoic and Cenozoic deeper water sediments
   organically rich with planktonic plant and animal
   debris

   Palezoic deep marine (oceanic) sediments "sterile"
   (this does not apply to "cratonic black shales")

Permeable sands and carbonates may be completely enclosed by impermeable deeper water lutites, chalks, marls, etc.

Helps preserve original porosity and permeability

Creates perfect stratagraphic traps

Abnormally high reservoir pressures

Fractured cherts and chalks are potential source and reservoir rocks

1. Turbidite Sequence

2. Grand Banks "Turbidite", 1929

3. Monterey Canyon Turbidite Fan

4. Turbidite Characteristics

5. Turbidite Cores, South Texas

6. Los Angeles Basin

7. Turbidite Exploration (Figure 22)

   Paleogeography, Miocene Times, S.E. Texas and Southwest Louisiana

8. Carbonate Turbidites

   Poza Rica Field, Tampico Basin, Mexico

9. Carbonate Turbidite exploration, South Texas (Figure 22-A)

10. Upper Cretaceous Turbidite "sand Piles" - Southeast U.S. (Figure 22-A)

11. Examples of Major Productive Turbidites

12. Seismic Examples of Turbidite Sequences

F. Keys to Interpretation of Sedimentary Environments

1. Basin Geometry

2. Paleontology

3. Sedimentology

4. Paleogeographic maps

5.   Basins and sedimentary environments

6.   Persian Gulf (Figure 23)

     "RSSTT"

III. PLATE TECTONICS & THE OCCURRENCE OF MAJOR HYDROCARBON ACCUMULATIONS

A. Basic Hypotheses

1. Laurasia and Gondwana (Figure 24)

   The super-continent, Pangaea, of late Paleozoic and early Mesozoic times.

   The major hydrocarbon accumulations genetically related to the break-up of the continents during Mesozoic and Cenozoic times.

   Mesozoic basins predominately extensional.

   Cenozoic basins predominately "shear zones".

2. Plate Tectonics Requires New Hypotheses as to Structural Styles of Basins

3. Major Cratonic Basins (Figure 25)

   Only about 5% of oil found in Paleozoic basins.

   Paleozoic basins once present along or near continental margins destroyed by continental collisions, subduction, etc.

   Many Paleozoic basins deeply eroded and oil fields exhumed.

4. Major Earthquake Epicenter Zones

   Focal mechanism studies indicate three basic structural styles for origin and deformation of basins:

   a. Extension ("pull-apart"): normal faulting (45 degrees to 60 degrees)

   b. Subduction (compression) and collision: thrust faulting

   c. Shearing: vertical to high angle faulting (with near-surface overturning)

   Many basins throughout their life history may have been subjected to two or even three of these basic styles; i.e. many extensional basins have a strong antithetic shear overlay; and most major shear-zone basins have a large component of extension.

5.   Rigid Plates of the Earth's Crust

6.   Sea-floor Spreading - Possible Causes:
     (Figure 26)

     a.   Convection currents

     b.   Plate "geometry" - thickness, density,
          sediment thickness, etc.

     c.   Plates pushed apart

     d.   Gravity tectonics

     e.   Lithosphere sinkers

     f.   Mainstream creep

     g.   Viscosity changes

     h.   Mantle plumes ("hot spots") (Figures 26-A)

7.   Rigid Plates and "Hot Spots"

8.   Hawaiian Islands "Hot Spot"?

     Hypothesis: Islands of Hawaiian chain
     formed as Pacific oceanic crust moving
     northwest passed over a relatively fixed
     "hot spot".

9.   Hawaiian Ridge & Emperor Seamounts (Figure 27)

     At western end of Hawaiian Islands, a line
     of sea-mounts is an apparent continuation
     of the Hawaiians now trending northerly.
     This "bend" is dated at circa 40 MY.

     Hypothesis: About 40 M years ago, the
     Pacific plate "pole of opening" shifted
     to a new pole. This resulted in the
     Pacific plate changing from a northerly
     drift to a more westerly direction of
     drift.

     This change to a westerly drift of the
     Pacific plate affected the margins of the
     plate. The North America margin changed from
     subduction to predominately shear creating
     the rich shear zone basins of California.
     The change along the western margin of the
     U.S. from subduction to shear "released" the
     western U.S. from compression, creating the
     (extensional) basin and range province?

In the Western Pacific, the Mariana Arc began
a pulse of volcanic activity in early Miocene
times. The Pareca Vela basin began opening.
The Japan arc began tectonic activity in
middle Tertiary times and the Sea of Japan
developed as a back-arc basin as the Japanese
archipelago migrated away from Asia.

Increased rate of subduction in Oligocene-
Miocene times along margins of the S.E. Asia
plate created major extensional basins
behind volcanic arcs; extensive flooding of
extension and shear-zone basins with fluvial,
lacustrine, and deltaic sediments; major
period of Miocene reefs and carbonate platforms "growing" in favorable "ecologic
niches".

10.   Yellowstone "Hot Spot"? (Figure 27-A)

11.   Colorado Plateau "Hot Spot"?

12.   Great Basin "Hot Spot"?

13.   "Hot Spots", Continental Domes and Rift
       Basins: Red Sea, East Africa

14.   "Hot Spots", Continental Rifting, and New
       Oceans Forming. "Failed arms" of triple
       junctions preserved as rift-valley basins.

15.   Offshore Sediment Thickness

       Basins formed and pre-existing basins deformed
       as a result of three basic structural
       styles, or combinations of styles.

B.   Extensional Basins

   1.   "Model Study": Extensional ("Pull-Apart")
         Rifting

   2.   Red Sea and Gulf of Aden: Mantle domes and
         triple junctions. (Figures 28 & 29)

         Major production found in Gulf of Suez (not
         the Red Sea): the "cold" sweet spot;
         Miocene "salt lid" on top of "Nubian kettle".
         Reservoirs of post-rift Miocene carbonates
         (reefs) and rift and pre-rift sands ("Nubian")

3.   Rift Valley Sedimentation (Figure 30)

    a.   Alluvial stage

          Good "sialic" reservoir rocks;
          "lacustrine" source rocks.

    b.   Evaporite (may be absent) stage

          Chemical precipitants; environments may
          be favorable for both deep and/or
          shallow water "salts".

    c.   Normal Marine stage

          Chalks, marls, reefs, black shales, etc.

4.   Africa - Triple Junctions (Figure 30-A)

5.   "Atlantic Break-Up" & Rift Valley Grabens (Figure 30-B)

6.   Africa - Mantle Domes, Basins and Extensional
Margins (Figure 31)

    a.   Gabon Basin - map (Figure 31-A)

    b.   Gabon Basin - cross sections (Figure 31-B)

          Cocoa Beach fm. (lacustrine and continental)
          excellent source rock. Major potential in
          pre-salt sediments"

    c.   Gabon Basin - seismic sections

    d.   Angola Basin - cross section

          Major potential in pre-salt sediments?

    e.   Malagasy

7.   Basins of Brazil

    a.   Reconcavo Basin - map (Figure 31-C)

    b.   Reconcavo Basin - cross section
          Lacustrine and continental source rocks (Figure 31-D)

    c.   Espiritu-Santo Basin
          Major potential in pre-salt sediments?

8.   Basins of Argentina (Figure 44-A)

9.   N.W. Australia: Mesozoic extensional margin;
Paleozoic aborted rift valleys (failed-arms?)
(Figure 32)

N.W. Australia - cross section (Figure 32-A)

N.W. Australia - seismic section (Figure 32-B)

> Where are the "sweet spots"? Where
> are the "pot-holes" containing good
> source rocks, good reservoir rocks,
> and good seals?

10. Idealized Cross Sections of "Extensional"
     Continental Shelves (Figure 32-C, 32-D)

     Most continental shelves at margins of
     continents are relatively barren. Major
     exceptions are Mississippi River and
     Niger River depocenters where sediment
     load has depressed the crust. Extensional
     continental shelves are usually characterized
     by slow sedimentation, slow burial of
     organic debris and passive structural
     deformation (except in the "deep", early,
     "root systems" of rift basins). Possible
     major potential for "deep water deltas"
     (Amazon, Nile, etc.).

C. Shear-Zone Basins

   1. Gulf of California

       Extensional (pull-apart motion) at mouth of
       Gulf "transformed" into shear-zone deformation
       to the north.

       San Andreas shear-zone system: a wide, "soft"
       plate boundary.

   2. Shear Diagram

       Components of both compression and extension
       present in parallel shear zone deformation

       Both synthetic (primary) and antithetic
       (secondary) deformation

   3. Model Study: Shear Zone Deformation

       Development of both basins and structural
       traps. Deformation of pre-existing basins.

   4. Convergent Shear Zone Basin vs. Divergent
       Shear Zone Basin

Basins may exhibit both structural styles; "multi-history".

5.   Structural Styles: Shear Zone "Traps"

En-echelon folds and faults
Major, through-going synthetic faults
Major basin-margin faults and folds

6.   California Basins - The San Andreas Shear Zone (Figure 33)

Imperial Valley: Inadequate source rocks; Salton and Agua Prieta geothermal fields; "bleeding" shear zone?; "friction" geothermal source?

Los Angeles Basin

Note the 200 mile wide "soft plate boundary" and the many shear zone basins of the California Continental Borderland.

Ventura Basin, Santa Maria Valley, Cuyama Valley, Salinas-San Ardo, and the S.W. Margin of the San Joaquin Valley.

Santa Cruz Basin: - "Smeared" - structural deformation too intense.

Geysers Geothermal field: "bleeding" shear zone?; fresh waters; "friction" geothermal source?

7.   Los Angeles Basin

   a.   Regional map of basin and "blocks"

        Divergent extensional basin; turbidite reservoirs; one of the world's richest "pot-holes" of source rock

   b.   S.W. Los Angeles Basin

        En-echelon folds and faults

   c.   Eastern Los Angeles Basin

        Oblique convergence, "hanging wall" traps, half folds, etc.

   d.   San Andreas fault and the Inglewood-Newport fault zone

8. Central California Basins (Figure 34)

    a. S.W. Margin San Joaquin Valley
       Basin margin fault, folds and strati-
       graphic traps. Right lateral shear
       zone deformation during Miocene, Pliocene,
       Pleistocene and Recent of Mesozoic-
       Early Cenozoic fore-arc basin.

    b. Santa Maria Valley
       Shallow, heavy oil

    c. Salinas Valley
       Shallow, heavy oil

    d. Cuyama Valley
       Small "sweet spot" preserved in wide,
       "barren", complex shear zone

9. Cook Inlet, Alaska (Figure 35)

Right lateral shear zone deformation during
Miocene, Pliocene, Pleistocene and Recent
of Mesozoic-Early Cenozoic fore-arc basin.

10. Eastern Venezuela and Trinidad

The Caribbean "Tongue of the Pacific" creates
major right-lateral shear zone deformation
along the northern margin of South America.
Sialic cratonic crust yields good reservoir
sands.

11. N.W. Venezuela and N.E. Columbia (Figure 36)

Northerly-trending Cordilleran shear zones
plus east-west Caribbean shear.
Long, narrow ("isoclinal") basins of Magdalena.

12. "Sumatra" Shear Zone (Figure 37)

Oblique subduction of India plate under S.E.
Asia plate creates major right-lateral
deformation of back-arc basins.

13. Philippines

Volcano-clastics contain poor reservoir sands.

14. New Zealand

Gas-prone reservoirs due to high temperatures?
Geothermal field; "bleeding" shear zone?;
fresh waters; "friction" geothermal source?

15. Dead Sea "Rift"

Rhombochasm resulting from left-lateral deformation. "Half domes".

16. "Collision Tectonics": (Figures 38, 39 & 40)

   1. Erasia-India collision (Figure 40-A

   2. Recent tectonics India-Asia (Figures 41 & 42)

      Eastward displacement of "Tibet block" to accommodate collision of Indian block with Asian block.

   3. Arabia-India-Asia Tectonic Patterns

   4. Western Mediterranean (Figure 42-A)

   5. Eastern Mediterranean (Figure 42-B)

   6. Rhine Graben "Impactogen" (Figure 42-C)

17. Major Shear Zones "Ripping" the Craton of N. America

   Subduction and collision along the "Atlantic-Gulf" margins of Paleozoic times "cracked" the continent and created major shear zone deformation of pre-existing basins, (horst blocks, folds, faults, etc.).

18. Carboniferous Paleogeography, Southern U.S. (Figures 43, 43-A & 43-B)

   a. Anadarko Shear Zone - Major snythetic through-going shear zone deformation. Carboniferous deformation of pre-existing Lower Paleozoic "Oklahoma basin".

   b. Hunton Arch, Nemaha Ridge and Matador-Red River Complex - Folds and faulting antithetic to snythetic deformation.

   c. Delaware Basin - Central Basin Platform - Midland Basin; shear zone deformation of pre-existing "Texas basin". Ft. Chadbourne "Antithetic" Fault Zone.

   d. Dip of Benioff Zone, Andean Margin, South America (Figure 44)

19. Mesozoic Shear Zones "Ripping" Western U.S. (Figure 45)

Lewis & Clark Lineament: "Wyoming" fault block
mts. and rift-valley basins. Formed as a
result of tangential compression, uplift and
left-lateral shear during Mesozoic-Cenozoic.
Epicontinental seas filled basins with favorable
source and reservoir rocks.

Arizona fault block mts. and rift-valley basins
filled with continental and lacustrine sediments.
No Known source rocks except for Tertiary
lacustrine sediments. (Possibility of thick,
flat thrust plates overlying favorable Mesozoic
and Paleozoic sediments.)

20. Precambrian Sedimentary Basins, Western U.S.:
(Figure 46)

21. Seismic Examples - Shear Zone Styles

Vertical, high angle faults, with some near-
surface overturning.

D. 1. Marginal (back-arc; arc-continent) and Frontal
(fore-arc; arc-trench) Basins (Figures 47, 47-A & 48)

Frontal basins generally have poor reservoir
quality sands, (volcano-clastics). Carbonates
and fractured cherts may offer reservoir
objectives. Marginal basins, possibly filled
with favorable source and reservoir rocks,
may have temperature problems.

2. Major Structural Features of the Western
Pacific (Figure 48-A)

Pacific: "Ring of Fire" vs. "Leading Edges
of Advancing Plates"?

3. Marginal and Frontal Basins - N.W. Pacific

"Eastern" Japan: reservoir quality?

Sea of Japan: source, reservoir, structure
problems.

"China Sea": Possible high potential shear
zone basins filled with turbidites and
deltaic clastics.

4. First and Second Marginal Basins Behind
"Migrating" Arc

Complex structural and sedimentary histories.
Reservoir and temperature problems.

5. Marginal Basins "Complicated" by Arc Reversal
and Arc-Arc Collision

Very complex "histories".

6. Relative Plate Motion and Types of Frontal
and Marginal Basins.

7. Andaman "Basin Complex"

Continent-arc basin; arc-ridge basin; ridge-
trench basin. Reservoir problems. Very
complex structural deformation.

8. Sumatra

Arc-ridge-trench "basin". Reservoir problems.

9. Java (Figure 49)

10. Eastern Caribbean Margin (Barbados) (Figure 50)

11. Sacramento Valley, California

12. Talara Basin, Peru

13. Cook Inlet, Alaska

14. Cenozoic Sedimentary Rates

15. Dip of Benioff Zone, Andean Margin, South
America (Figure 44)

16. Basins of Argentina (Figure 44-A)

17. Seismic Examples

18. Subduction Margin Summary

E. Eustatic Sea Level Changes & Plate Tectonics (Figure 51)

Worldwide changes of sea level related not only
to periods of continental glaciation but also to
rates of sea floor spreading (and volumes of
oceanic ridge systems).

F. "Stand-Still" Domes and Basins (Figures 31, 52 & 53)

1. Africa: Neogene times, encircled by "ridges".

2.   North America: Paleozoic times, encircled by "subduction and collision margins".

3.   S.E. Asia: Encircled by subduction.

G.   Continental Drift Scenarios and Basin "Development"

1.   Mesozoic-Cenozoic break-up of Pangaea

2.   The basins of the margins of the north and south Atlantic genetically related to the "openings" of the Atlantic - and eustatic sea level changes. (Figure 54, 54-A & 54-B)

3.   Possible Paleozoic "assembly" of Gondwana and Laurasia.

The proto-Atlantic of Paleozoic times? Soft data! (Figures 43 & 55)

Paleo-magnetic latitudes, sedimentary environments, and radiometric dates of orogeny (subduction).

H.   Prudhoe Bay Field

Sadlerochit formation (Permo-Triassic clastics) derived from a sialic provenance located to the north. Today this is oceanic crust. (Figure 55-A)

I.   Gondwana "Break-up" and the Gippsland Basin, Australia

J.   The Basins of India and Pakistan (Figure 56)

1.   Gondwana: Triassic-Jurassic times

2.   India-Burma

3.   Cambay Basin (Figure 56-A)

Failed-arm of Late Cretaceous-Early Tertiary "triple junction"?

Deccan trap times: basalt flooding from mantle plume? (Figure 56-B)

4.   The hydrocarbon potential of N. W. India and Eastern Pakistan.

K. Plate Tectonics: Southeast Asia (Figure 57)

    1. Tertiary Basins of S.E. Asia (after Murphy '75)

       Types of crust vs. types of basins

    2. Shelfal basins

       Sumatra
       Structural styles
       Characteristics

    3. Continental margin basins

       Structural styles
       Characteristics

    4. Archipelagic basins

       Phillipines
       Characteristics

    5. Marginal seas: Small ocean basins?

       Sulu-Celebes
       Characteristics

L. Ouachita-Marathon Subduction-Collision

Carboniferous collision of South America and/or island arcs with the Marathon-Ouachita margin of North America

M. Gulf Basin Extensional - Shear Tectonics: Triassic-Jurassic Times

The great extensional (divergent) shear zone gore of Jurassic times, and the quasi-oceanic crust forming as North America "moved away" northwesterly from Africa and South America; the rift basins and the "ridges" that formed.

N. Exploration of Orogenic belts

    1. Types of Deformation and Hydrocarbon Accumulations

    2. Thrust Plate Terminology

    3. Typical Oil and Gas Traps

15.   Cenozoic "Break-up"

16.   Basin and Range and East Pacific Rise

17.   Great Basin Tertiary Volcanic Province

18.   Central Nevada

19.   Foreland Basement Deformation and Tangential Compression ("Wyoming" Rocky Mountain Province) (Figures 45, 65, 66, 67 & 68)

20.   Dip of Benioff Zones, Andean Margin, South America (Figure 44)

      <u>Spatial Distribution of Earthquakes and Subduction of the Nazca Plate Beneath South America</u>
      M. Barazangi and B. L. Isacks; Geology 11 (1976) 686-692

21.   Colorado Plateau

22.   Western Cordillera

23.   Mega "Drag Folds"

24.   Lewis & Clark Lineament

25.   Ridge-Trench "collision" and Mantle Diapirs

26.   Crustal Fracture Systems, North America

      <u>Lineaments - Ineffective Guide to Ore Deposits</u>, J. Gillully; Economic Geology (1976) 1507-1514

27.   Back-arc basins of Western North America (Figure 22-A)

R.   <u>Zagros Mountains</u>

S.   <u>Caribbean</u>

      Major accumulations (Venezuela, Trinidad and Columbia) related to continental margins-sialic crust, not oceanic crust. Tertiary reefs offer reservoir potential.

T.   <u>Ouachita-Marathon</u>

U.   Appalachians

V.   Mexican "Rockies"

"Reforma" Fields - S.E. Mexico

Shear zone folds (Middle Cretaceous and Lower
Tertiary carbonate reservoirs). Shear related to
Tehuantepec fracture zone of the Guatemalan plate?

"Flat Dipping" Benioff Zone?

W.   Oil & Gas Accumulations of the North Sea

Viking Graben - "Failed Arm" of Mesozoic Triple
Junction? (Figure 69)

X.   Assessment of Potential Petroleum Provinces - United
States   (Figures 70 & 71)

Gulf Basin

Atlantic Shelf

California Borderland

Alaska Basins

Y.   The "Deepwater" Potential

Submerged Production Systems (SPS)

Continental Slopes, Rises, and Abyssal Plains

Continental Fragments: Indian Ocean, Atlantic
Ocean, Pacific Ocean

Z.   The Basins of Russia and China

IV. PLATE TECTONICS & THE OCCURRENCES OF MAJOR METAL DEPOSITS

A.   Major Types of Deposits

B.   Gondwana Metalliferous Belts

V. <u>INTRA-CRUSTAL (BASEMENT) REFLECTIONS & CRUSTAL MODEL</u>
(Figures 66, 67 & 68)

Earth History, Geothermal Accumulations, Metalliferous
Deposits.

BIOGRAPHICAL DATA

Hunter Yarborough

Hunter Yarborough, a Consulting Geologist and Geophys-
icist and Executive Vice President of Global Exploration
Analysts, Inc. & Associates, attended the University of
Texas, receiving a degree in Geology with highest honors and
minors in physics and petroleum engineering. Two years were
spent in graduate studies. During World Ware II, he served
as an officer and aviator of the U.S. Navy in both the
Atlantic and Pacific theaters. Following the War, Mr.
Yarborough worked for Exxon conducting geological, geophysical
and geochemical studies in the exploration for oil and gas
over much of the United States. He has been active in all
phases of geological, geophysical and geochemical research
and has traveled over much of the surface of the earth
working and consulting with active exploration groups.

Mr. Yarborough is a Certified Petroleum Geologist; a
member of The American Association of Petroleum Geologists;
a Fellow of The Geological Society of America; a member of
The American Geophysical Union; a Registered Professional
Engineer, and a member of Sigma Gamma Epsilon and Rho Kappa,
honorary geological fraternities. He has served as Distinguished Lecturer of The American Association of Petroleum
Geologists, and has given technical addresses on oil finding
and energy and mineral problems to most of the universities
and geological and geophysical societies of the United
States. He is a two-time recipient of the A. I. Levorsen
Memorial Award. Mr. Yarborough is a member of the Governor's
Energy Advisory Council for the State of Texas.

BASIN ENVIRONMENTS
RESERVOIR & SOURCE ROCKS
MARINE AND/OR LACUSTRINE (CONTINENTAL)
LAND
ABUNDANT PLANT AND ANIMAL LIFE
LAND
AERATED ZONE
(OXIDIZING CONDITIONS)
WAVE BASE
STAGNANT ZONE
(REDUCING CONDITIONS)
"RAPIDLY" SUBSIDING
LAGOON OR SHELF
"RAPIDLY" SUBSIDING
DELTA MARGIN
"REEF"
(SHELF MARGIN)
DETRITUS
TURBIDITE "SANDS"
ORGANIC RICH SHALES, MARLS, CHALKS, CHERTS,
ETC.
HY

FIGURE 1

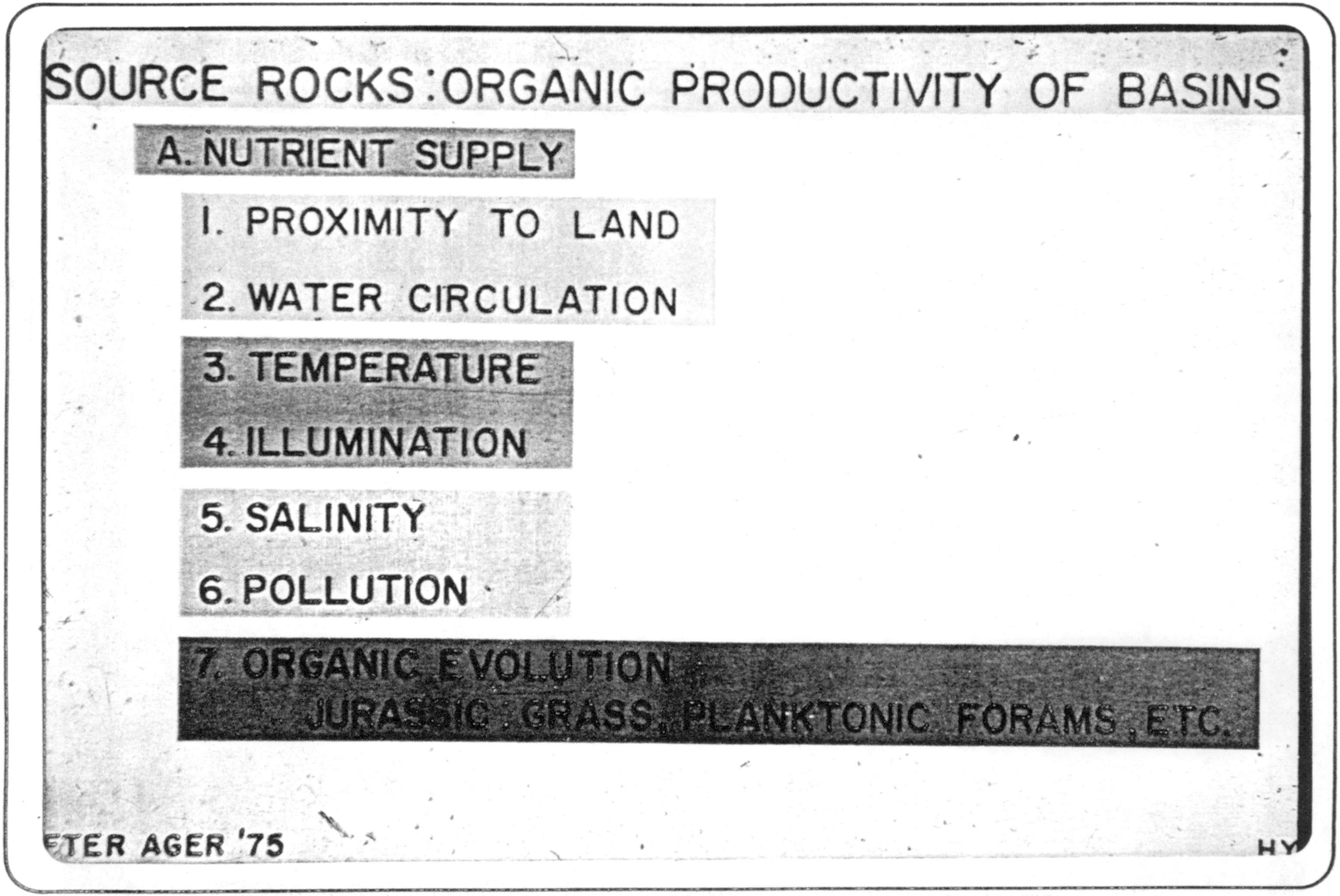

SOURCE ROCKS: ORGANIC PRODUCTIVITY OF BASINS

A. NUTRIENT SUPPLY

1. PROXIMITY TO LAND
2. WATER CIRCULATION
3. TEMPERATURE
4. ILLUMINATION
5. SALINITY
6. POLLUTION
7. ORGANIC EVOLUTION: JURASSIC GRASS, PLANKTONIC FORAMS, ETC.

AFTER AGER '75

HY

FIGURE 1-A

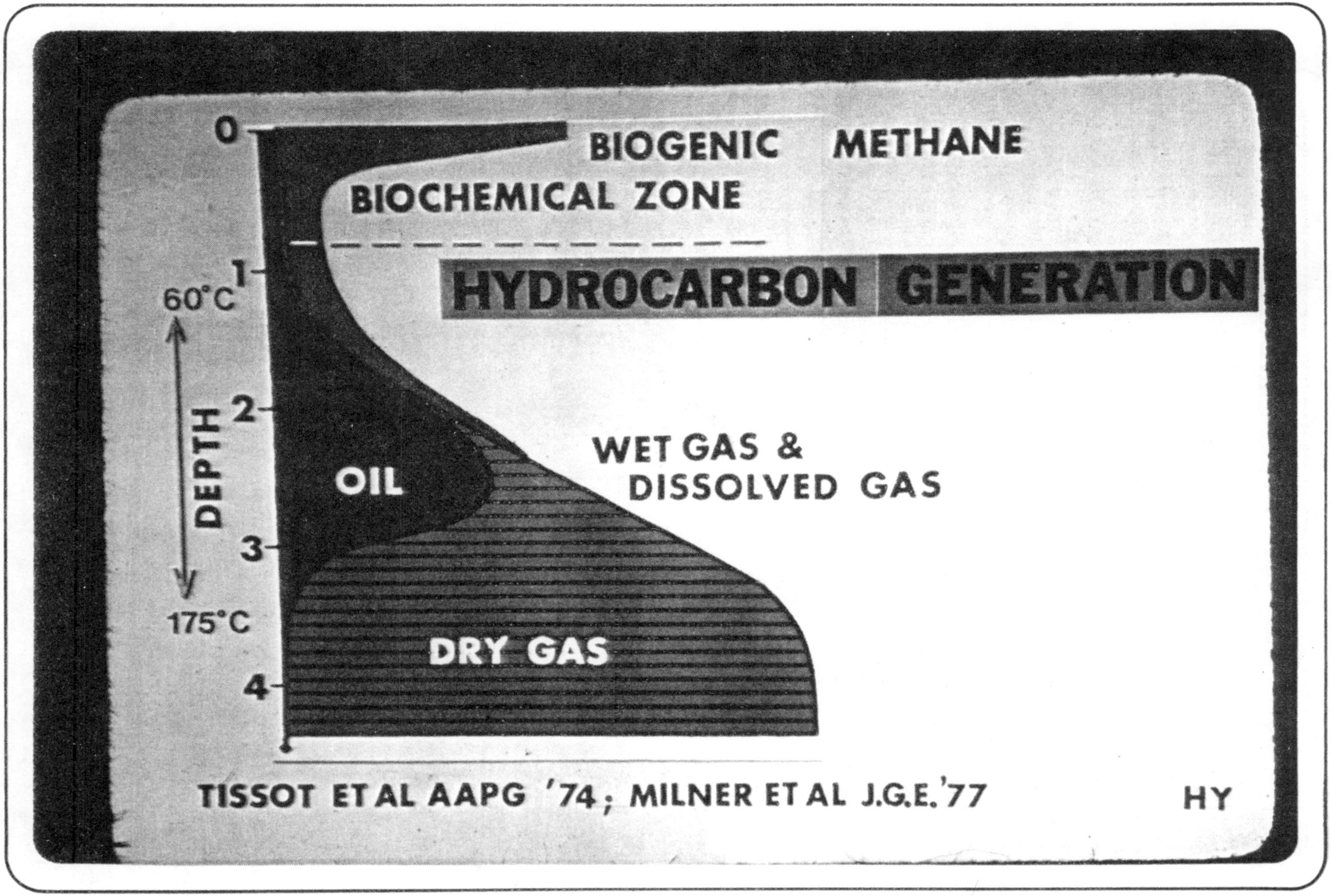
BIOGENIC METHANE
BIOCHEMICAL ZONE
HYDROCARBON GENERATION
0
1
2
3
4
60°C
DEPTH
175°C
OIL
WET GAS &
DISSOLVED GAS
DRY GAS
TISSOT ET AL AAPG '74; MILNER ET AL J.G.E.'77
HY

FIGURE 2

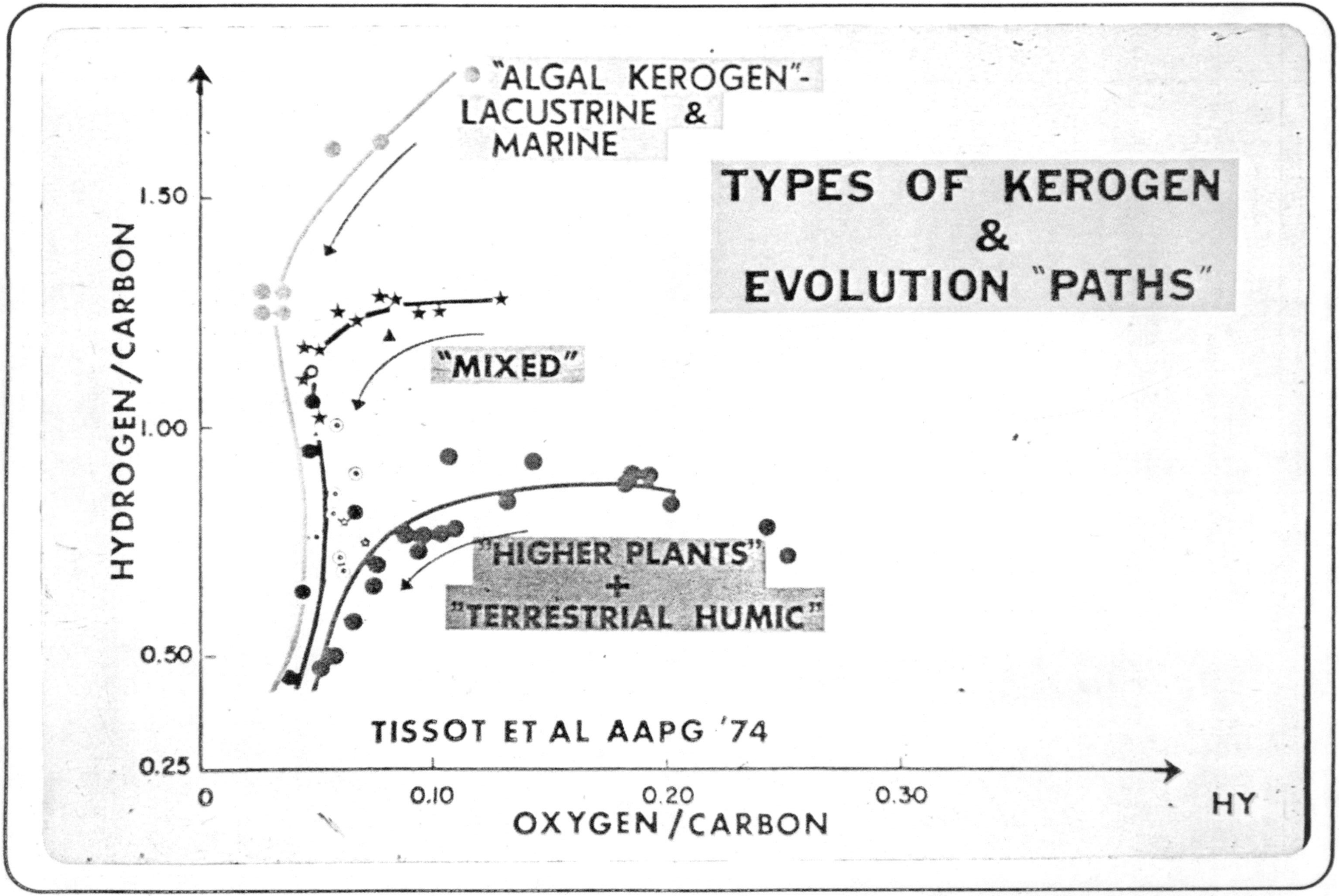

"ALGAL KEROGEN"-
LACUSTRINE &
MARINE
TYPES OF KEROGEN
&
EVOLUTION "PATHS"
"MIXED"
"HIGHER PLANTS"
+
"TERRESTRIAL HUMIC"
TISSOT ET AL AAPG '74
HYDROGEN/CARBON
1.50
1.00
0.50
0.25
0
0.10
0.20
0.30
OXYGEN/CARBON
HY

FIGURE 2-A

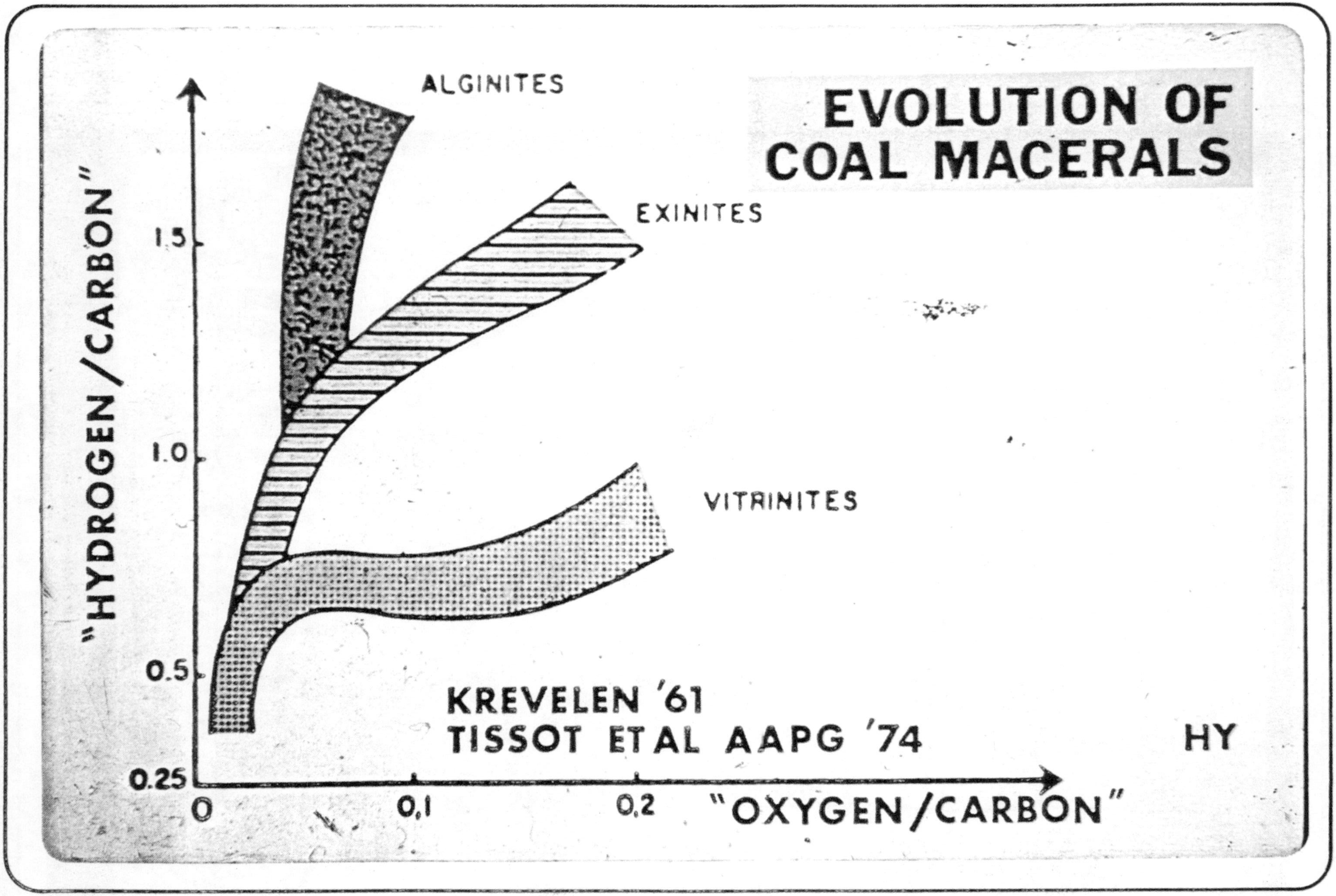
EVOLUTION OF
COAL MACERALS
ALGINITES
EXINITES
VITRINITES
"HYDROGEN/CARBON"
1.5
1.0
0.5
0.25
0
0,1
0,2
"OXYGEN/CARBON"
KREVELEN '61
TISSOT ET AL AAPG '74
HY

FIGURE 2-B

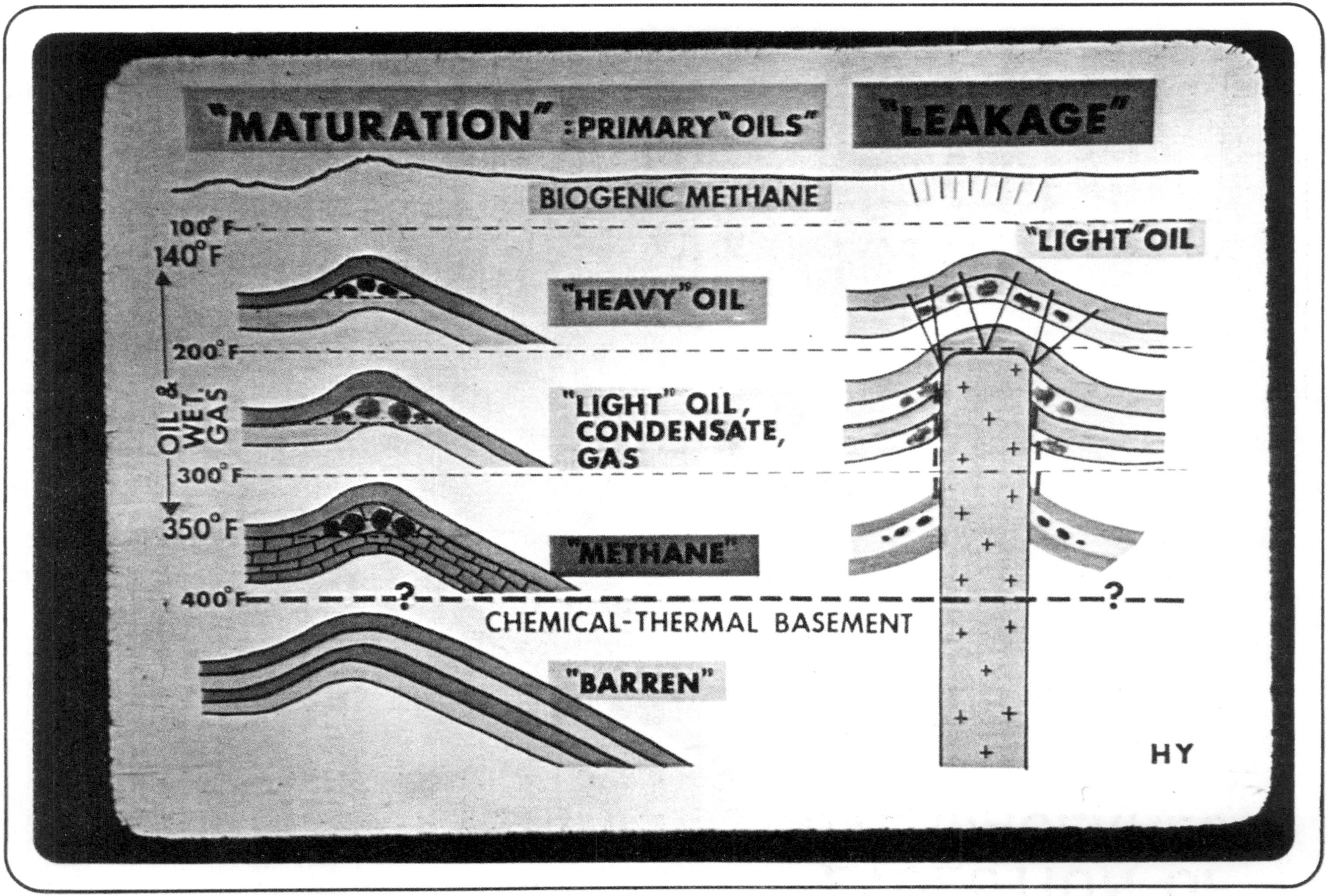
"MATURATION" :PRIMARY "OILS"
"LEAKAGE"
BIOGENIC METHANE
100° F
140° F
"LIGHT" OIL
"HEAVY" OIL
200° F
OIL & WET GAS
"LIGHT" OIL, CONDENSATE, GAS
300° F
350° F
"METHANE"
400° F
?
?
CHEMICAL-THERMAL BASEMENT
"BARREN"
HY

FIGURE 3

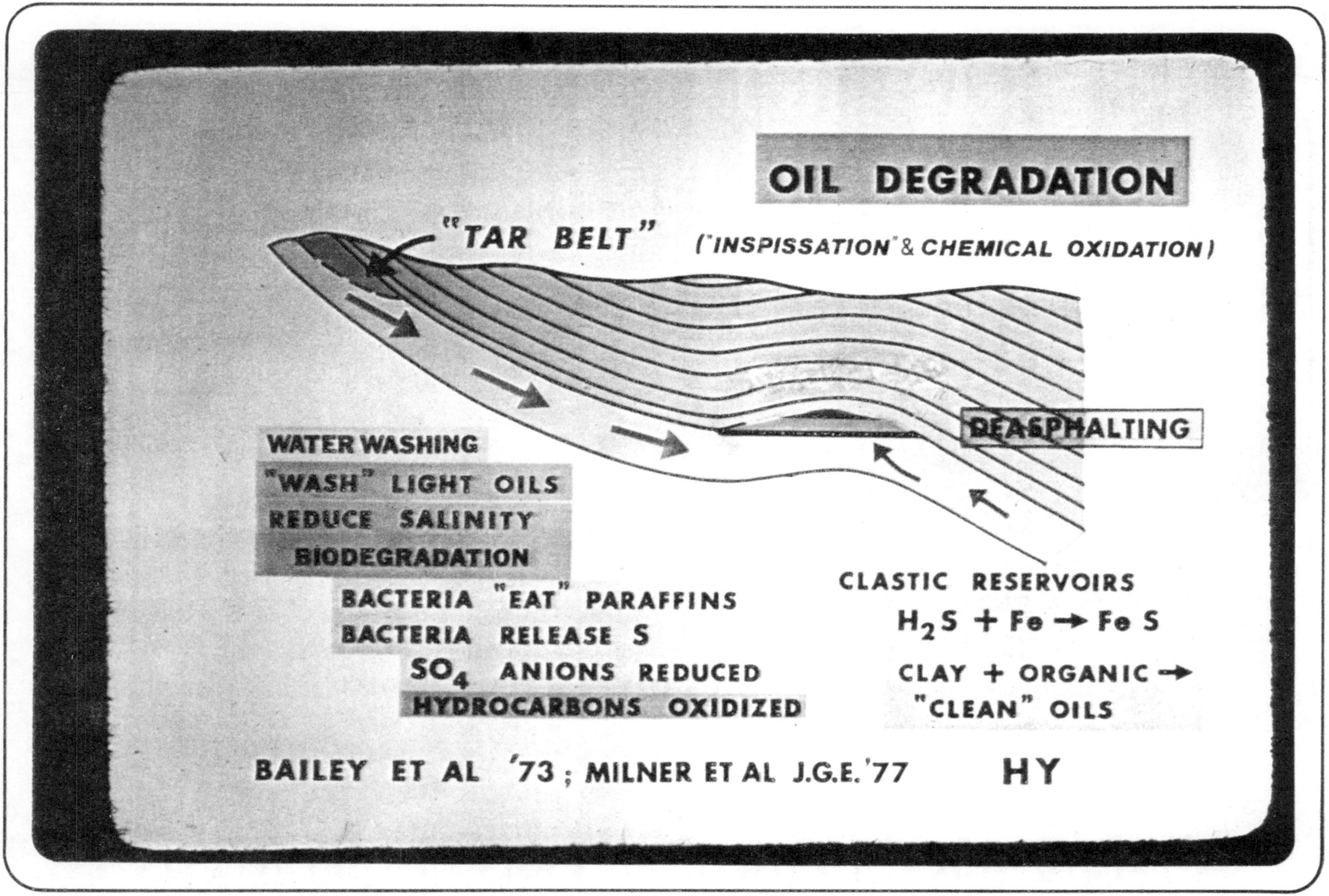
OIL DEGRADATION
"TAR BELT"
("INSPISSATION" & CHEMICAL OXIDATION)
DEASPHALTING
WATER WASHING
"WASH" LIGHT OILS
REDUCE SALINITY
BIODEGRADATION
BACTERIA "EAT" PARAFFINS
BACTERIA RELEASE S
SO_4 ANIONS REDUCED
HYDROCARBONS OXIDIZED
CLASTIC RESERVOIRS
$H_2S + Fe \rightarrow FeS$
CLAY + ORGANIC →
"CLEAN" OILS
BAILEY ET AL '73 ; MILNER ET AL J.G.E.'77
HY

FIGURE 4

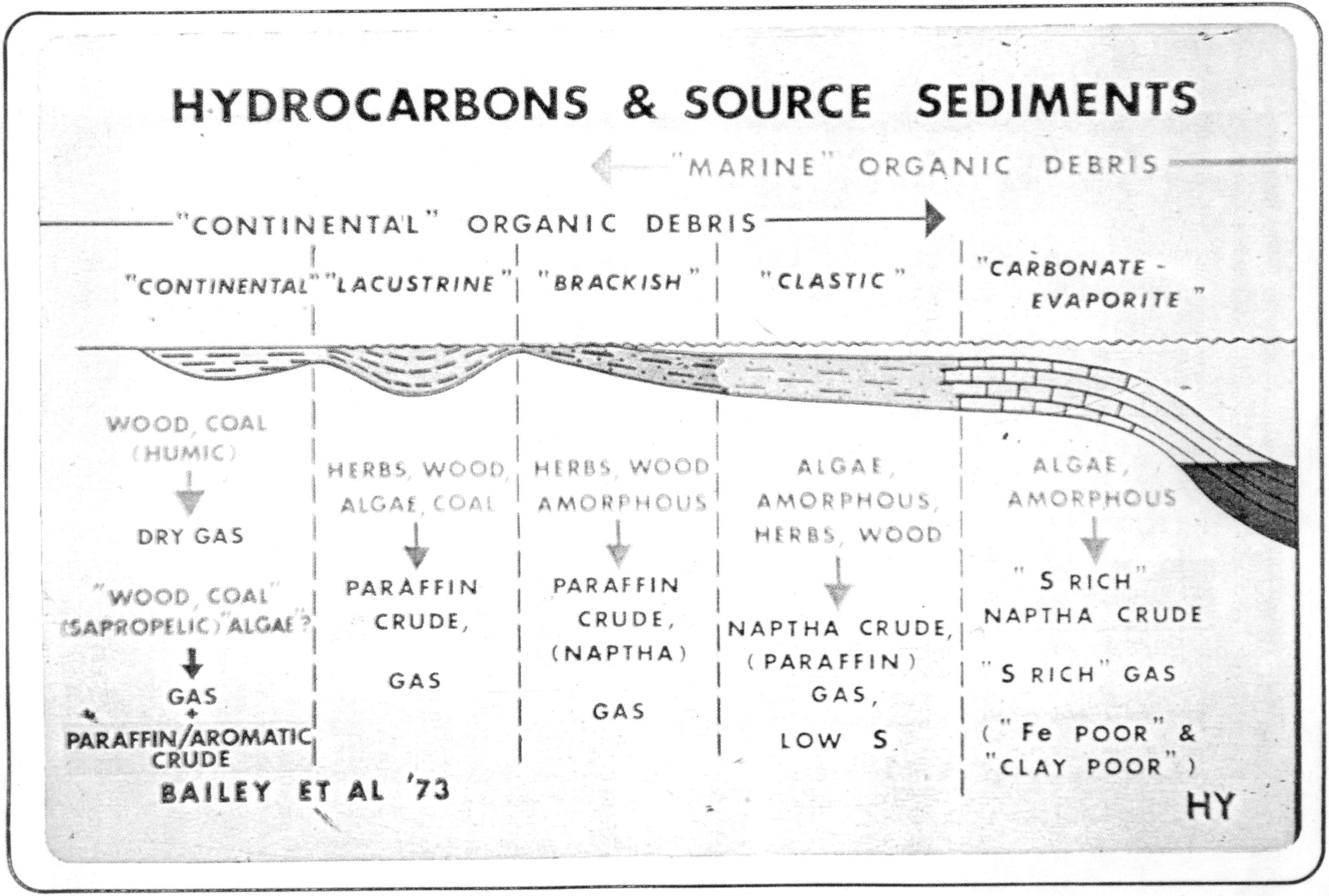
HYDROCARBONS & SOURCE SEDIMENTS
"MARINE" ORGANIC DEBRIS
"CONTINENTAL" ORGANIC DEBRIS
"CONTINENTAL"
"LACUSTRINE"
"BRACKISH"
"CLASTIC"
"CARBONATE - EVAPORITE"
WOOD, COAL (HUMIC)
DRY GAS
"WOOD, COAL" (SAPROPELIC) ALGAE?
GAS + PARAFFIN/AROMATIC CRUDE
HERBS, WOOD, ALGAE, COAL
PARAFFIN CRUDE,
GAS
HERBS, WOOD AMORPHOUS
PARAFFIN CRUDE, (NAPTHA)
GAS
ALGAE, AMORPHOUS, HERBS, WOOD
NAPTHA CRUDE, (PARAFFIN) GAS,
LOW S
ALGAE, AMORPHOUS
"S RICH" NAPTHA CRUDE
"S RICH" GAS
("Fe POOR" & "CLAY POOR")
BAILEY ET AL '73
HY

FIGURE 5

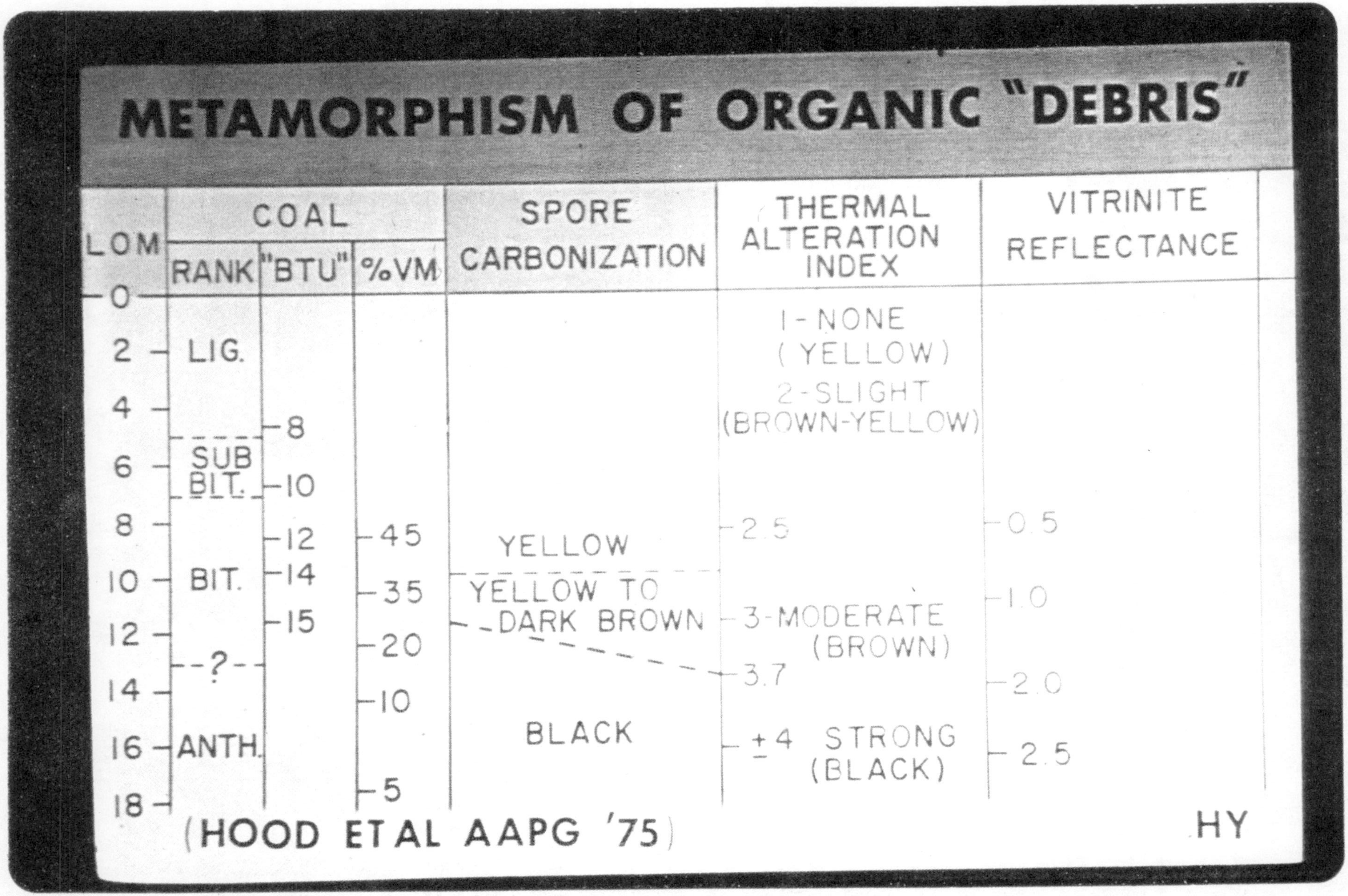

METAMORPHISM OF ORGANIC "DEBRIS"

LOM	COAL RANK	"BTU" %VM	SPORE CARBONIZATION	THERMAL ALTERATION INDEX	VITRINITE REFLECTANCE
0				1 - NONE (YELLOW)	
2	LIG.			2 - SLIGHT (BROWN-YELLOW)	
4					
6	SUB BIT.	—8 / —10			
8		—12 / —14 —45 —35	YELLOW		—0.5
10	BIT.	—15 —20	YELLOW TO DARK BROWN	2.5 / 3 - MODERATE (BROWN)	—1.0
12		—10		3.7	—2.0
14	—?—		BLACK	+4 STRONG (BLACK)	
16	ANTH.	—5			—2.5
18					HY

(HOOD ET AL AAPG '75)

FIGURE 6

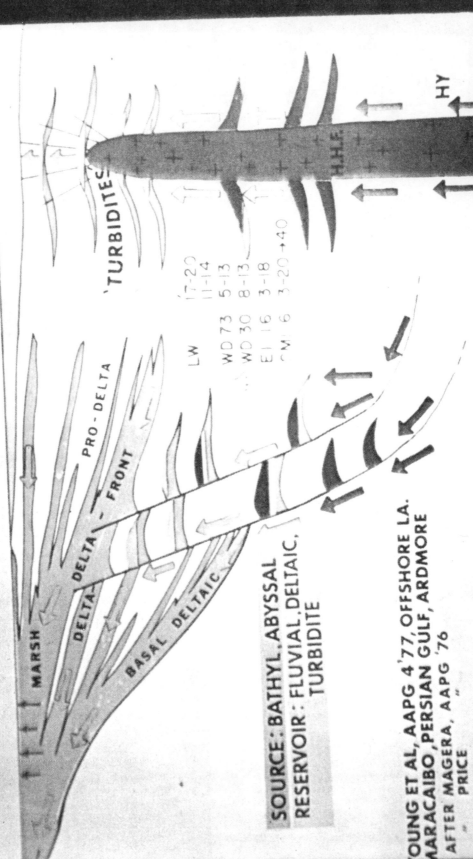

FIGURE 7

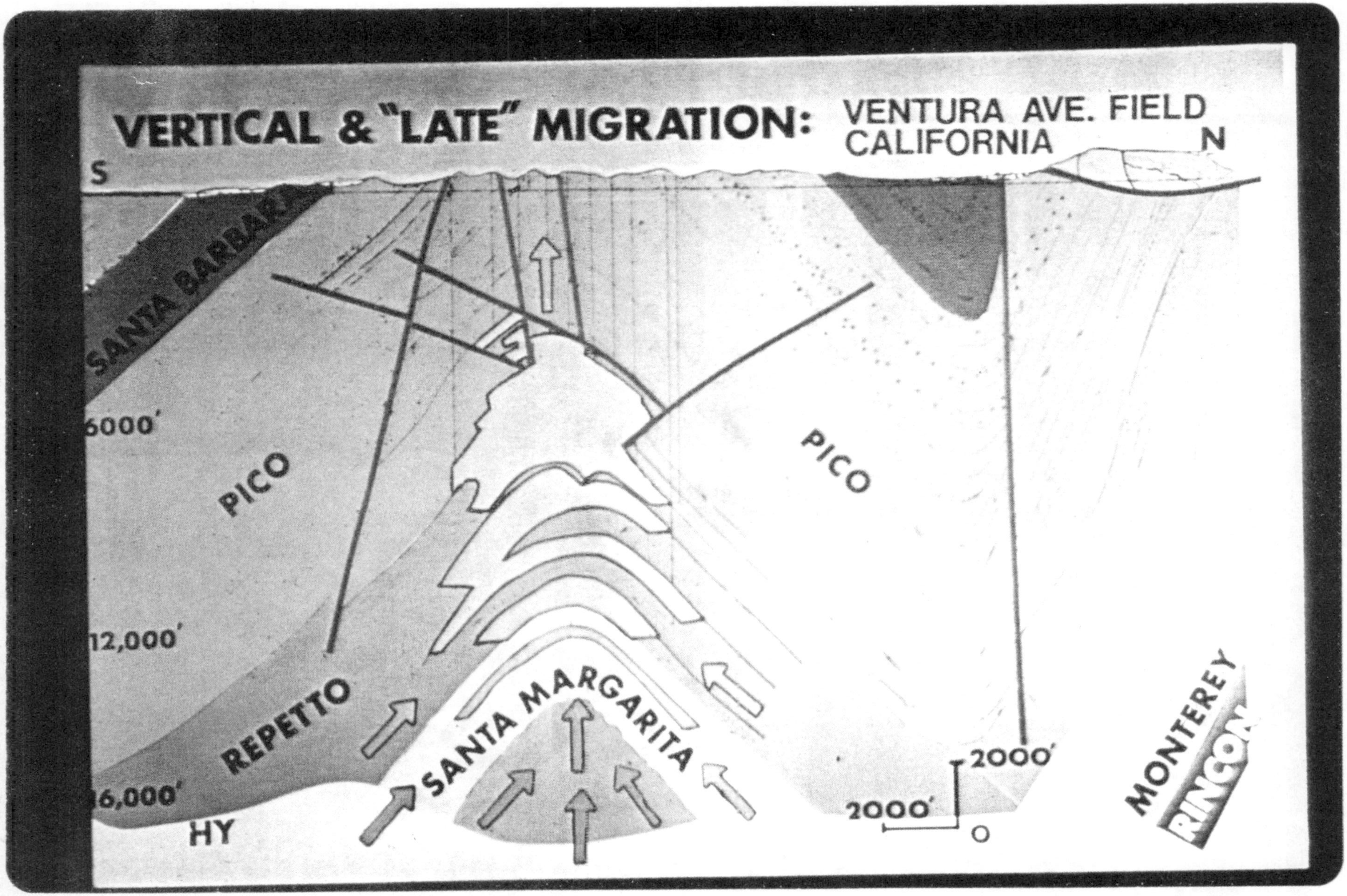
VERTICAL & "LATE" MIGRATION:
VENTURA AVE. FIELD
CALIFORNIA
S
N
SANTA BARBAR
6000'
PICO
12,000'
REPETTO
6,000'
HY
SANTA MARGARITA
PICO
2000'
2000'
O
MONTEREY
RINCO

FIGURE 8

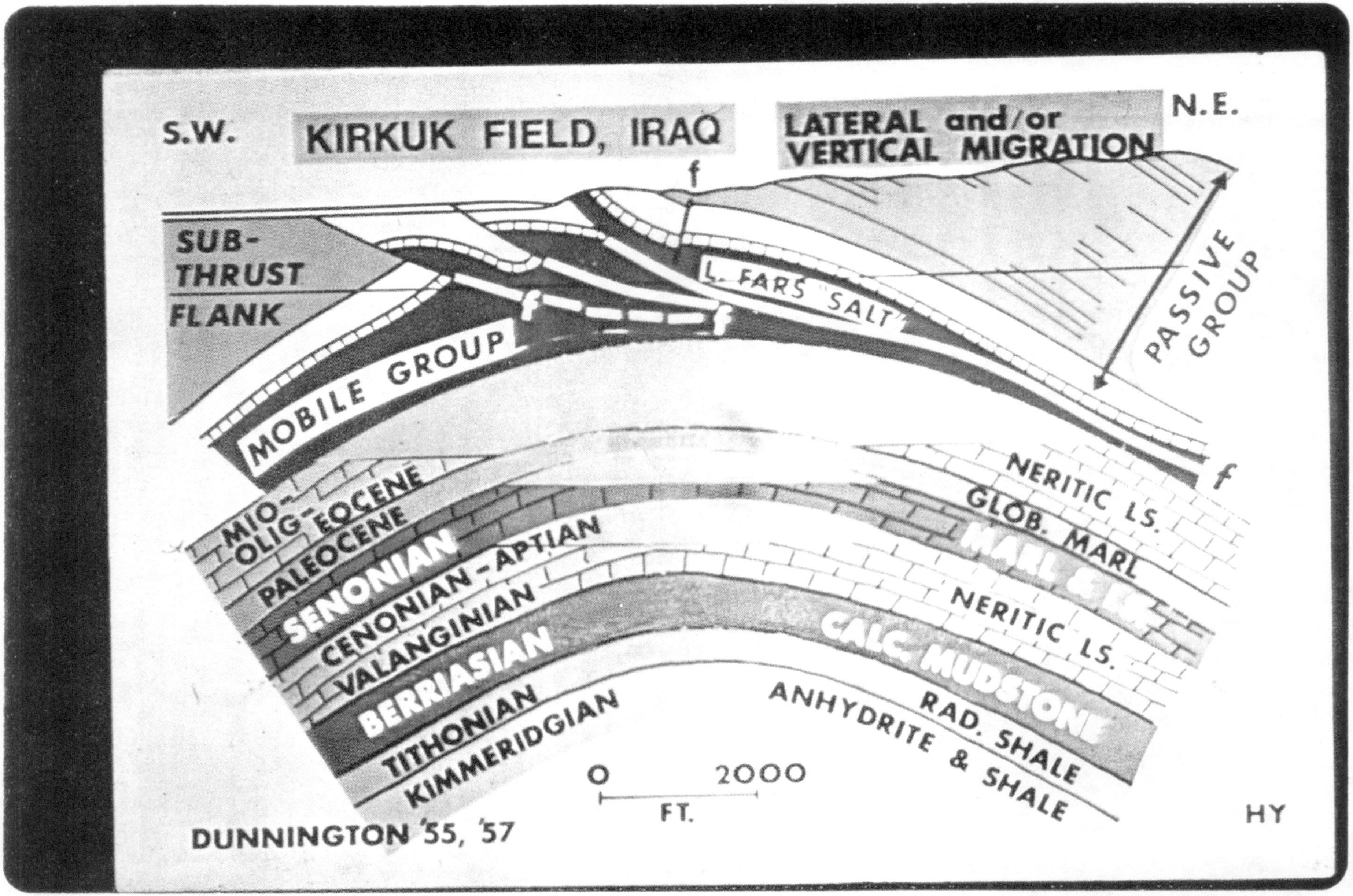
S.W.
KIRKUK FIELD, IRAQ
LATERAL and/or VERTICAL MIGRATION
N.E.
SUB-THRUST FLANK
f
L. FARS "SALT"
PASSIVE GROUP
MOBILE GROUP
MIO-OLIG-EOCENE
PALEOCENE
SENONIAN
CENONIAN-APTIAN
VALANGINIAN
BERRIASIAN
TITHONIAN
KIMMERIDGIAN
NERITIC LS.
GLOB. MARL
NERITIC LS.
CALC. MUDSTONE
RAD. SHALE
ANHYDRITE & SHALE
0 2000
FT.
DUNNINGTON '55, '57
HY

FIGURE 9

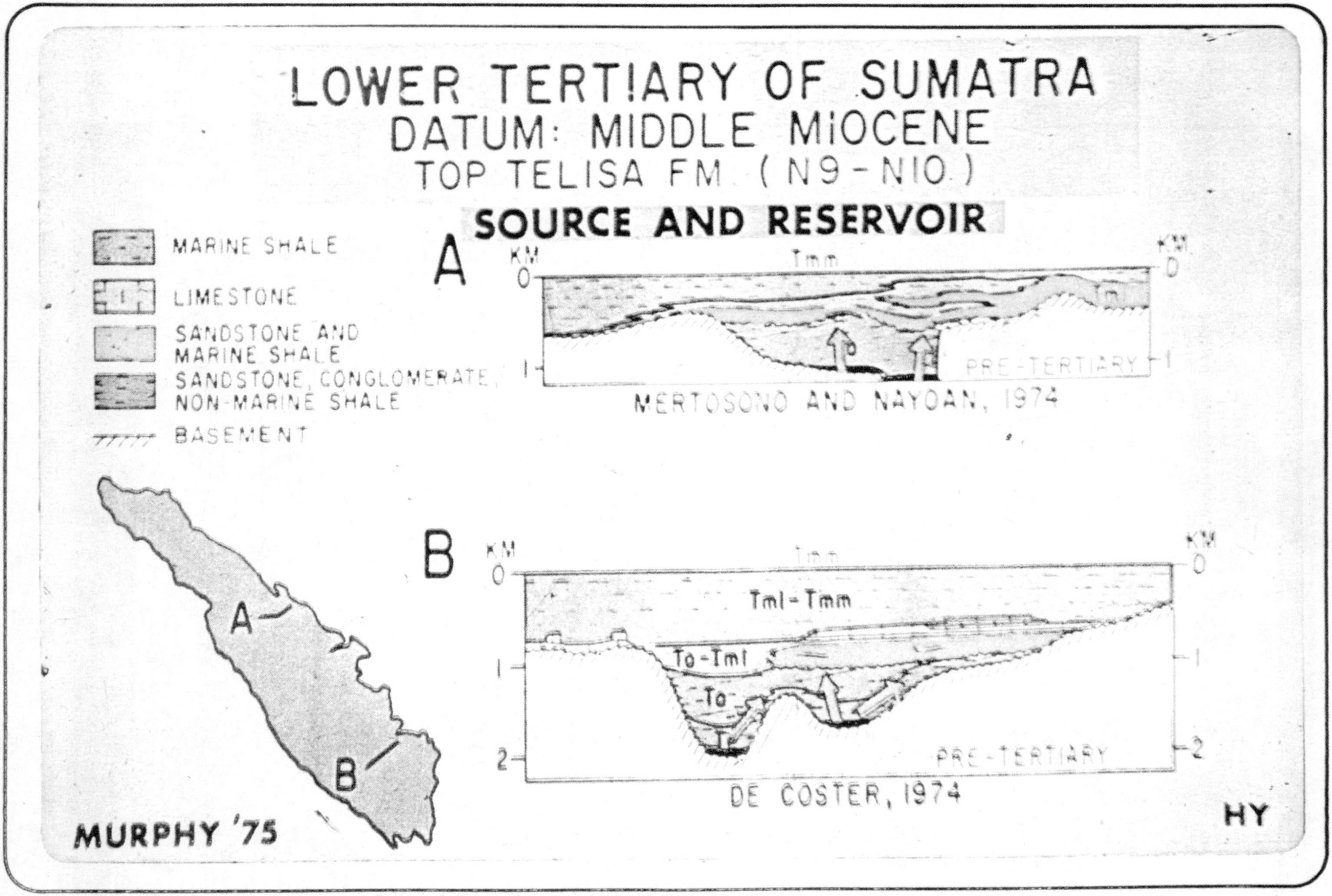
LOWER TERTIARY OF SUMATRA
DATUM: MIDDLE MIOCENE
TOP TELISA FM (N9-N10)
SOURCE AND RESERVOIR
MARINE SHALE
LIMESTONE
SANDSTONE AND MARINE SHALE
SANDSTONE, CONGLOMERATE, NON-MARINE SHALE
BASEMENT
A
KM
0
1
Tmm
PRE-TERTIARY
MERTOSONO AND NAYOAN, 1974
B
KM
0
1
2
Tmm
Tml-Tmm
To-Tml
To
PRE-TERTIARY
DE COSTER, 1974
A
B
MURPHY '75
HY

FIGURE 9-A

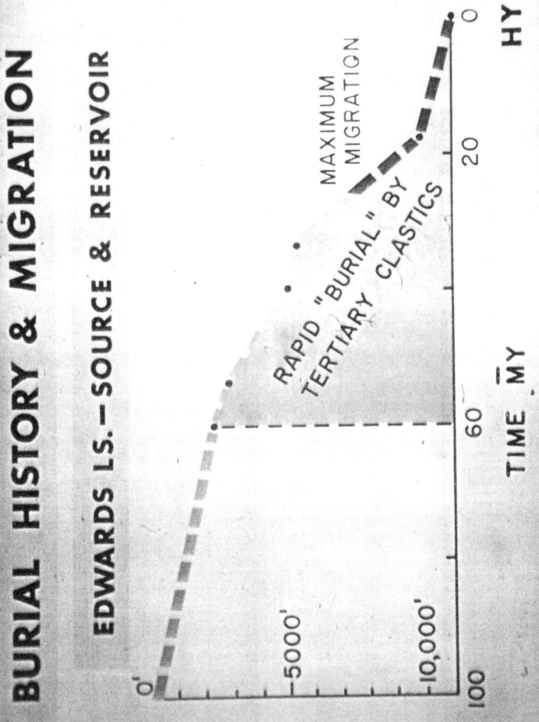

FIGURE 10

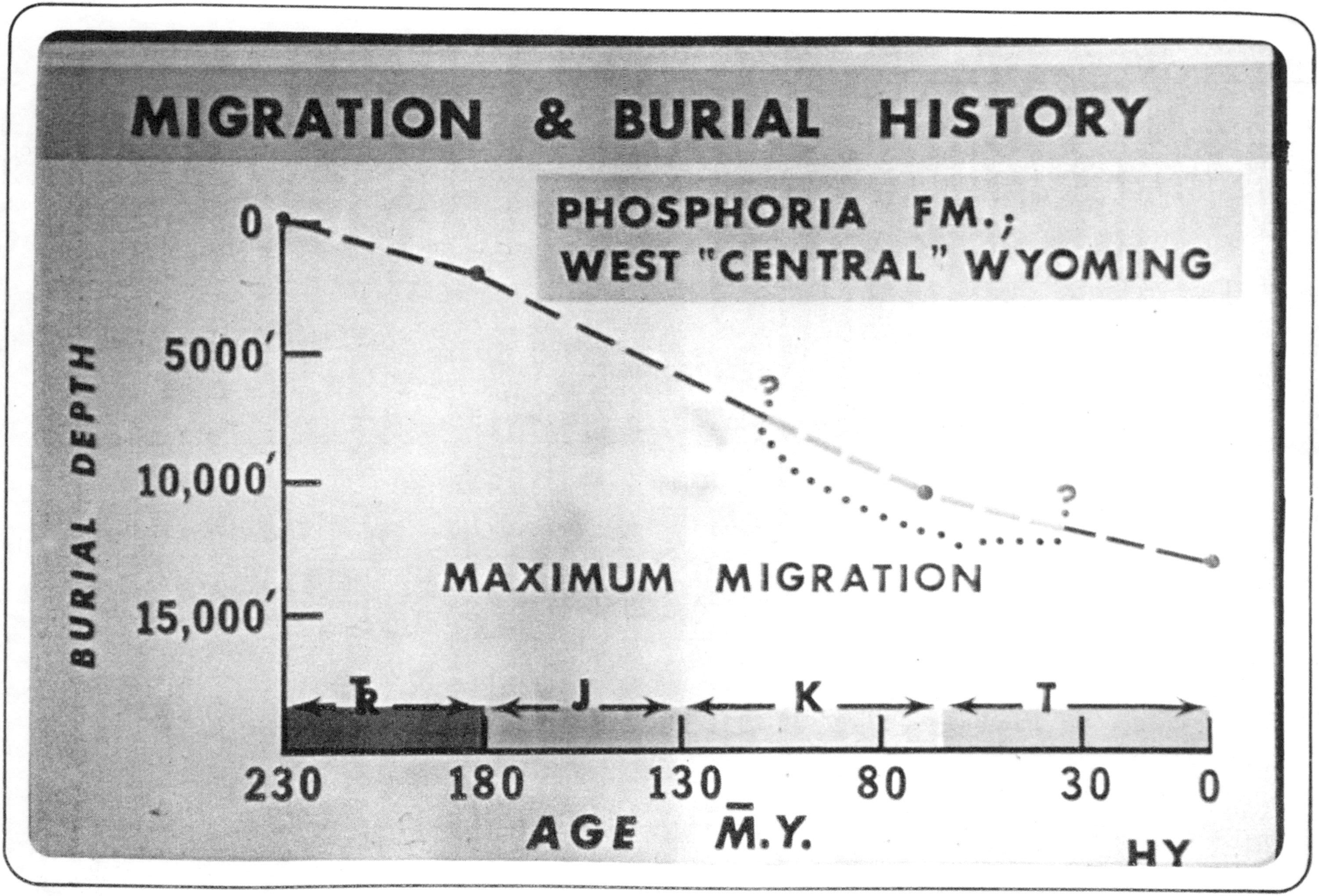

FIGURE 11

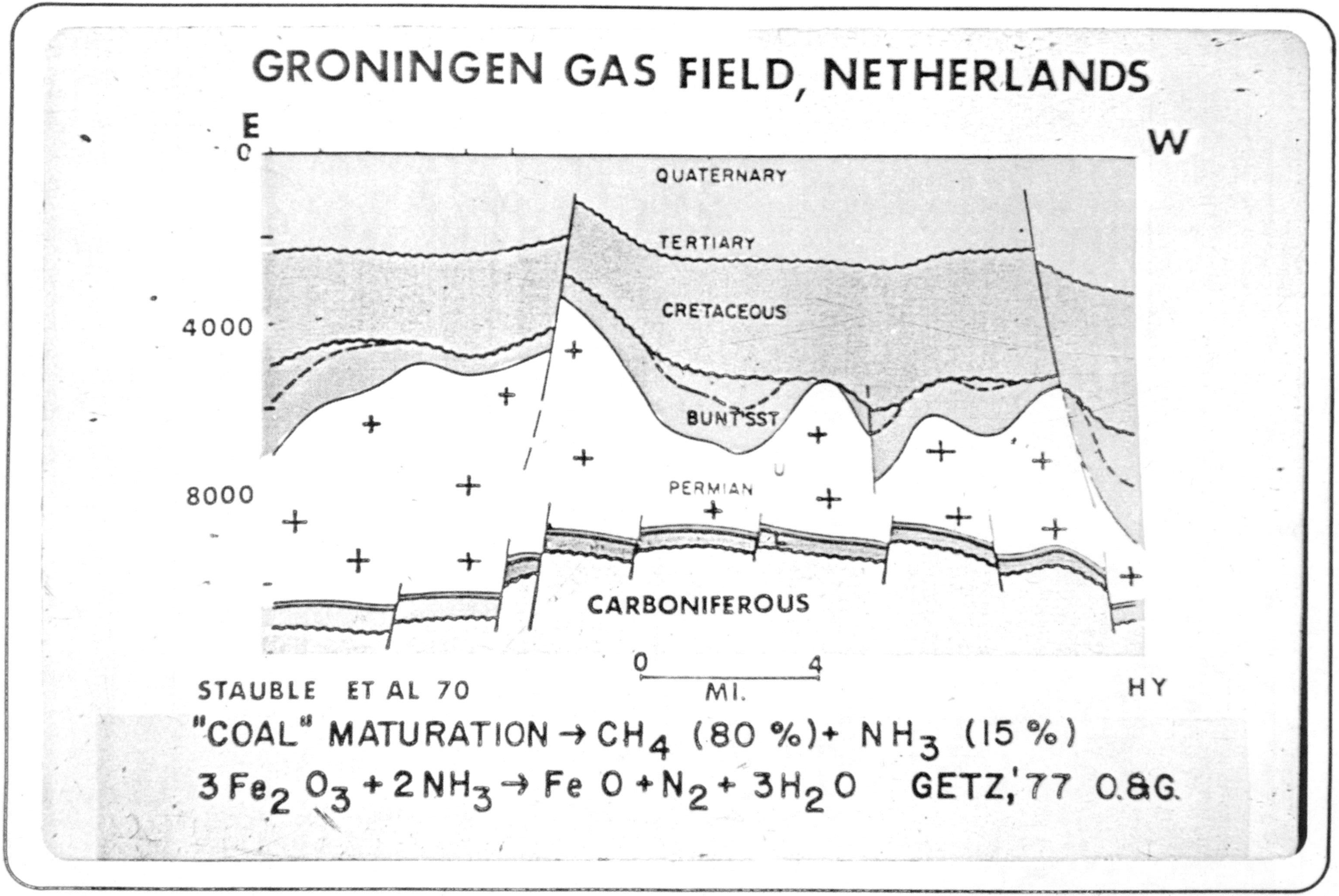
GRONINGEN GAS FIELD, NETHERLANDS
E
W
0
4000
8000
QUATERNARY
TERTIARY
CRETACEOUS
BUNT SST
PERMIAN
CARBONIFEROUS
0
4
MI.
STAUBLE ET AL 70
HY
"COAL" MATURATION → CH_4 (80 %) + NH_3 (15 %)
$3Fe_2O_3 + 2NH_3 \rightarrow FeO + N_2 + 3H_2O$
GETZ, '77 O.&G.

FIGURE 11-A

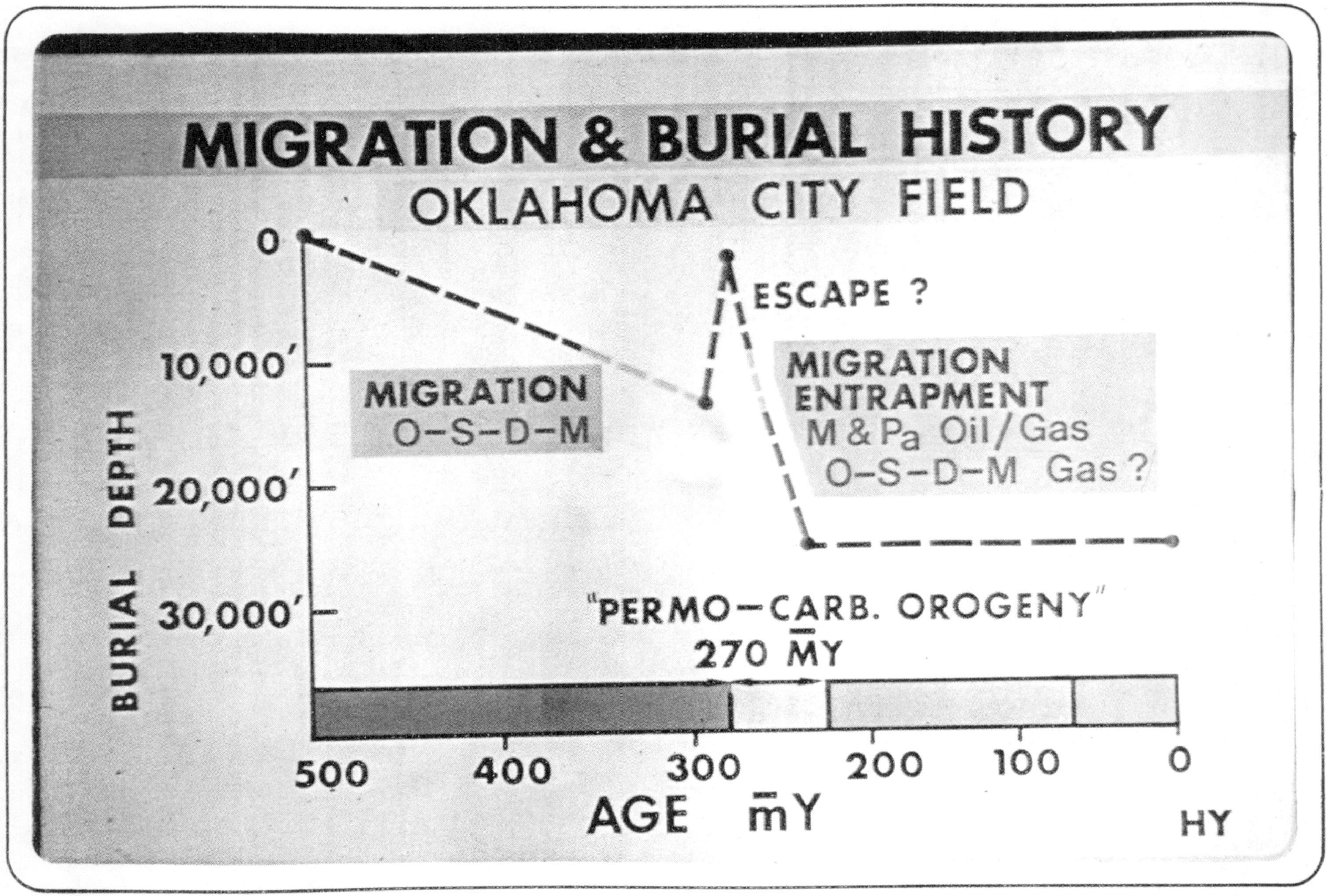
MIGRATION & BURIAL HISTORY
OKLAHOMA CITY FIELD
BURIAL DEPTH
0
10,000'
20,000'
30,000'
MIGRATION
O-S-D-M
ESCAPE ?
MIGRATION
ENTRAPMENT
M & Pa Oil/Gas
O-S-D-M Gas ?
"PERMO-CARB. OROGENY"
270 MY
500
400
300
200
100
0
AGE mY
HY

FIGURE 12

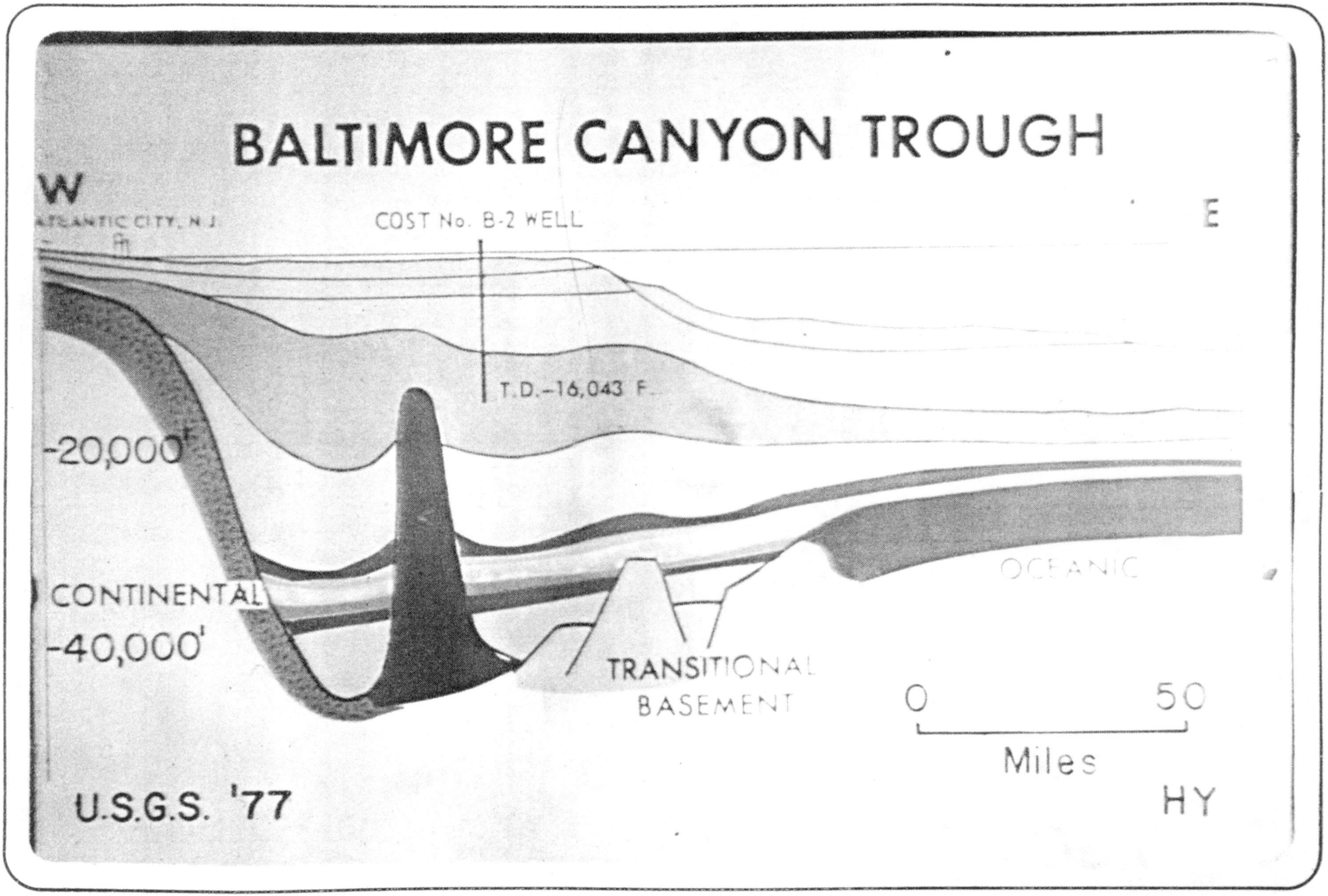
BALTIMORE CANYON TROUGH
W
ATLANTIC CITY, N.J.
COST No. B-2 WELL
E
T.D.-16,043 F
-20,000'
CONTINENTAL
-40,000'
TRANSITIONAL
BASEMENT
OCEANIC
0
50
Miles
U.S.G.S. '77
HY

FIGURE 13

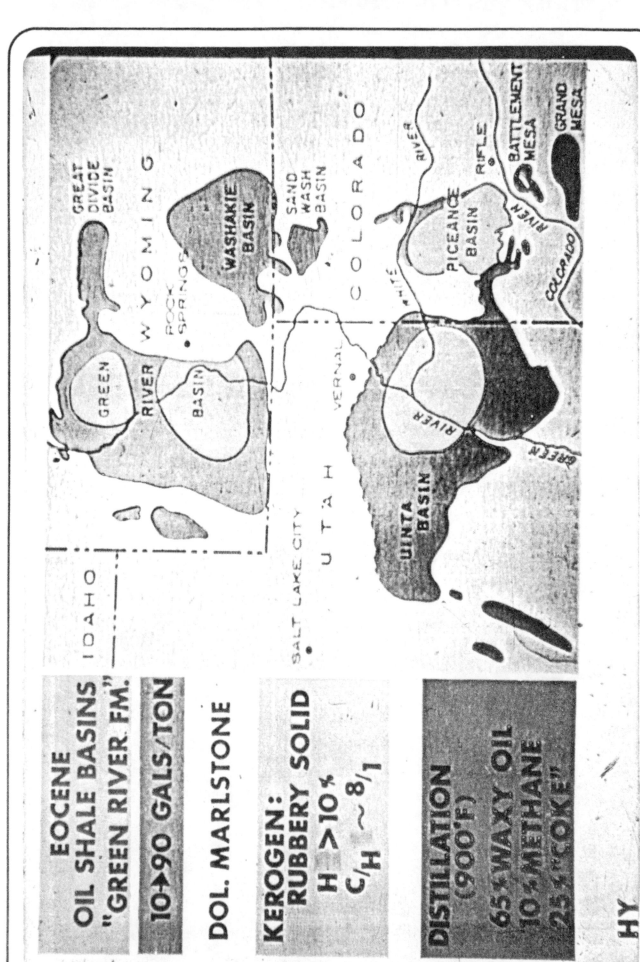

FIGURE 13-A

SOURCE ROCKS: LATE JURASSIC TIMES

NUTRIENT SUPPLY & SURFACE CURRENTS

FIGURE 14

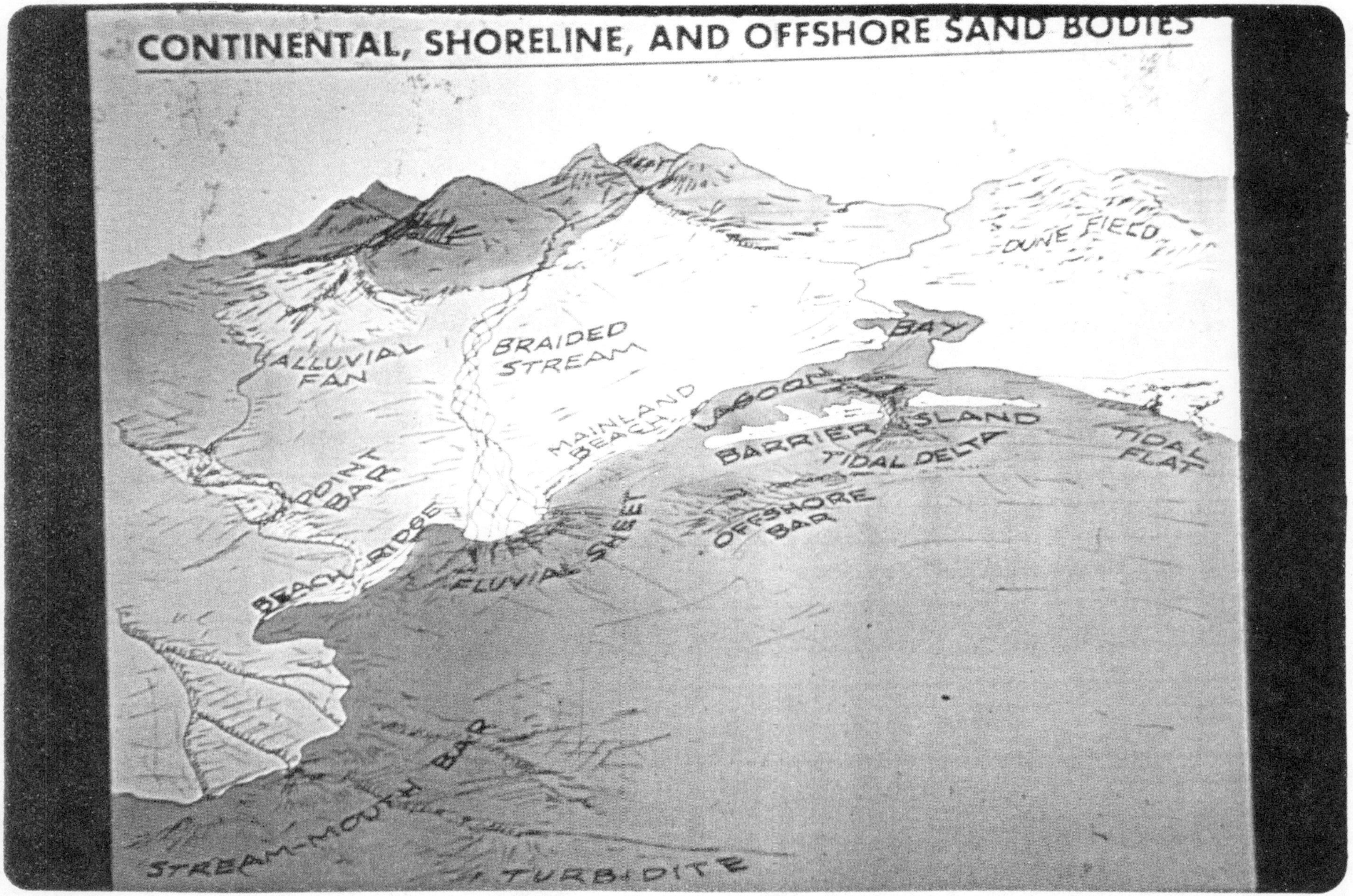
CONTINENTAL, SHORELINE, AND OFFSHORE SAND BODIES
DUNE FIELD
BRAIDED STREAM
ALLUVIAL FAN
BAY
LAGOON
MAINLAND BEACH
BARRIER ISLAND
TIDAL FLAT
TIDAL DELTA
POINT BAR
BEACH RIDGE
FLUVIAL SHEET
OFFSHORE BAR
STREAM-MOUTH BAR
TURBIDITE

FIGURE 15

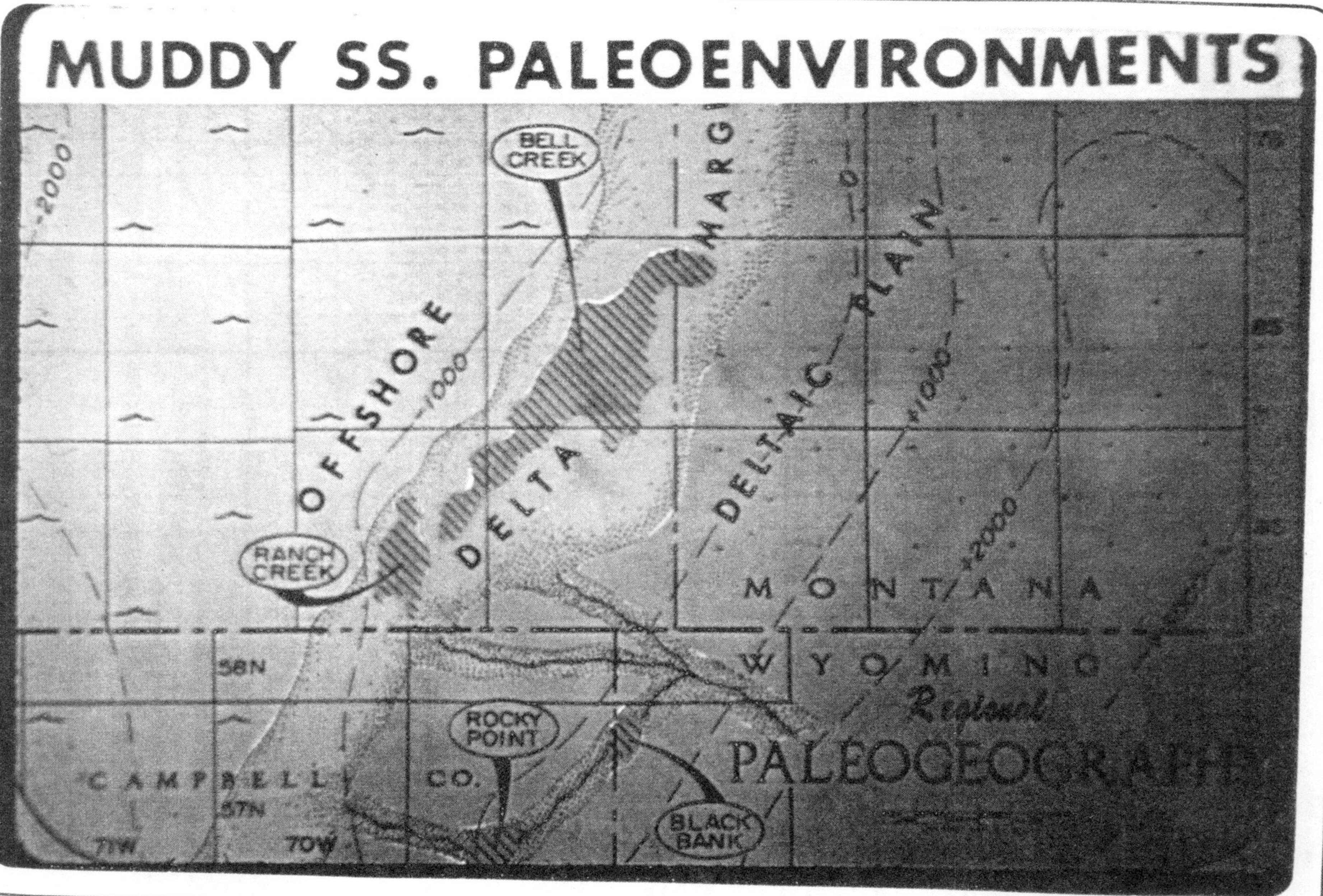
MUDDY SS. PALEOENVIRONMENTS
BELL CREEK
RANCH CREEK
ROCKY POINT
BLACK BANK
OFFSHORE
DELTA
DELTAIC PLAIN
MONTANA
WYOMING
CAMPBELL CO.
Regional
PALEOGEOGRAPHY
-2000
-1000
0
+1000
+2000
58N
57N
71W
70W

FIGURE 16

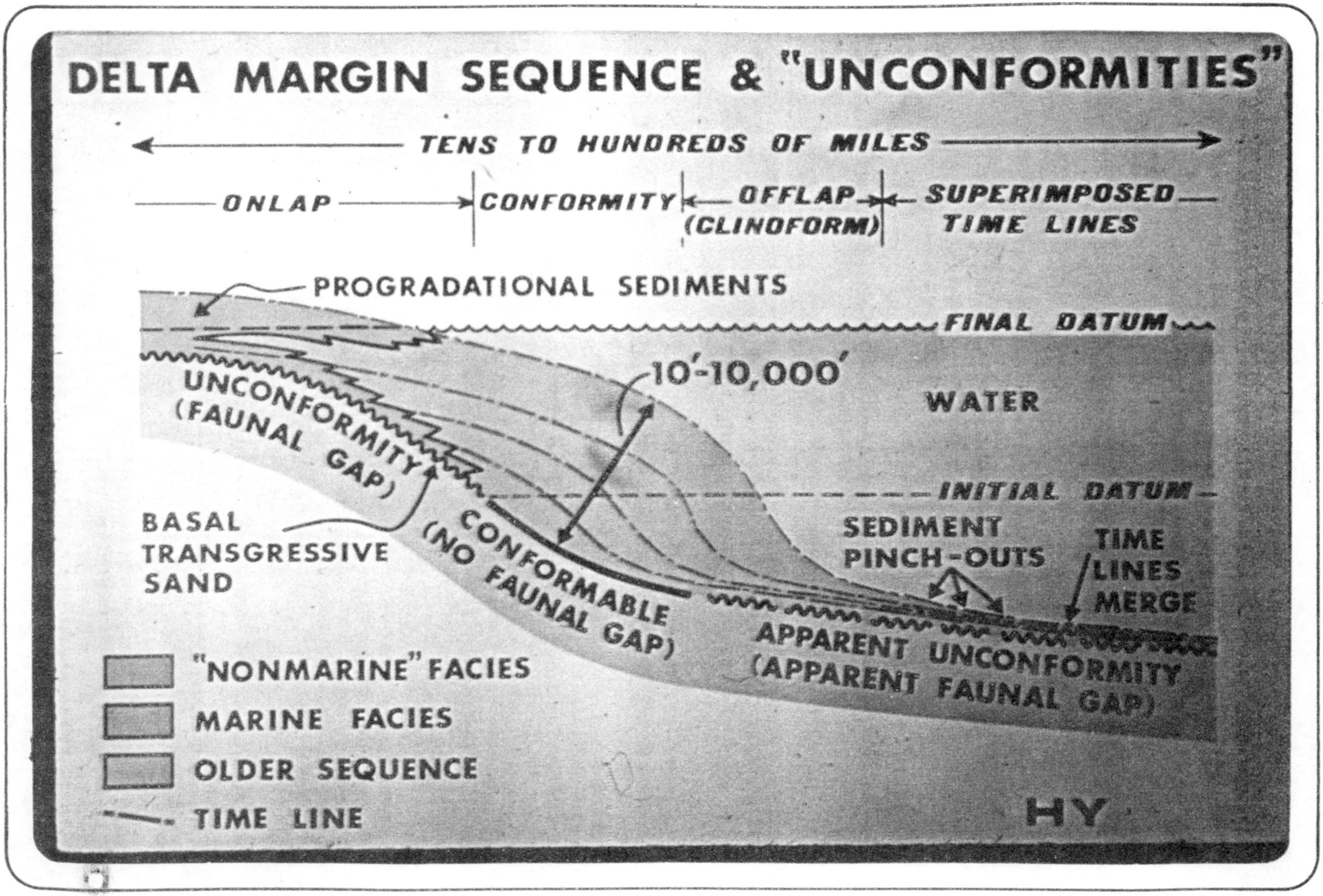
DELTA MARGIN SEQUENCE & "UNCONFORMITIES"
TENS TO HUNDREDS OF MILES
ONLAP
CONFORMITY
OFFLAP (CLINOFORM)
SUPERIMPOSED TIME LINES
PROGRADATIONAL SEDIMENTS
FINAL DATUM
10'-10,000'
WATER
UNCONFORMITY (FAUNAL GAP)
INITIAL DATUM
BASAL TRANSGRESSIVE SAND
CONFORMABLE (NO FAUNAL GAP)
SEDIMENT PINCH-OUTS
TIME LINES MERGE
APPARENT UNCONFORMITY (APPARENT FAUNAL GAP)
"NONMARINE" FACIES
MARINE FACIES
OLDER SEQUENCE
TIME LINE
HY

FIGURE 17

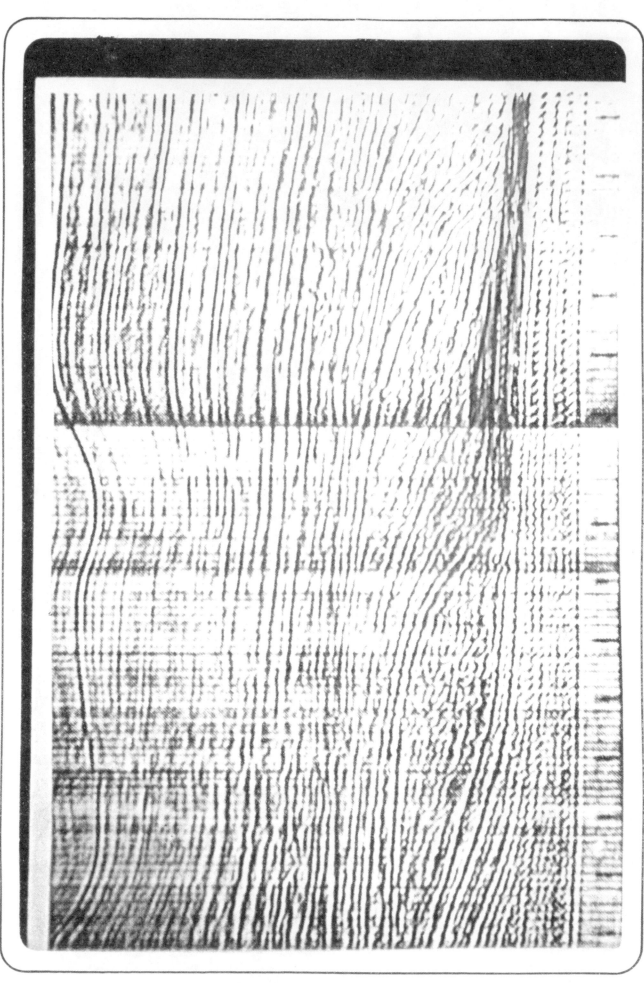

FIGURE 18

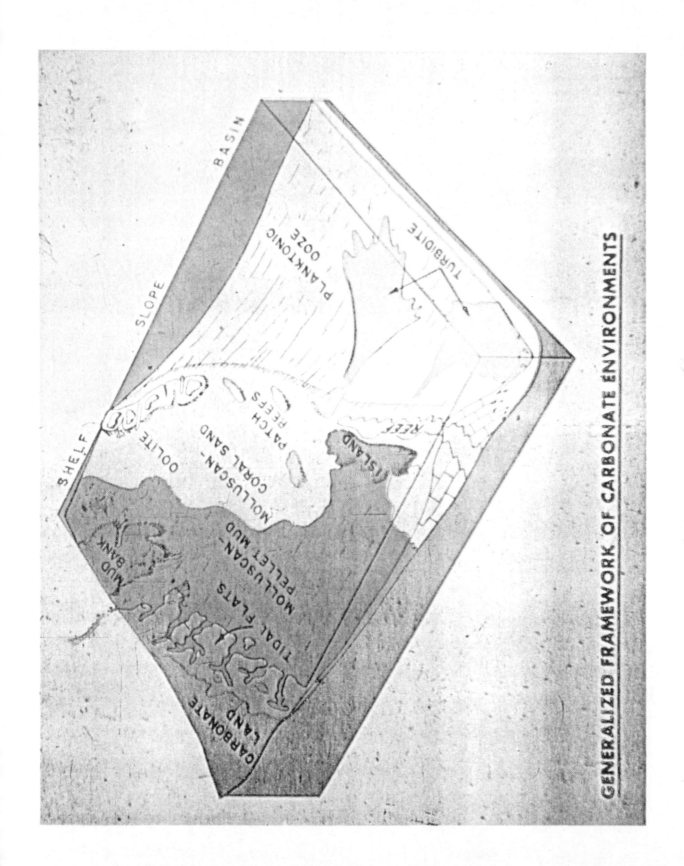

GENERALIZED FRAMEWORK OF CARBONATE ENVIRONMENTS

FIGURE 19

THEORIES OF EVAPORITE FORMATION

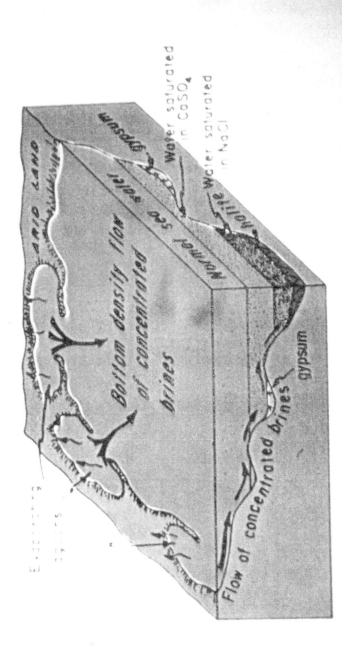

RICHTER-BERNBURG THEORY: Brines are concentrated in marginal evaporating lagoons and flow as density currents into deep parts of basin where they form density-stratified layers; different salts are precipitated where saturated brine layers are in contact with the irregular basin floor.

FIGURE 20

CARBONATE "BUILD-UPS" & "DETRITUS"

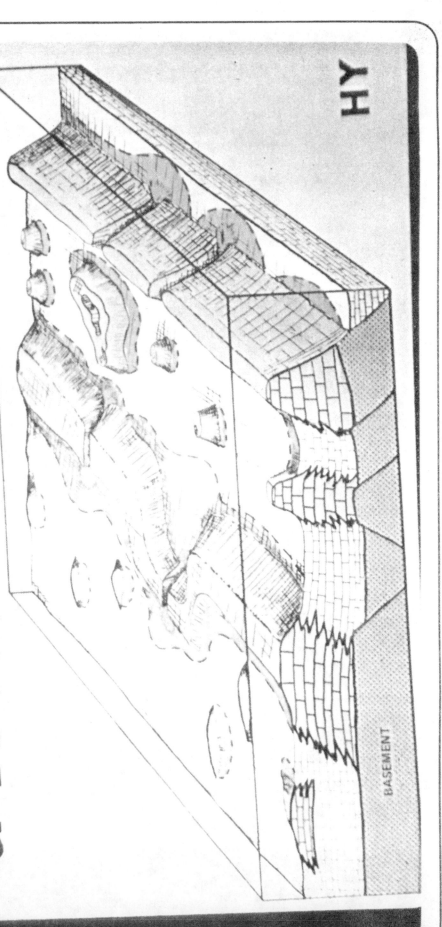

HY

BASEMENT

FIGURE 21

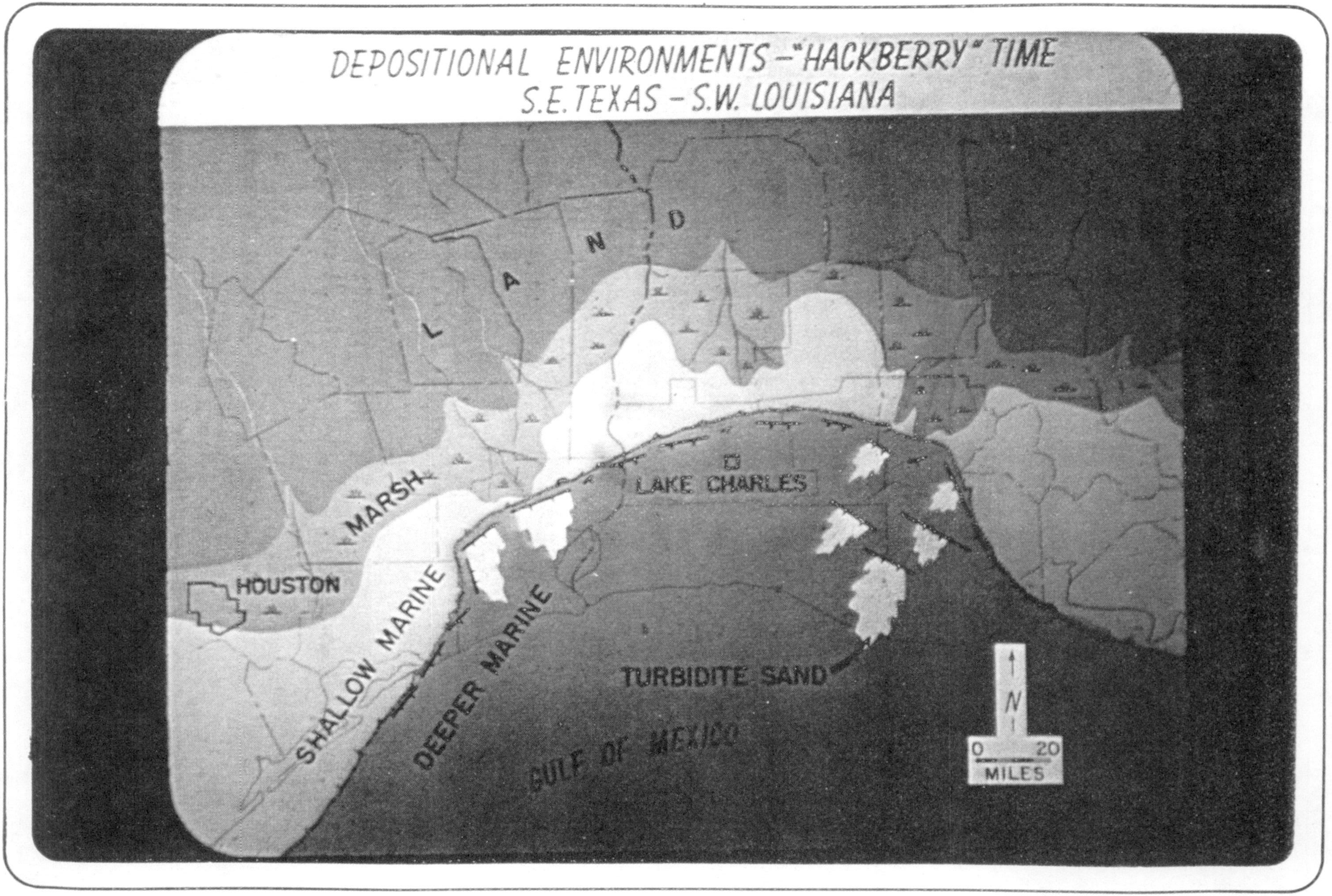
DEPOSITIONAL ENVIRONMENTS – "HACKBERRY" TIME
S.E. TEXAS – S.W. LOUISIANA
L A N D
MARSH
HOUSTON
LAKE CHARLES
SHALLOW MARINE
DEEPER MARINE
TURBIDITE SAND
GULF OF MEXICO
N
0 20
MILES

FIGURE 22

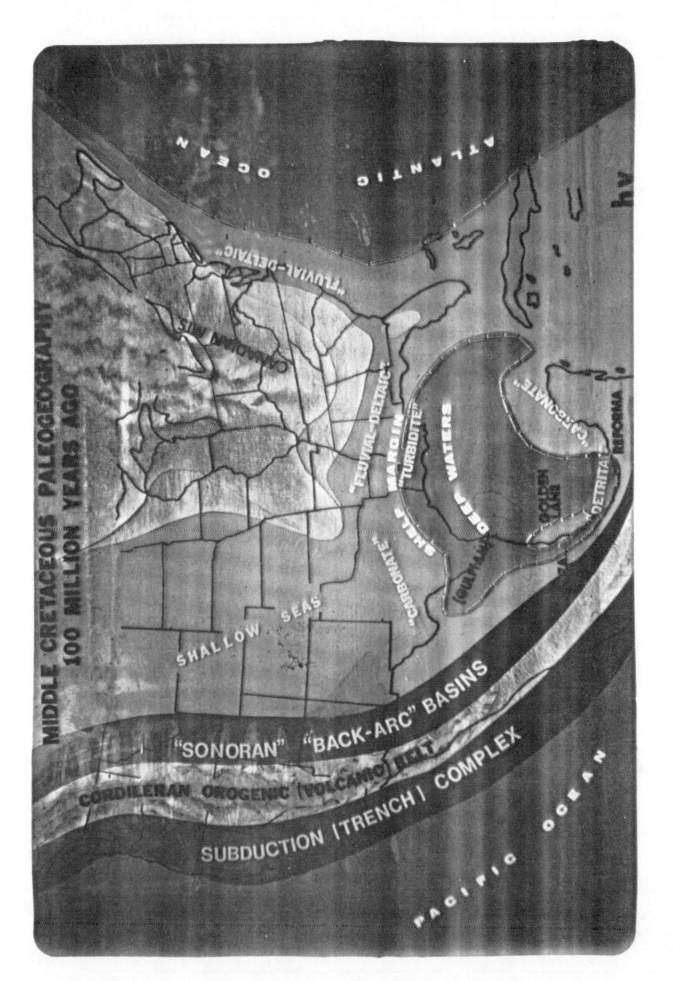

FIGURE 22-A

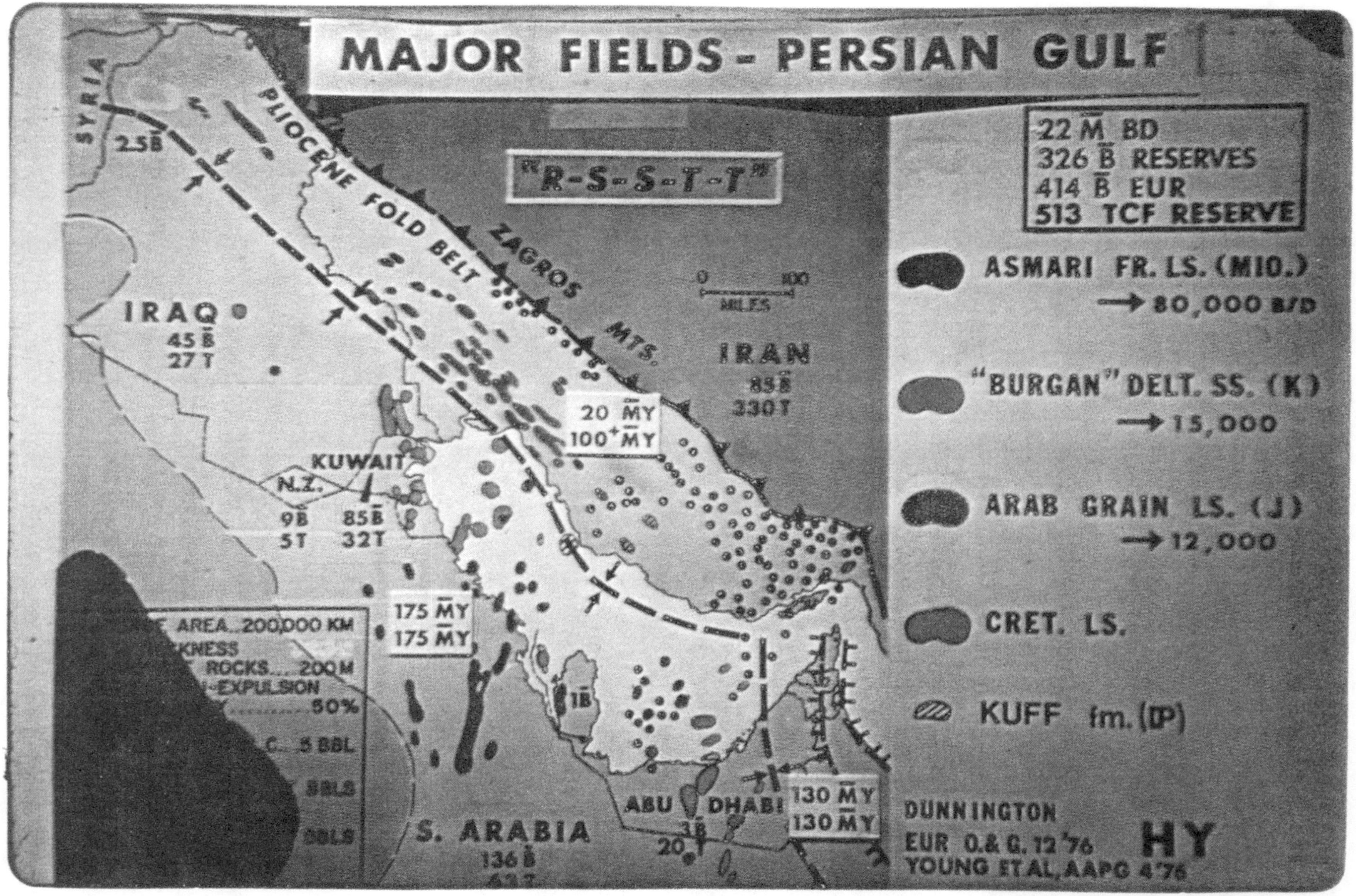
MAJOR FIELDS - PERSIAN GULF
22 M̄ BD
326 B̄ RESERVES
414 B̄ EUR
513 TCF RESERVE
"R-S-S-T-T"
ASMARI FR. LS. (MIO.)
→ 80,000 B/D
"BURGAN" DELT. SS. (K)
→ 15,000
ARAB GRAIN LS. (J)
→ 12,000
CRET. LS.
KUFF fm. (P)
DUNNINGTON
EUR O.& G. 12'76
YOUNG ET AL, AAPG 4'76
HY
SYRIA
2.5B̄
PLIOCENE FOLD BELT
ZAGROS MTS.
IRAQ
45 B̄
27 T
IRAN
85 B̄
330 T
0 100
MILES
20 M̄Y
100+ M̄Y
KUWAIT
N.Z.
9 B̄
5 T
85 B̄
32 T
175 M̄Y
175 M̄Y
1 B̄
ABU DHABI
3 B̄
20
130 M̄Y
130 M̄Y
S. ARABIA
136 B̄

FIGURE 23

LAURASIA & GONDWANA

"PLATE" MARGINS &
MAJOR OIL & GAS FIELDS •

HY 172

FIGURE 24

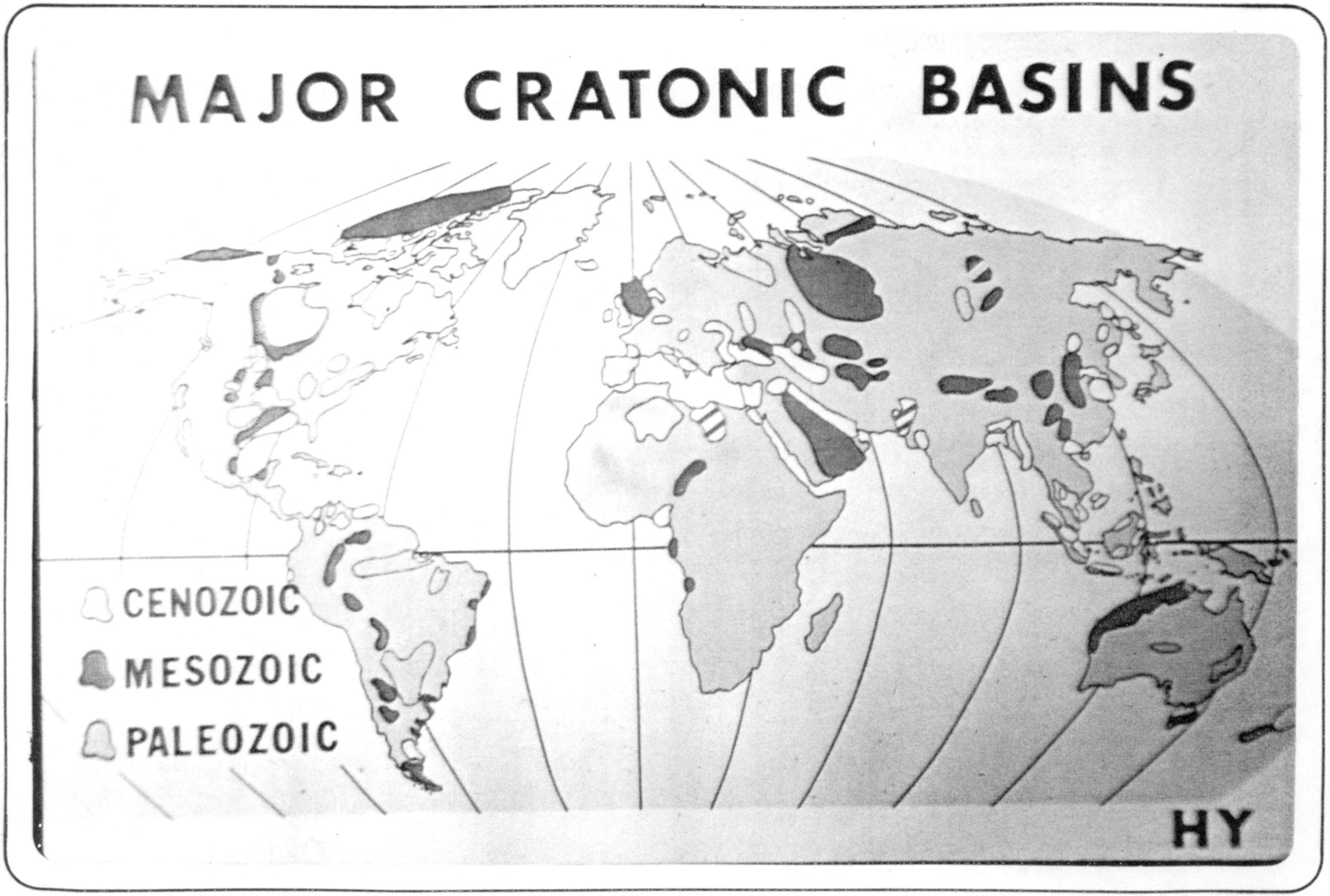

MAJOR CRATONIC BASINS

HY

CENOZOIC
MESOZOIC
PALEOZOIC

FIGURE 25

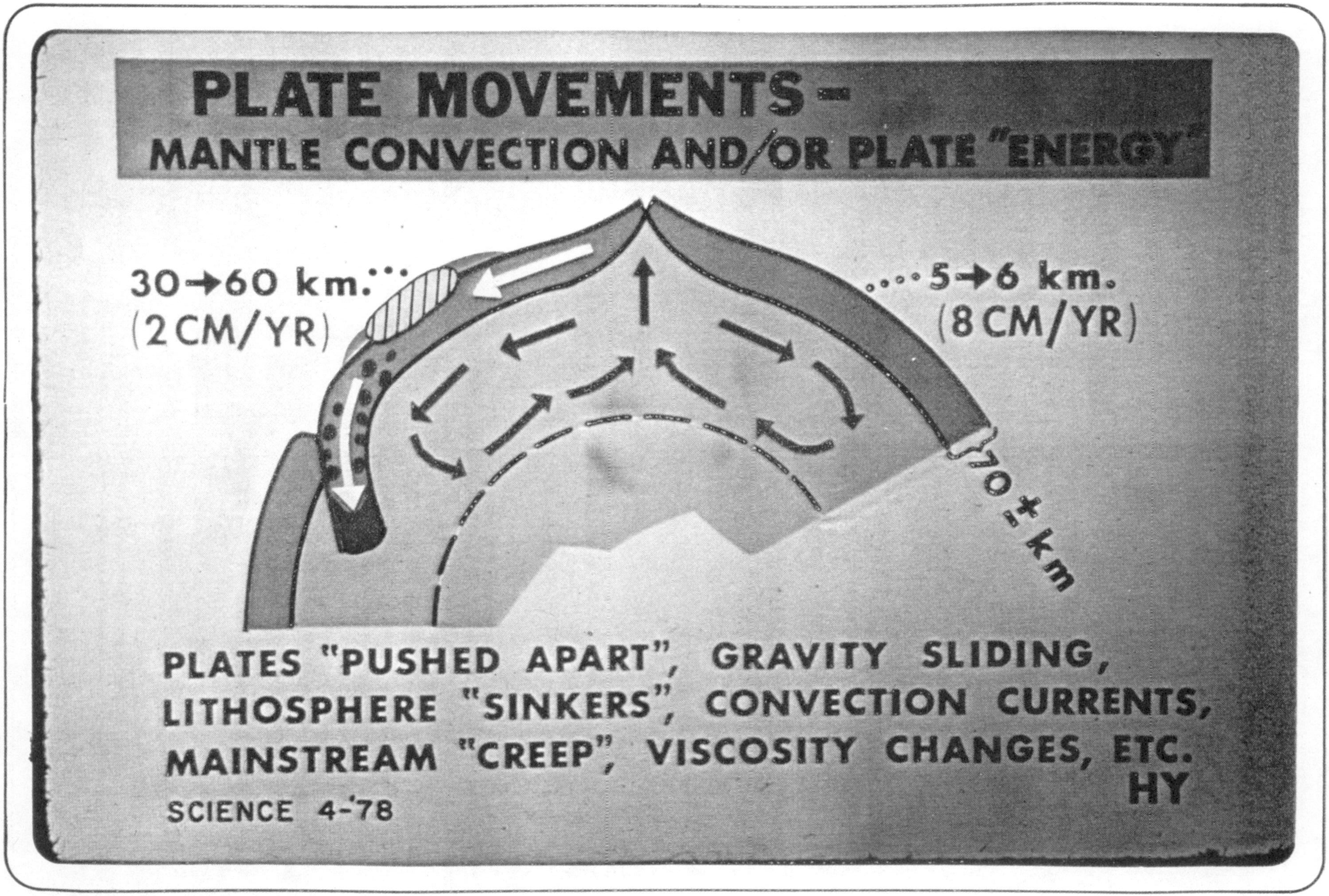

PLATE MOVEMENTS =
MANTLE CONVECTION AND/OR PLATE "ENERGY"

...5→6 km.
(8CM/YR)

70±km

30→60 km...
(2CM/YR)

PLATES "PUSHED APART", GRAVITY SLIDING,
LITHOSPHERE "SINKERS", CONVECTION CURRENTS,
MAINSTREAM "CREEP", VISCOSITY CHANGES, ETC.
HY

SCIENCE 4-'78

FIGURE 26

"HOT SPOTS", MANTLE PLUMES, CRUSTAL DOMES (TRIPLE JUNCTIONS), "BUMPS"?

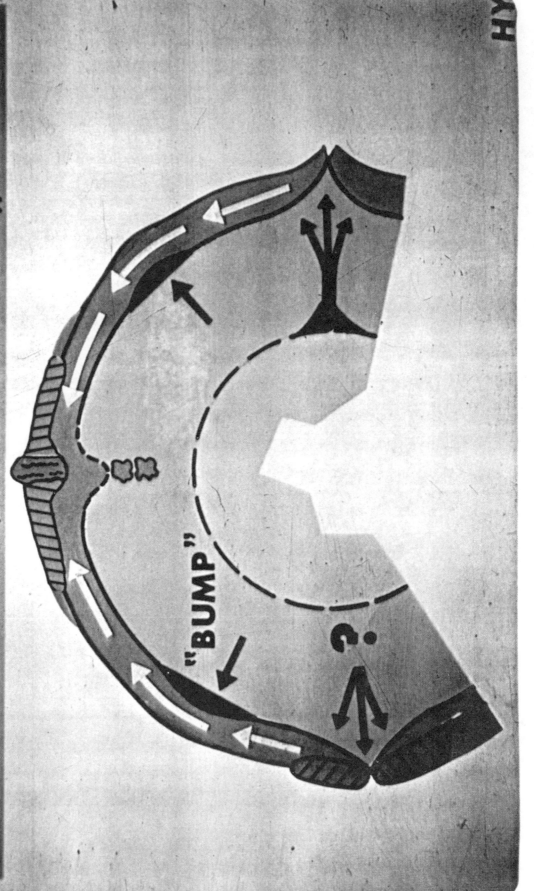

"BUMP"

?

FIGURE 26-A

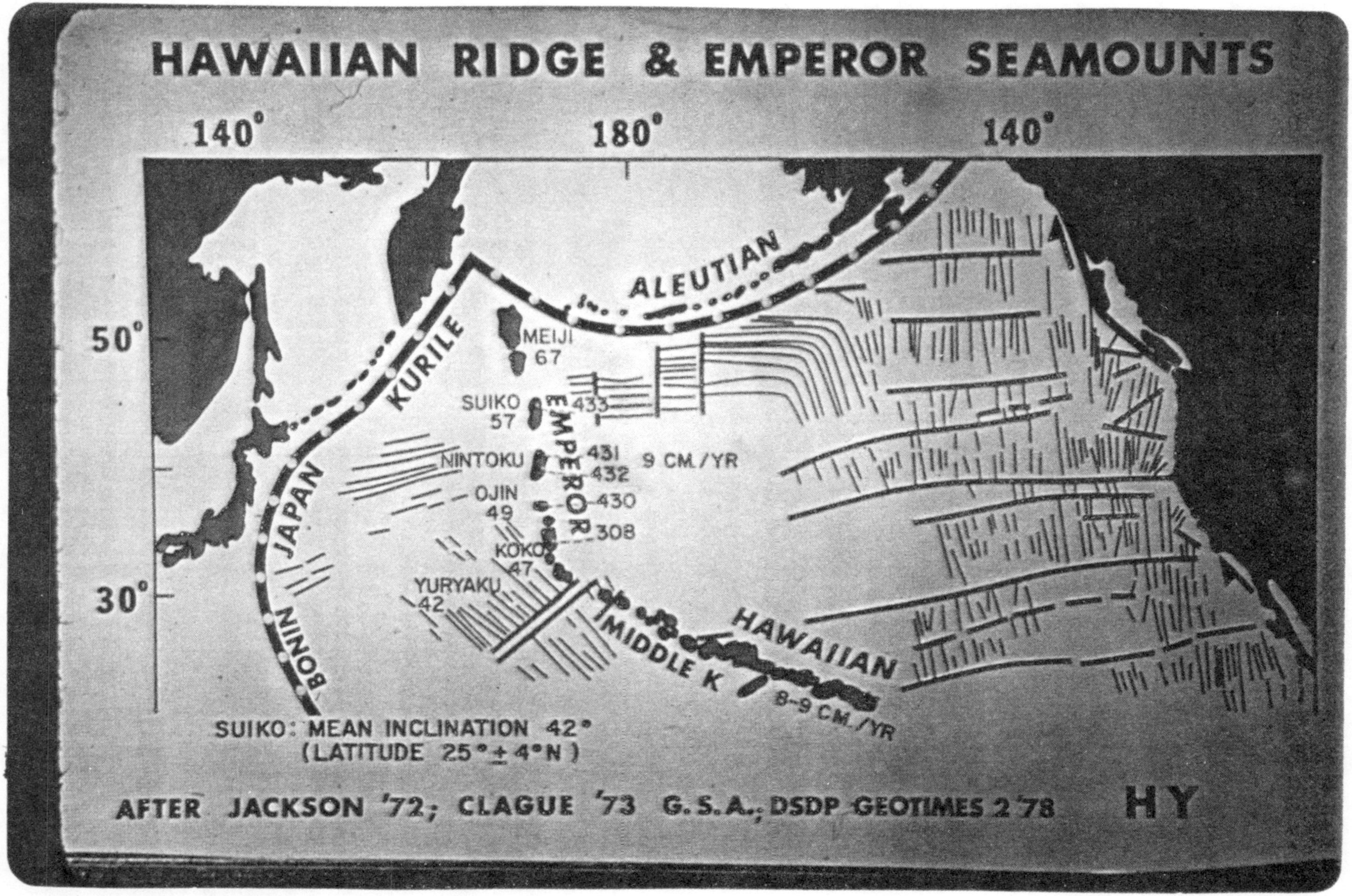

HAWAIIAN RIDGE & EMPEROR SEAMOUNTS

140°   180°   140°

50°

30°

MEIJI
67

SUIKO
57

433
432
431
430
308

9 CM./YR

NINTOKU
OJIN
49

KOKO
47

YURYAKU
42

EMPEROR

HAWAIIAN

MIDDLE K
8-9 CM./YR

ALEUTIAN

KURILE

JAPAN

BONIN

SUIKO: MEAN INCLINATION 42°
(LATITUDE 25°±4°N)

AFTER JACKSON '72; CLAGUE '73 G.S.A.; DSDP GEOTIMES 278   H Y

FIGURE 27

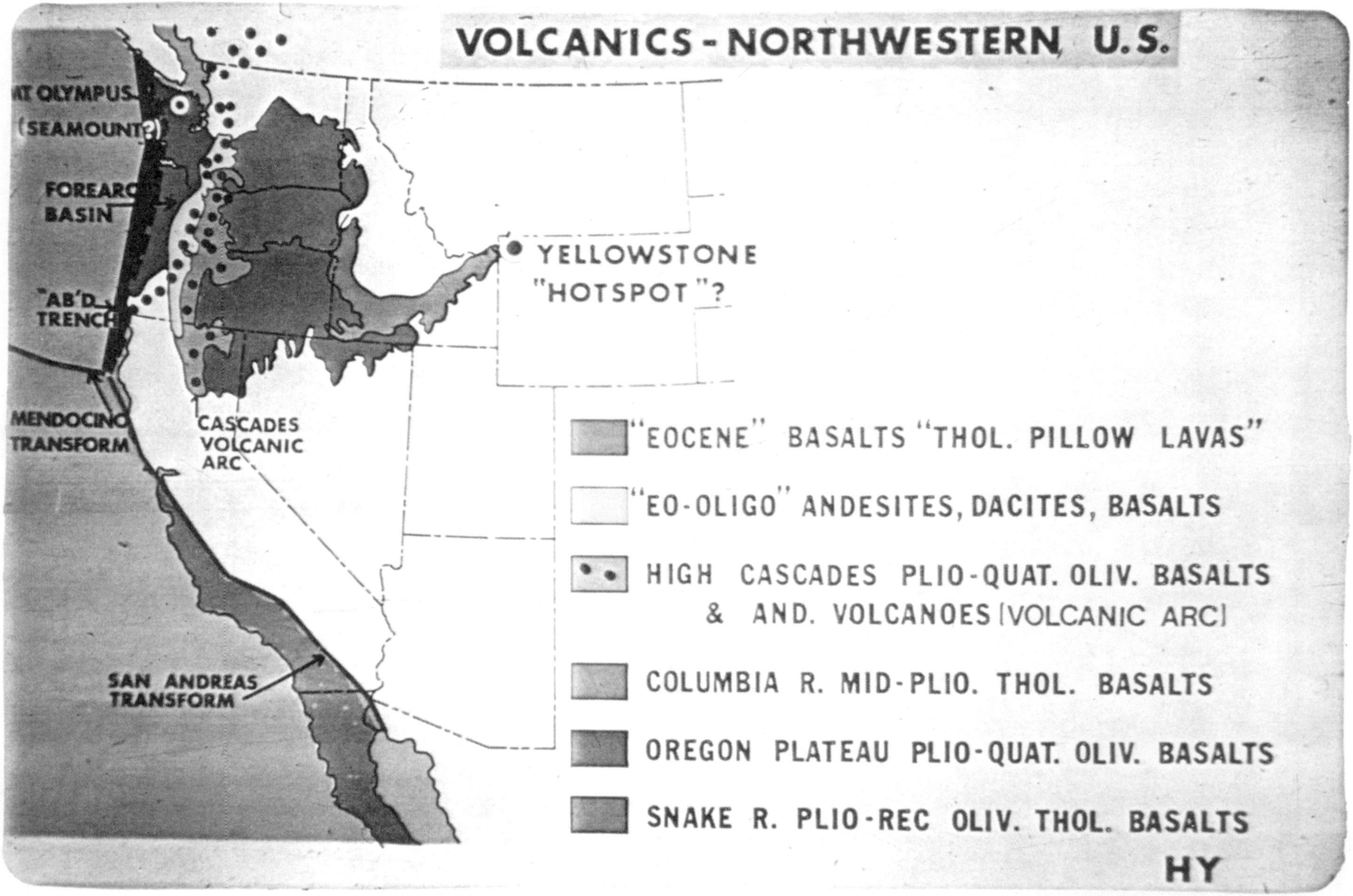

VOLCANICS – NORTHWESTERN, U.S.

"EOCENE" BASALTS "THOL. PILLOW LAVAS"

"EO-OLIGO" ANDESITES, DACITES, BASALTS

HIGH CASCADES PLIO-QUAT. OLIV. BASALTS
& AND. VOLCANOES (VOLCANIC ARC)

COLUMBIA R. MID-PLIO. THOL. BASALTS

OREGON PLATEAU PLIO-QUAT. OLIV. BASALTS

SNAKE R. PLIO-REC OLIV. THOL. BASALTS

YELLOWSTONE "HOTSPOT"?

MT. OLYMPUS (SEAMOUNT?)

FOREARC BASIN

"AB'D" TRENCH

MENDOCINO TRANSFORM

CASCADES VOLCANIC ARC

SAN ANDREAS TRANSFORM

HY

FIGURE 27-A

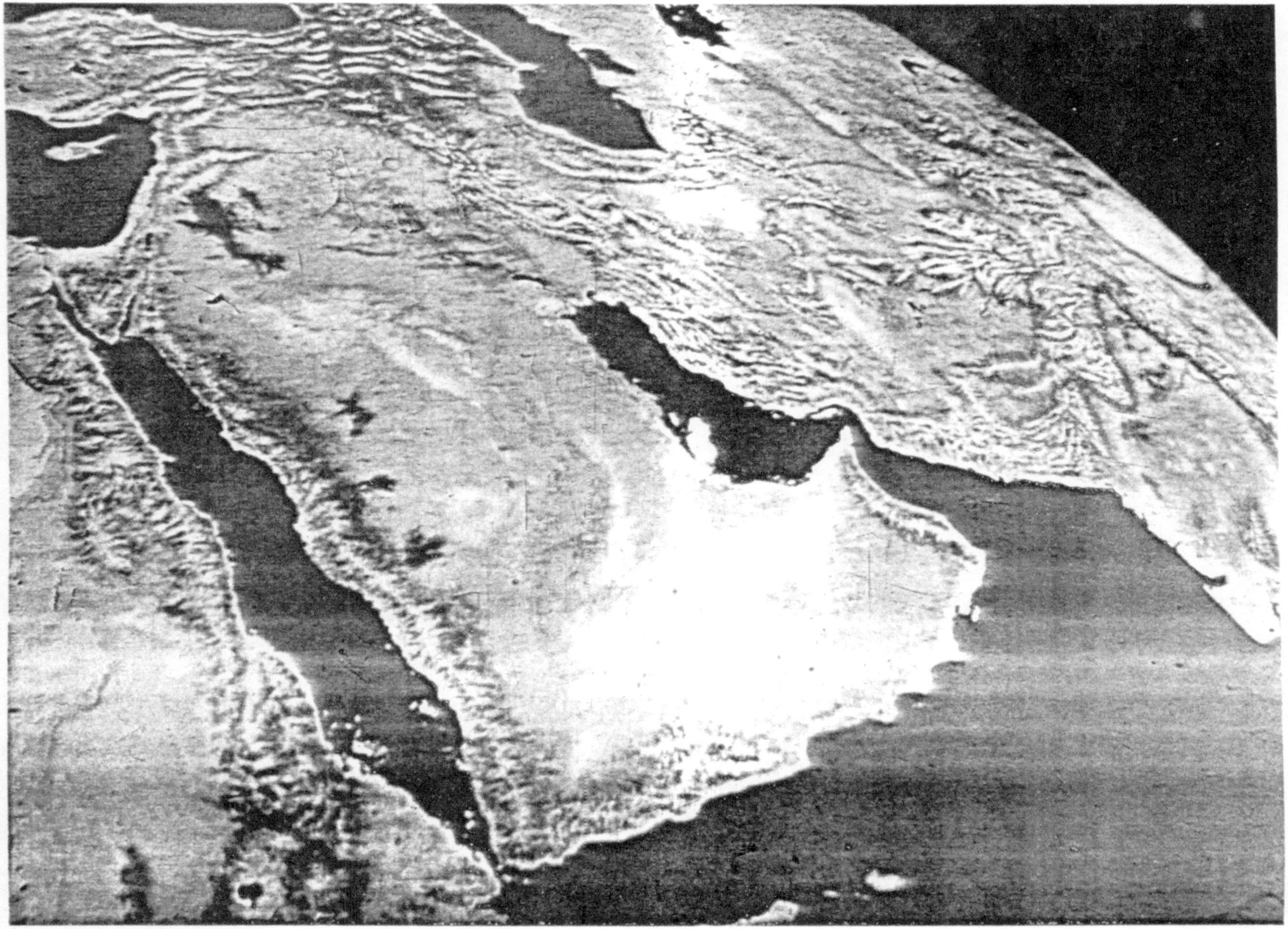

FIGURE 28

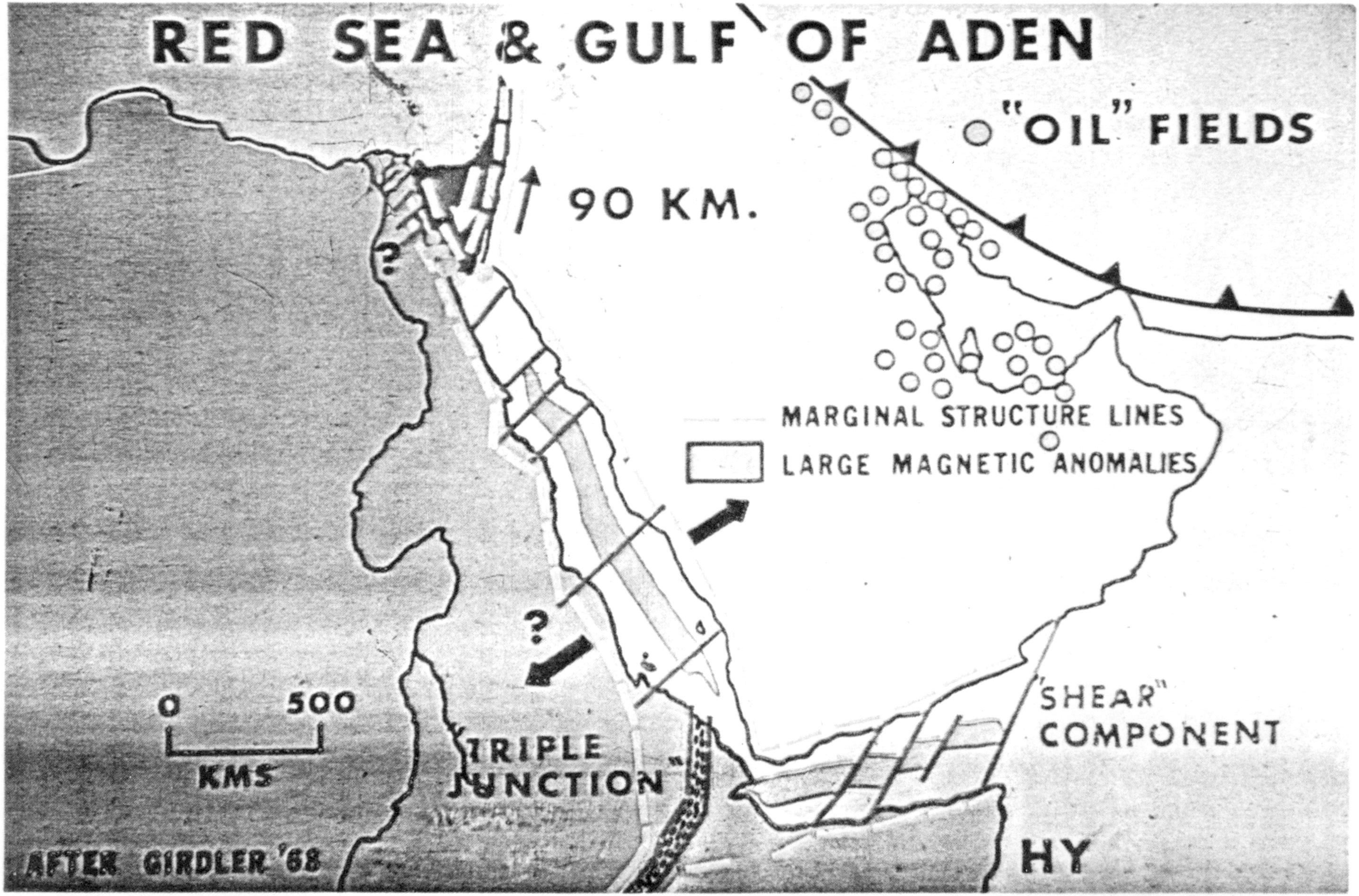

RED SEA & GULF OF ADEN

"OIL" FIELDS

90 KM.

MARGINAL STRUCTURE LINES

LARGE MAGNETIC ANOMALIES

"SHEAR" COMPONENT

TRIPLE JUNCTION

0   500
KMS

AFTER GIRDLER '68

HY

FIGURE 29

RIFT VALLEY SEDIMENTATION

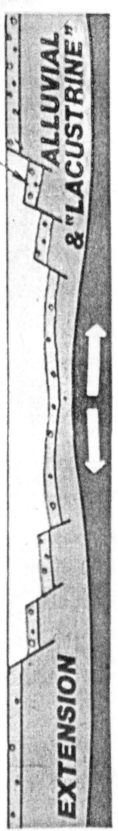

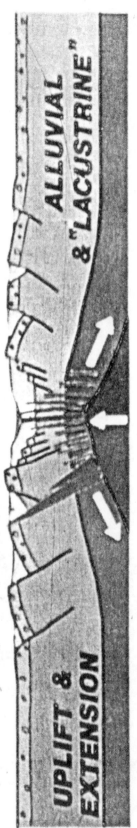

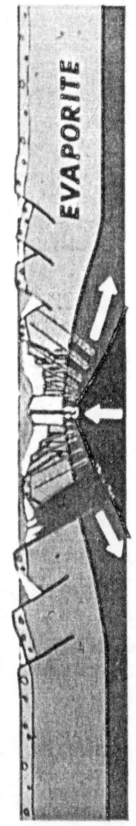

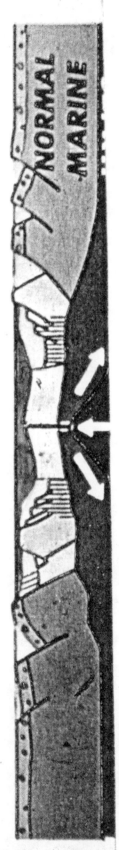

PRE-RIFT

EXTENSION

ALLUVIAL & "LACUSTRINE"

UPLIFT & EXTENSION

ALLUVIAL & "LACUSTRINE"

EVAPORITE

NORMAL MARINE

FIGURE 30

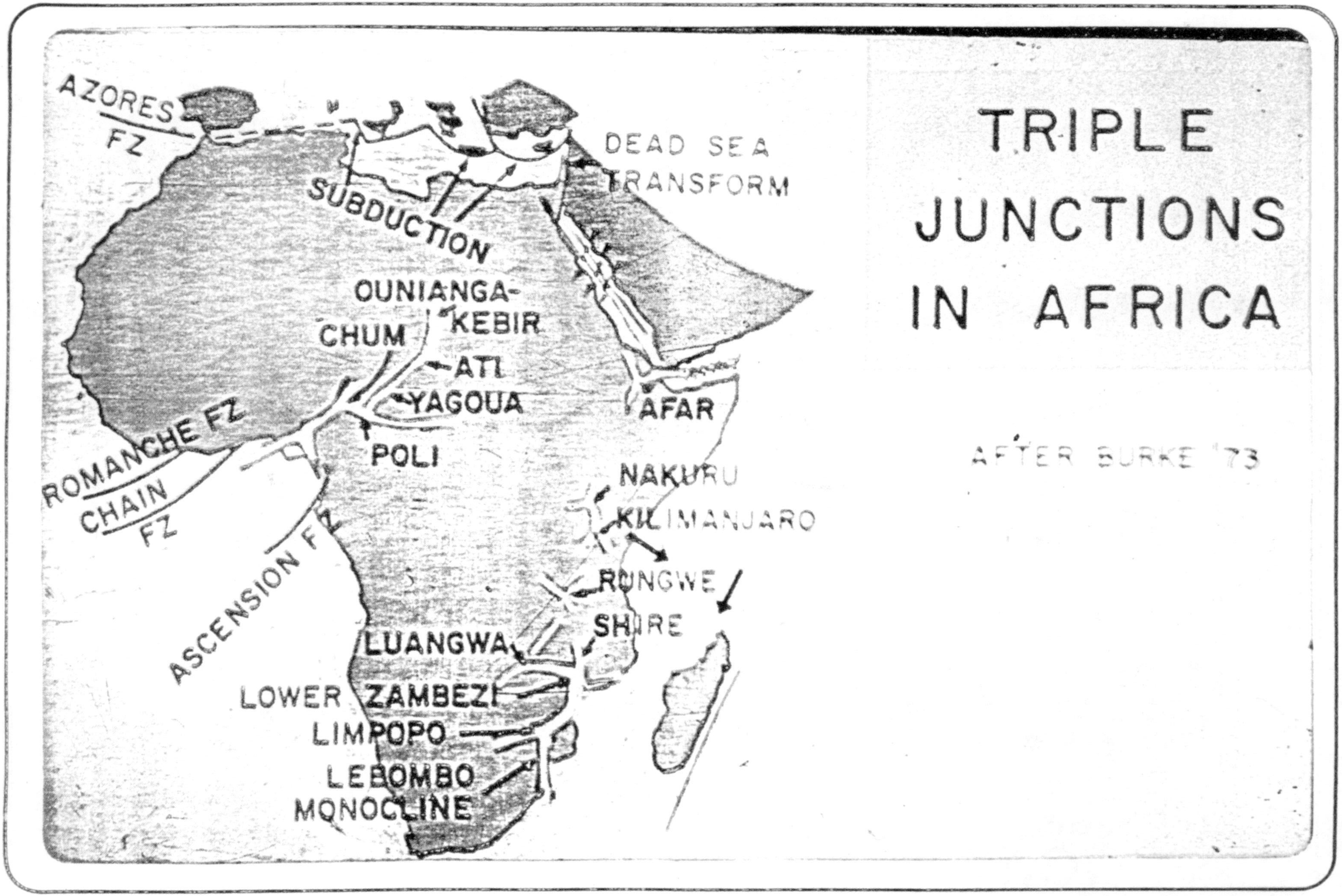
TRIPLE
JUNCTIONS
IN AFRICA
AFTER BURKE '73
AZORES FZ
DEAD SEA TRANSFORM
SUBDUCTION
OUNIANGA-KEBIR
CHUM
ATI
YAGOUA
POLI
AFAR
ROMANCHE FZ
CHAIN FZ
ASCENSION FZ
NAKURU
KILIMANJARO
RUNGWE
SHIRE
LUANGWA
LOWER ZAMBEZI
LIMPOPO
LEBOMBO MONOCLINE

FIGURE 30-A

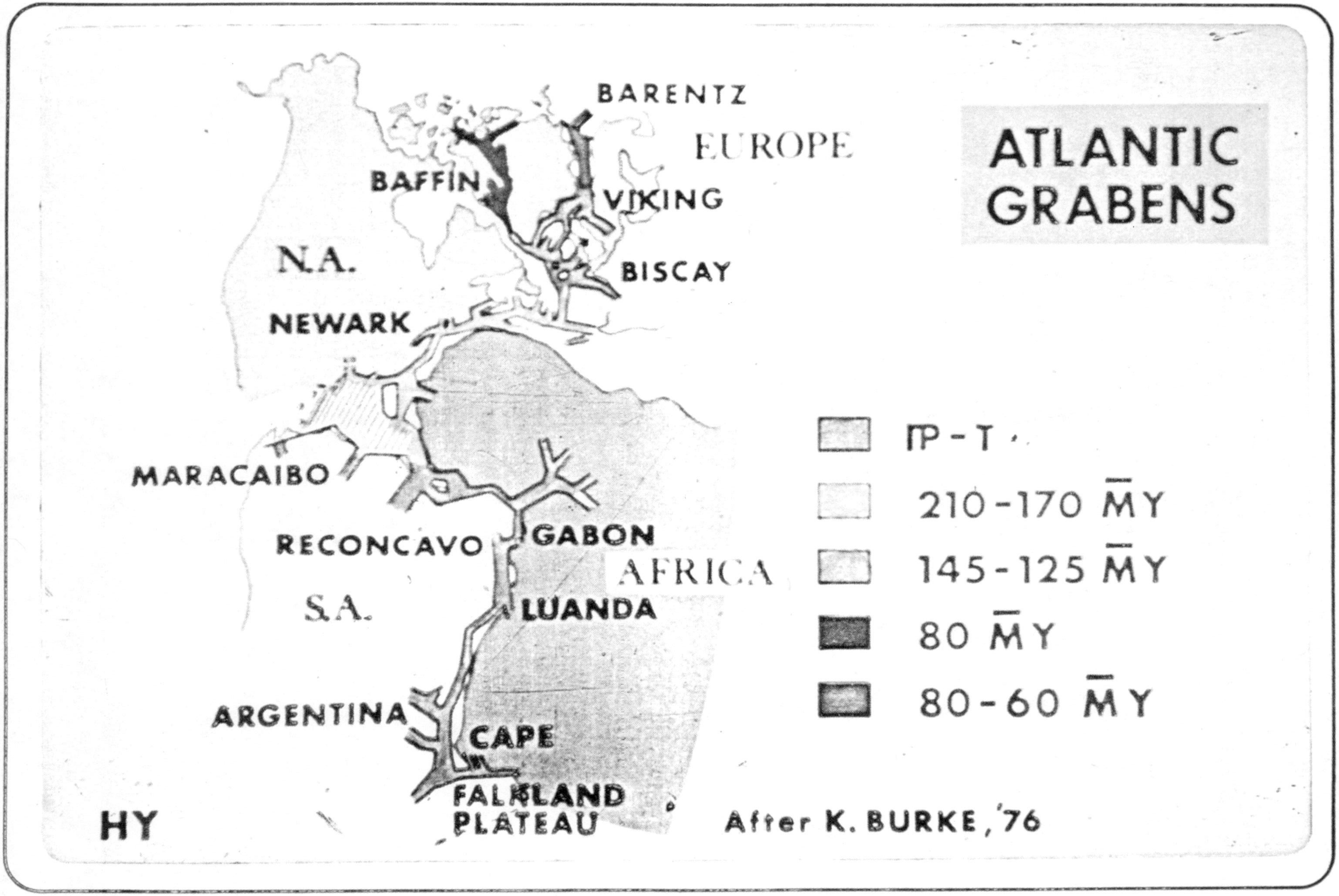
ATLANTIC
GRABENS
BARENTZ
EUROPE
BAFFIN
VIKING
N.A.
BISCAY
NEWARK
MARACAIBO
RECONCAVO
GABON
AFRICA
S.A.
LUANDA
ARGENTINA
CAPE
FALKLAND
PLATEAU
ΓP - T
210-170 M̄Y
145-125 M̄Y
80 M̄Y
80-60 M̄Y
HY
After K. BURKE, '76

FIGURE 30-B

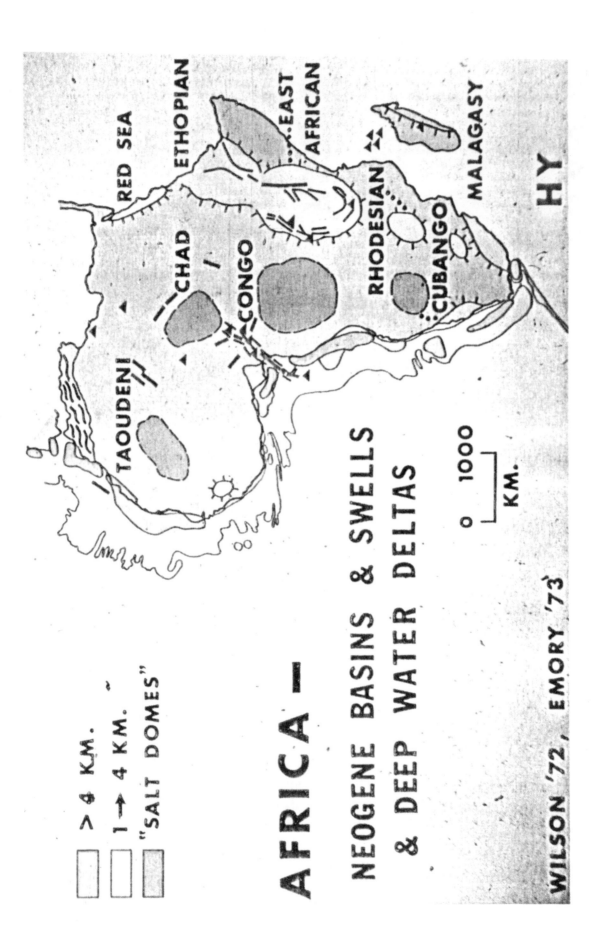

AFRICA —
NEOGENE BASINS & SWELLS
& DEEP WATER DELTAS

WILSON '72, EMORY '73

FIGURE 31

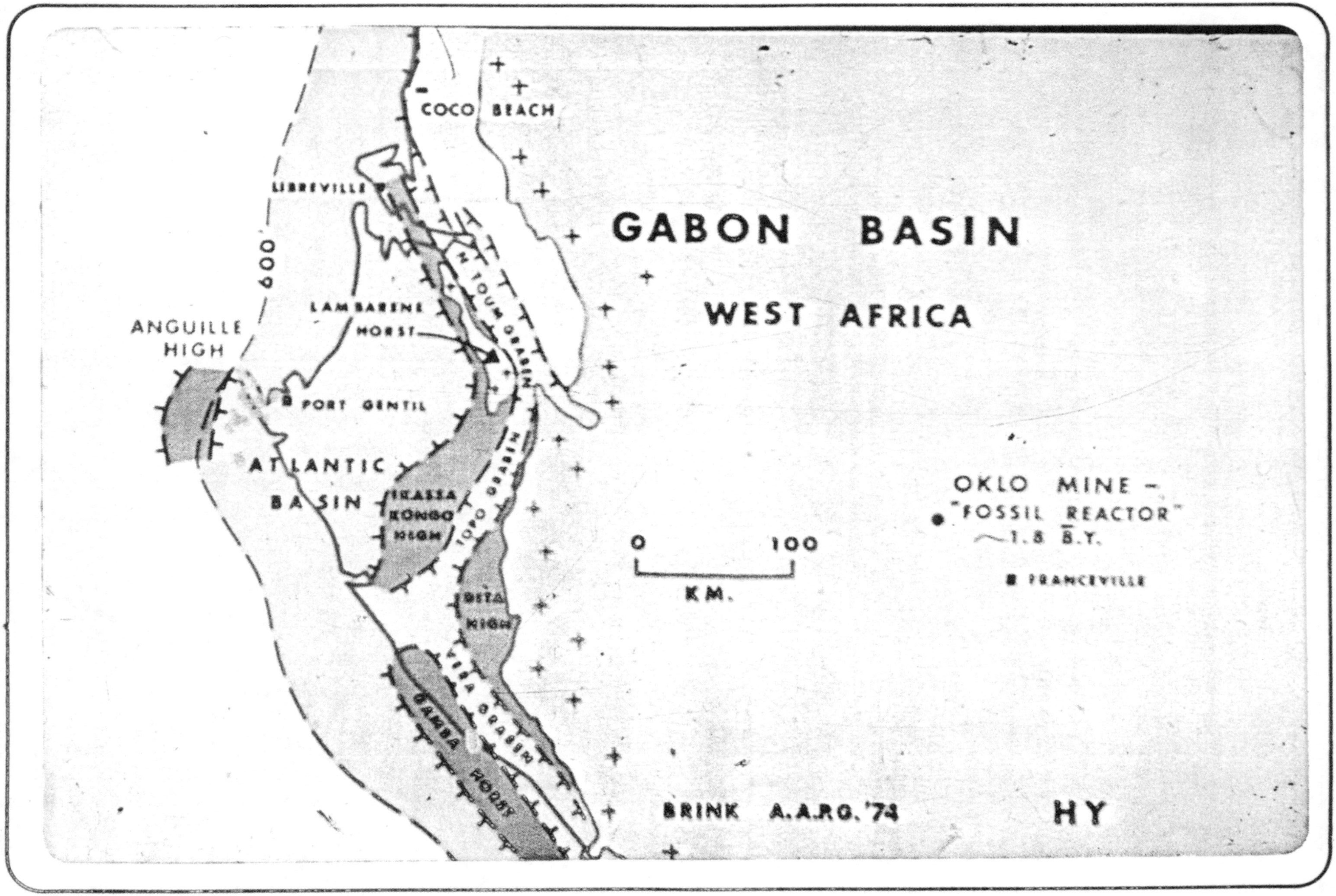

GABON BASIN

WEST AFRICA

OKLO MINE –
"FOSSIL REACTOR"
~1.8 B.Y.

● FRANCEVILLE

0   100
|___|___|
K.M.

COCO BEACH

LIBREVILLE

N'TOUM GRABEN

LAMBARENE HORST

PORT GENTIL

ANGUILLE HIGH

ATLANTIC BASIN

NDJOLE GRABEN

IKASSA KONGO HIGH

BITA HIGH

VIDA GRABEN

GAMBA HORST

600

BRINK A.A.P.G. '74

HY

FIGURE 31-A

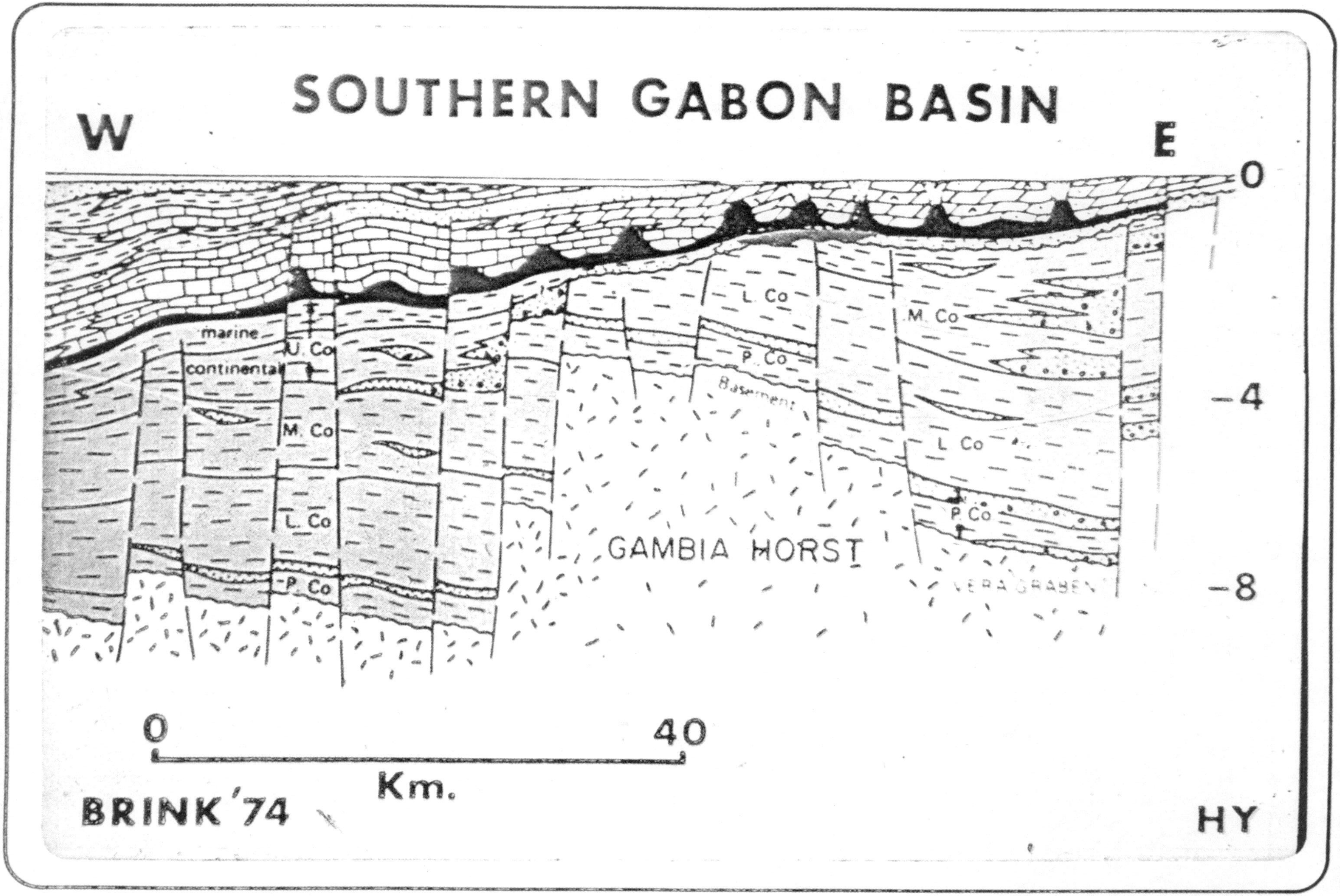

SOUTHERN GABON BASIN

W

E

0

-4

-8

marine

continental

U. Co

M. Co

L. Co

P. Co

M. Co

L. Co

P. Co

L. Co

P. Co

Basement

GAMBIA HORST

ERA GRABEN

0   40

Km.

BRINK '74

HY

FIGURE 31-B

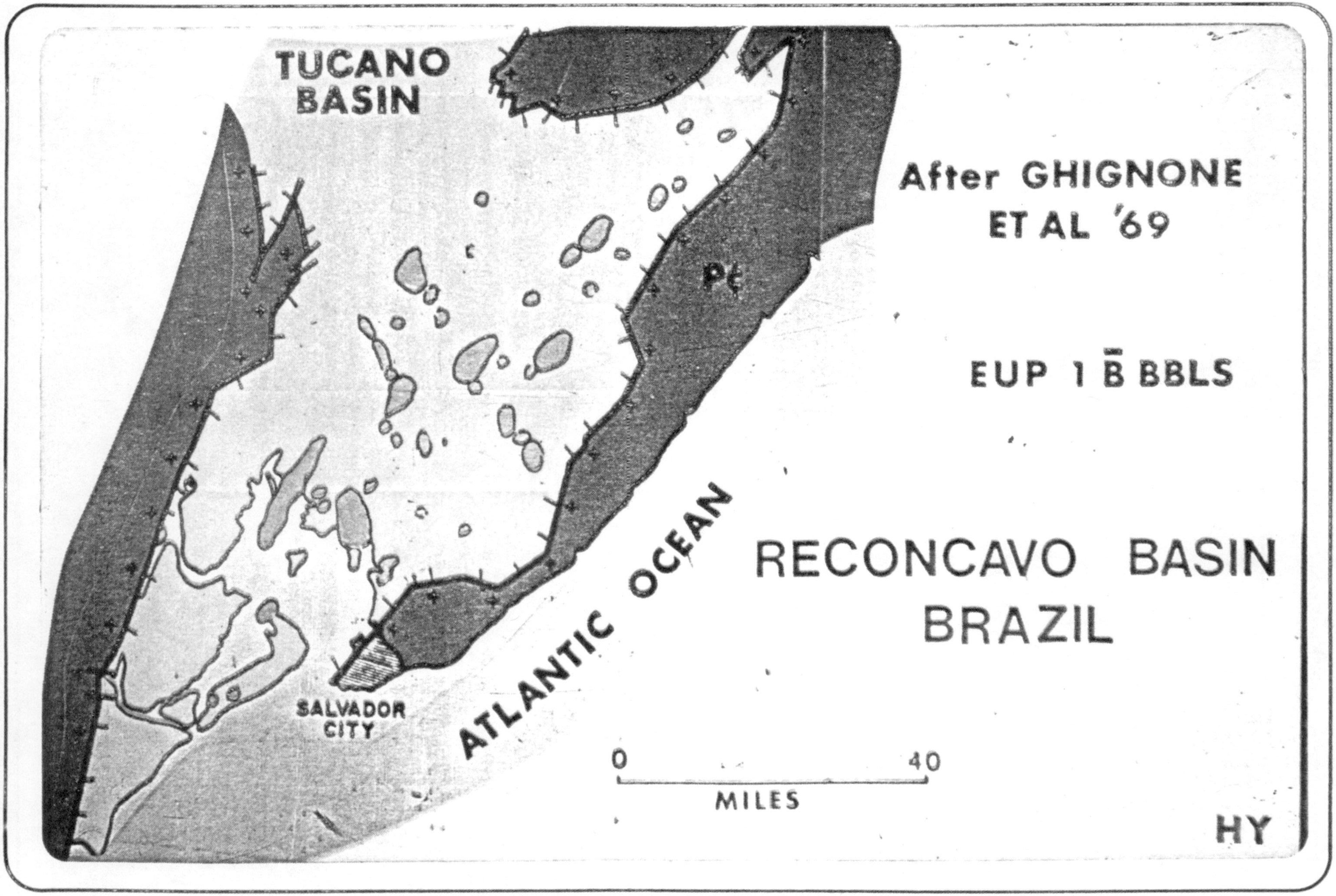

After GHIGNONE ET AL '69

EUP 1 $\overline{B}$ BBLS

RECONCAVO BASIN
BRAZIL

TUCANO BASIN

ATLANTIC OCEAN

SALVADOR CITY

0   40
MILES

HY

FIGURE 31-C

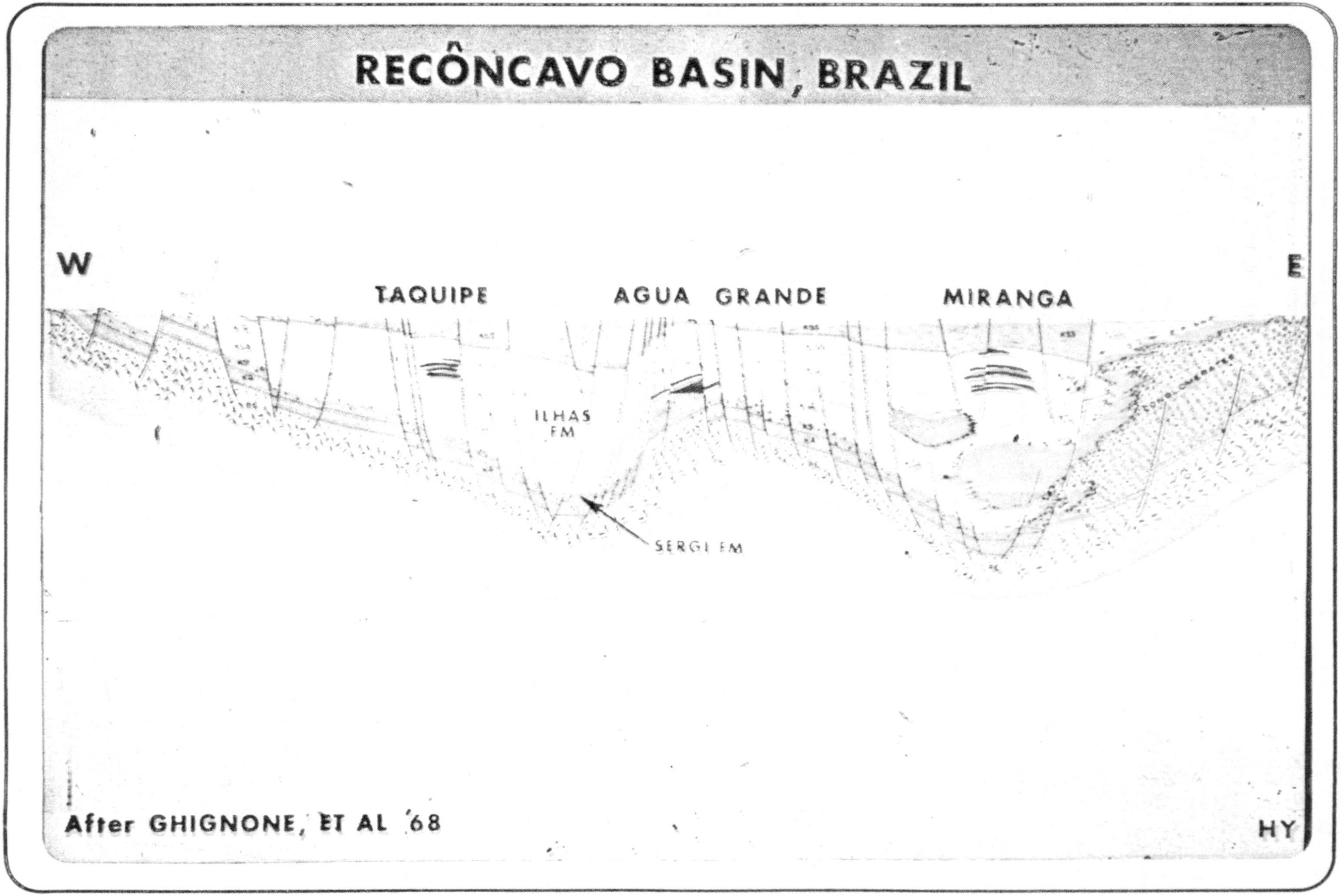

RECÔNCAVO BASIN, BRAZIL

W   E

TAQUIPE   AGUA GRANDE   MIRANGA

ILHAS FM

SERGI FM

After GHIGNONE, ET AL '68

FIGURE 31-D

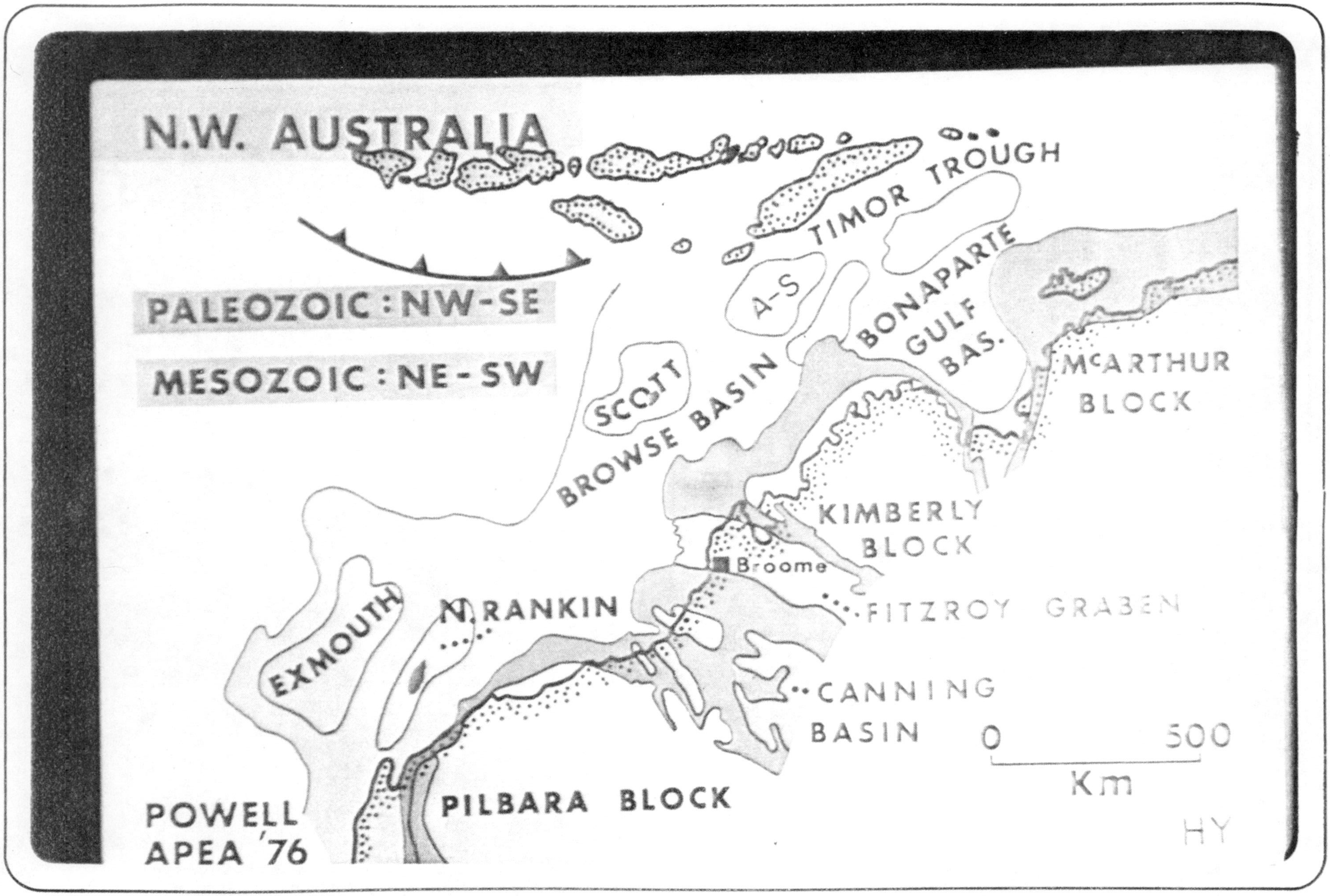

N.W. AUSTRALIA

PALEOZOIC: NW-SE

MESOZOIC: NE-SW

TIMOR TROUGH

BONAPARTE GULF BAS.

A-S

SCOTT

BROWSE BASIN

McARTHUR BLOCK

KIMBERLY BLOCK

Broome

FITZROY GRABEN

CANNING BASIN

N. RANKIN

EXMOUTH

PILBARA BLOCK

0   500
    Km
         HY

POWELL
APEA '76

FIGURE 32

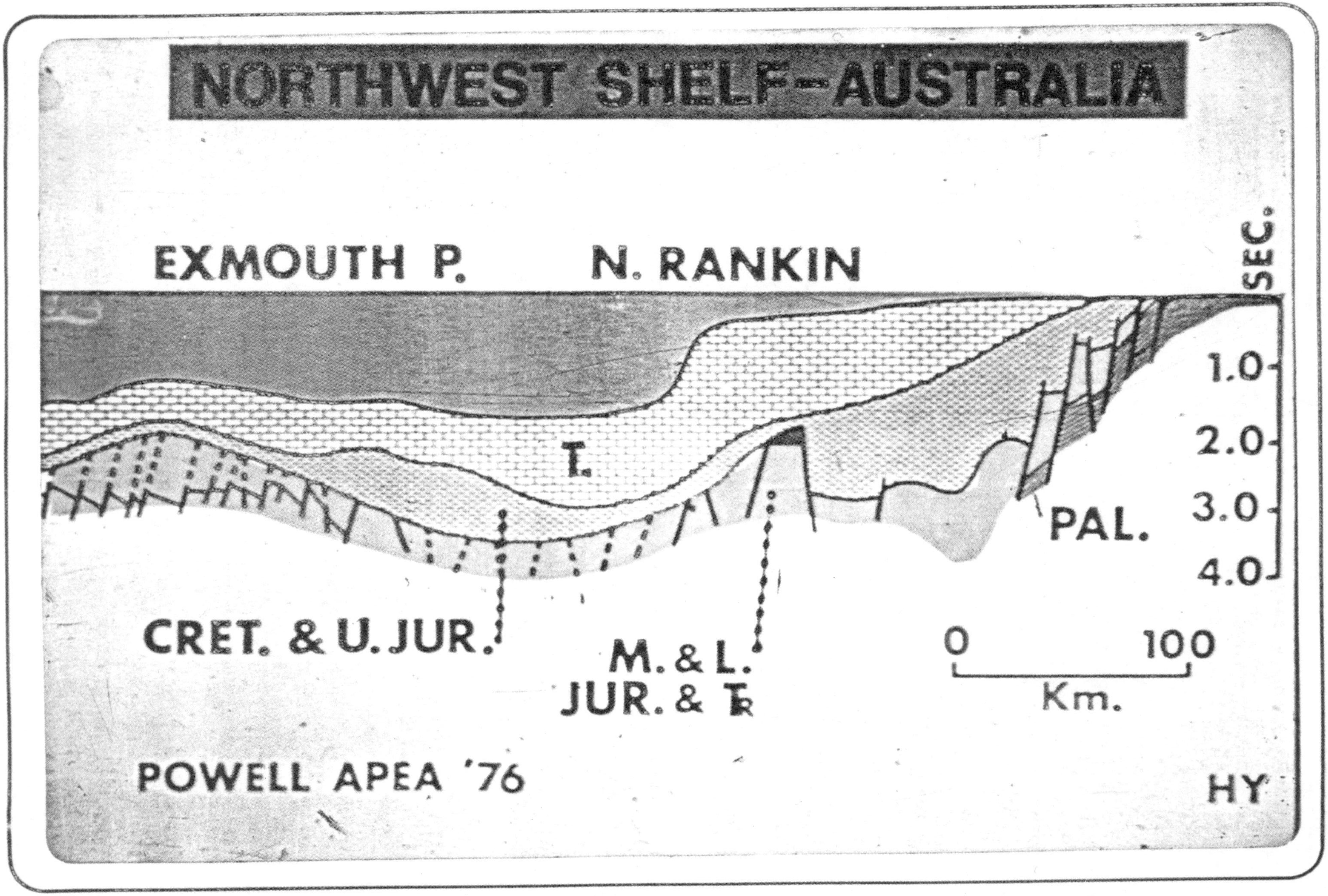

NORTHWEST SHELF—AUSTRALIA

EXMOUTH P.   N. RANKIN

SEC.

1.0
2.0
3.0
4.0

100

0   Km.

PAL.

CRET. & U. JUR.

M. & L.
JUR. & TR.

POWELL APEA '76

FIGURE 32-A

HY.

N.W. AUSTRALIAN SHELF

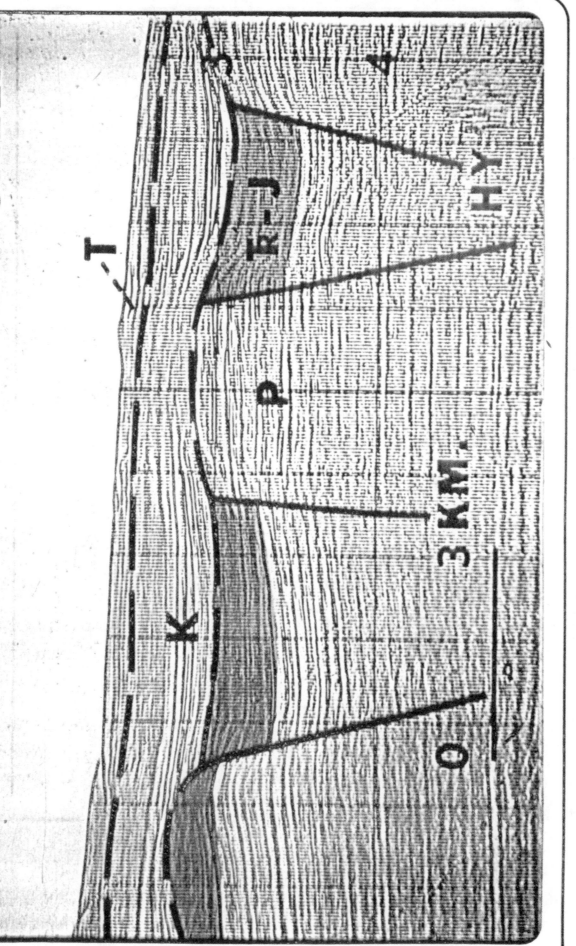

FIGURE 32-B

CONTINENTAL MARGINS-A

CLASTIC

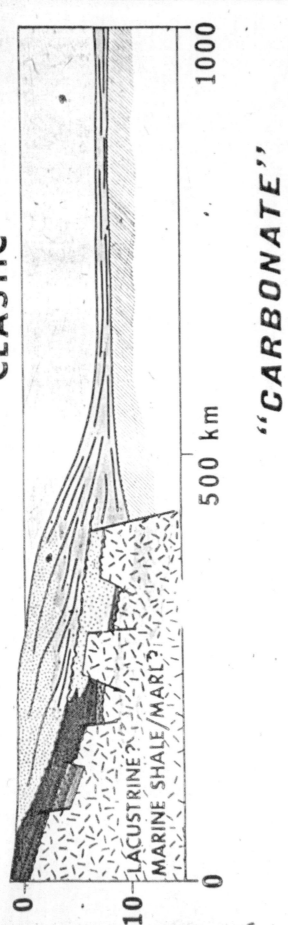

LACUSTRINE?
MARINE SHALE/MARL?

"CARBONATE"

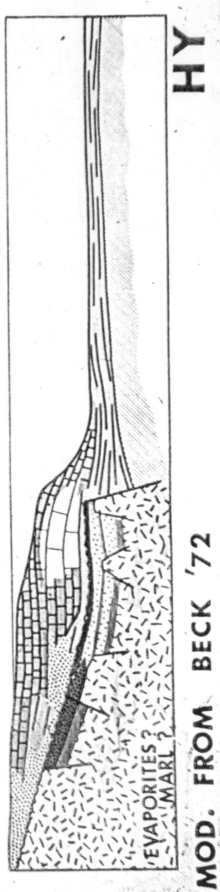

EVAPORITES?
MARL?

MOD. FROM BECK '72

HY

FIGURE 32-C

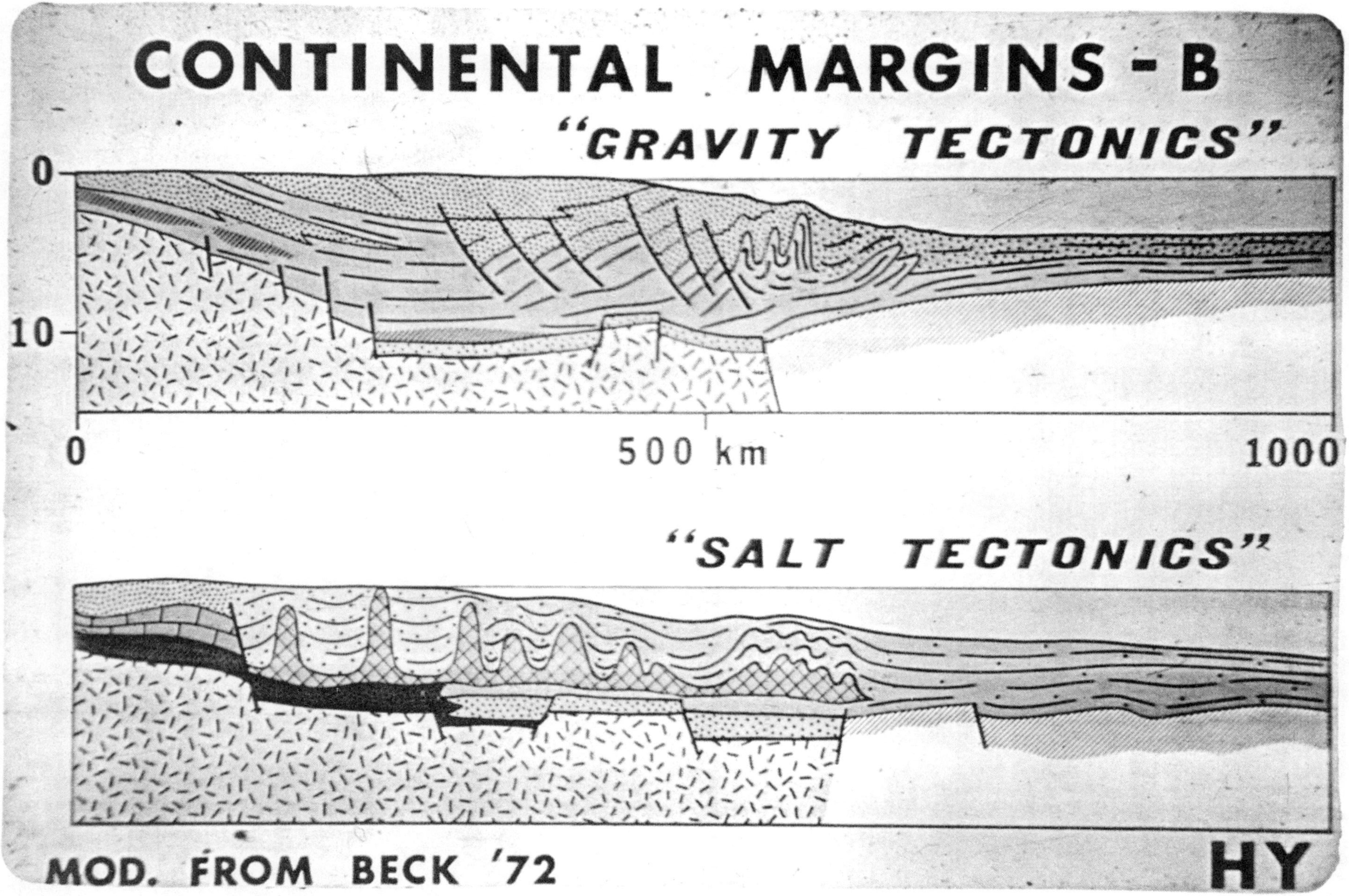
CONTINENTAL MARGINS - B
"GRAVITY TECTONICS"
0
10
0
500 km
1000
"SALT TECTONICS"
MOD. FROM BECK '72
HY

FIGURE 32-D

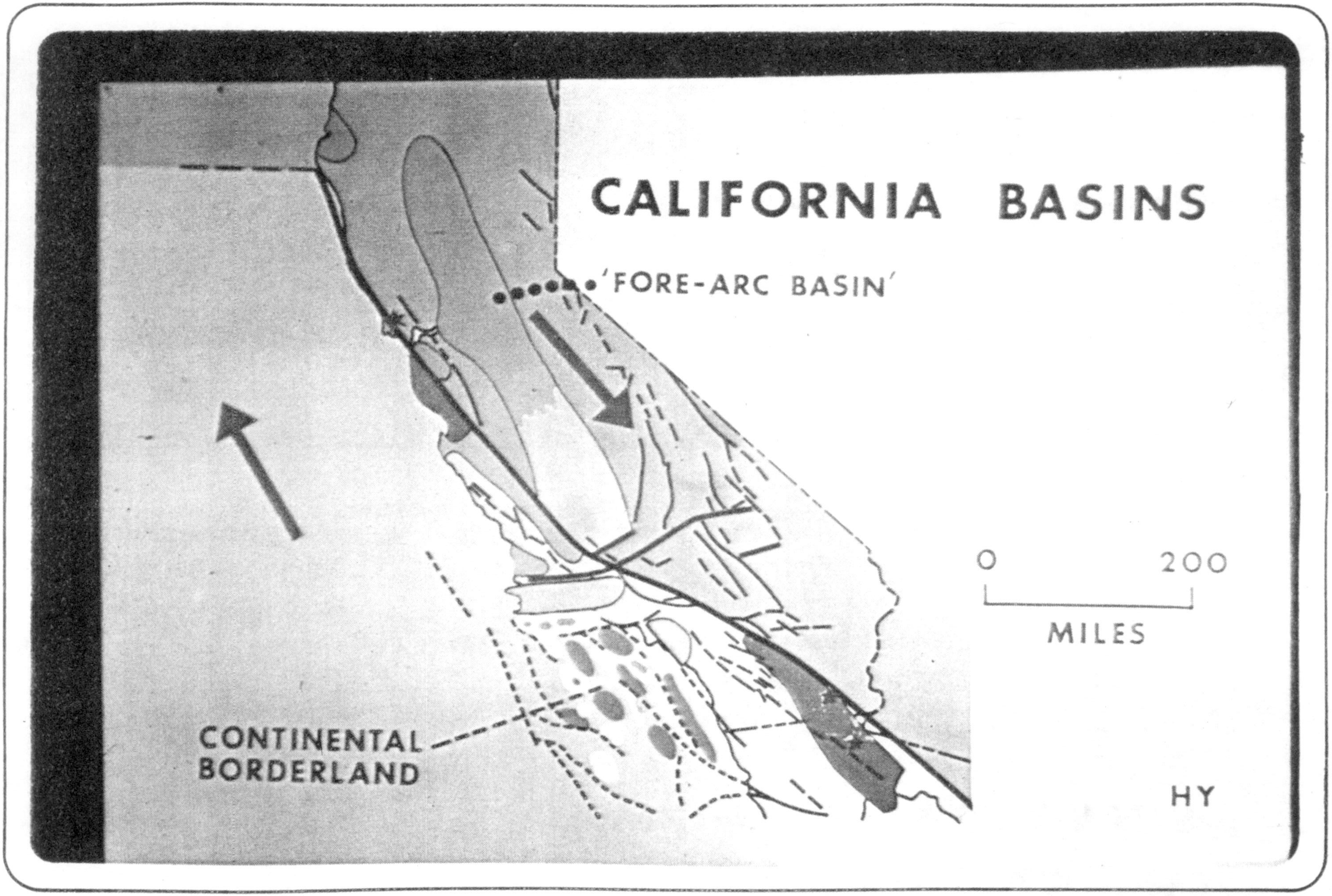

CALIFORNIA BASINS

'FORE-ARC BASIN'

CONTINENTAL BORDERLAND

0   200
MILES

HY

FIGURE 33

FIGURE 34

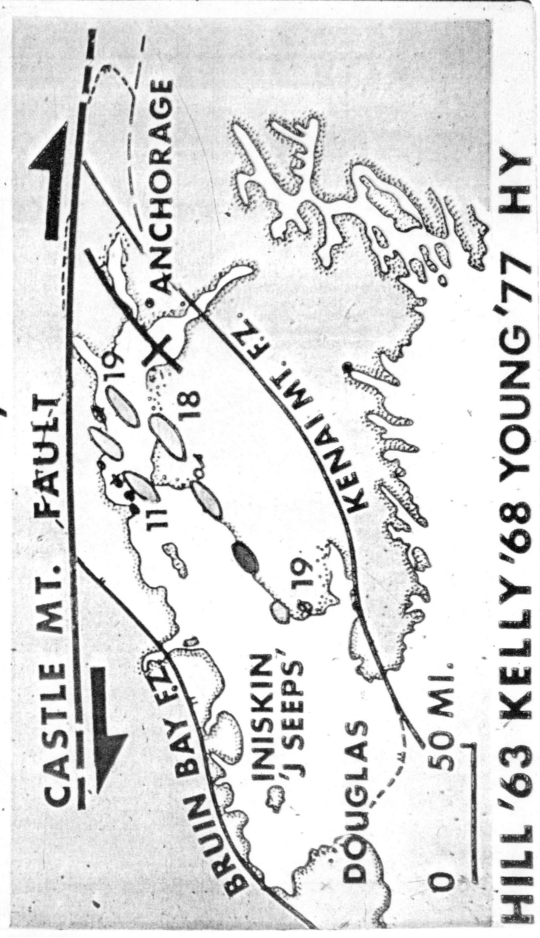

COOK INLET, ALASKA

FIGURE 35

HILL '63 KELLY '68 YOUNG '77 HY

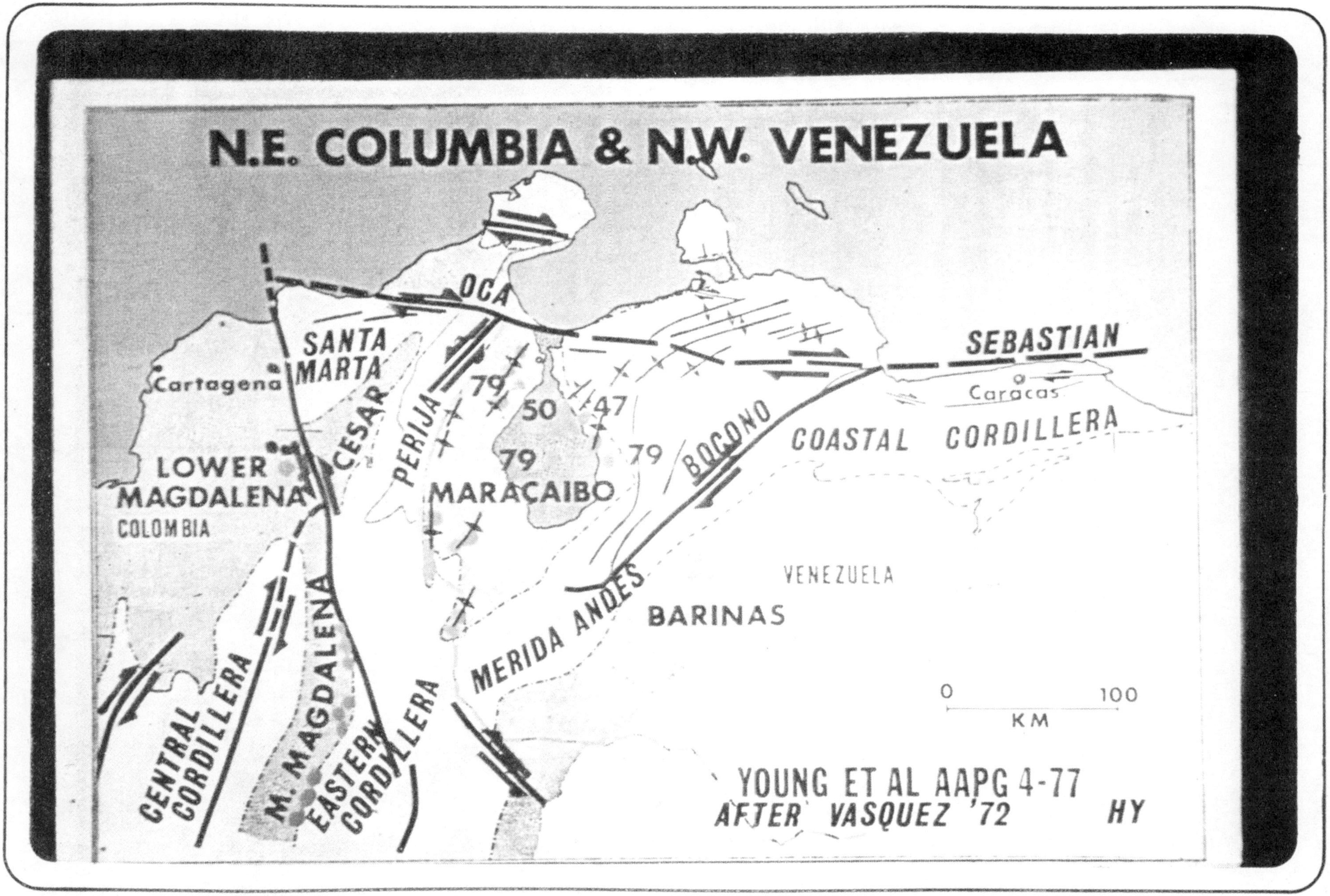

N.E. COLUMBIA & N.W. VENEZUELA

SEBASTIAN

Caracas

COASTAL CORDILLERA

BOCONO

VENEZUELA

BARINAS

MERIDA ANDES

MARACAIBO

PERIJA

CESAR

OCA

SANTA MARTA

Cartagena

LOWER MAGDALENA

COLOMBIA

M. MAGDALENA

EASTERN CORDILLERA

CENTRAL CORDILLERA

79 50 79 147 79 79

KM

0   100

YOUNG ET AL AAPG 4-77
AFTER VASQUEZ '72   HY

FIGURE 36

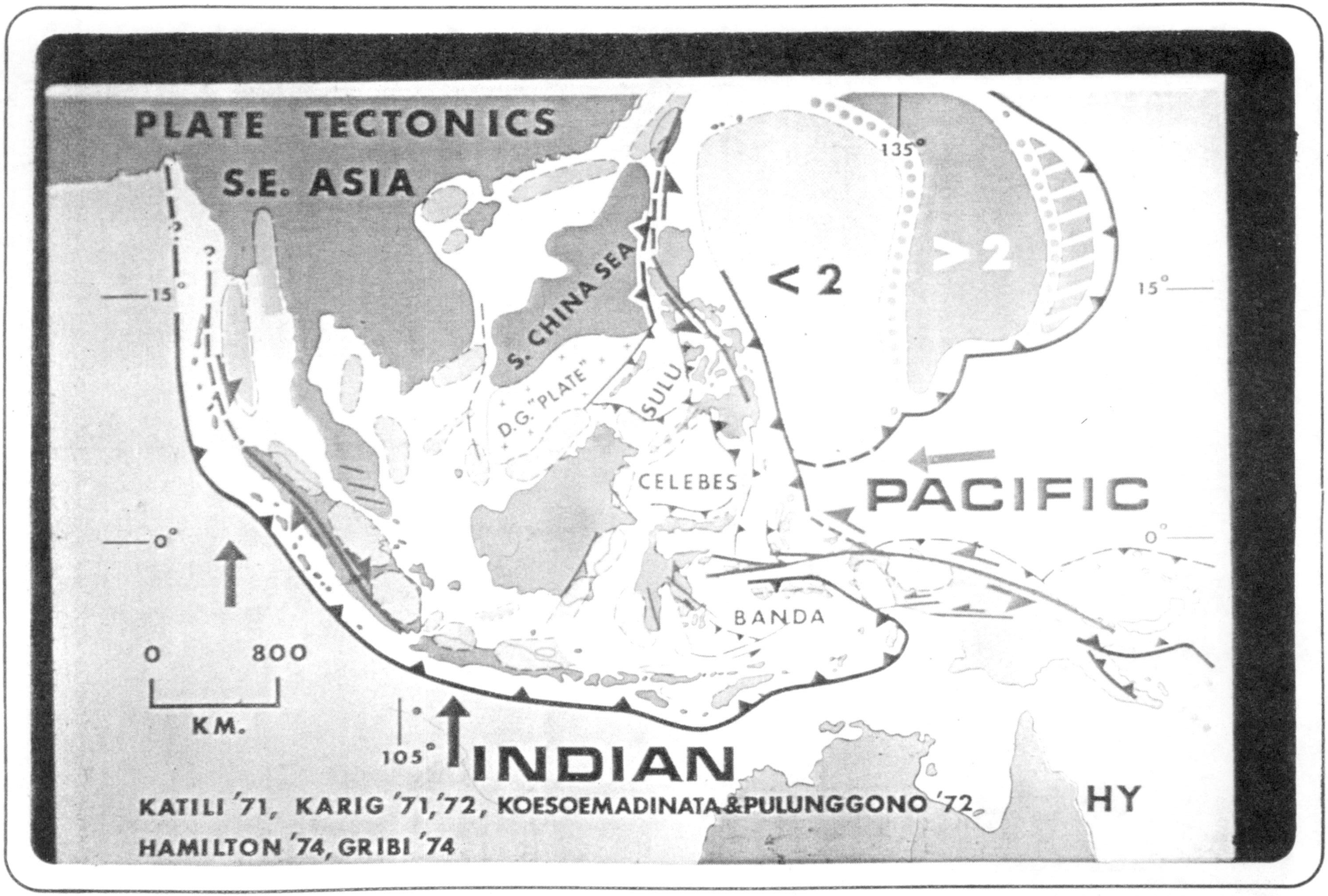
PLATE TECTONICS
S.E. ASIA
135°
15°
< 2
> 2
S. CHINA SEA
D.G. "PLATE"
SULU
CELEBES
PACIFIC
0°
BANDA
0 800
KM.
105°
INDIAN
HY
KATILI '71, KARIG '71,'72, KOESOEMADINATA & PULUNGGONO '72
HAMILTON '74, GRIBI '74

FIGURE 37

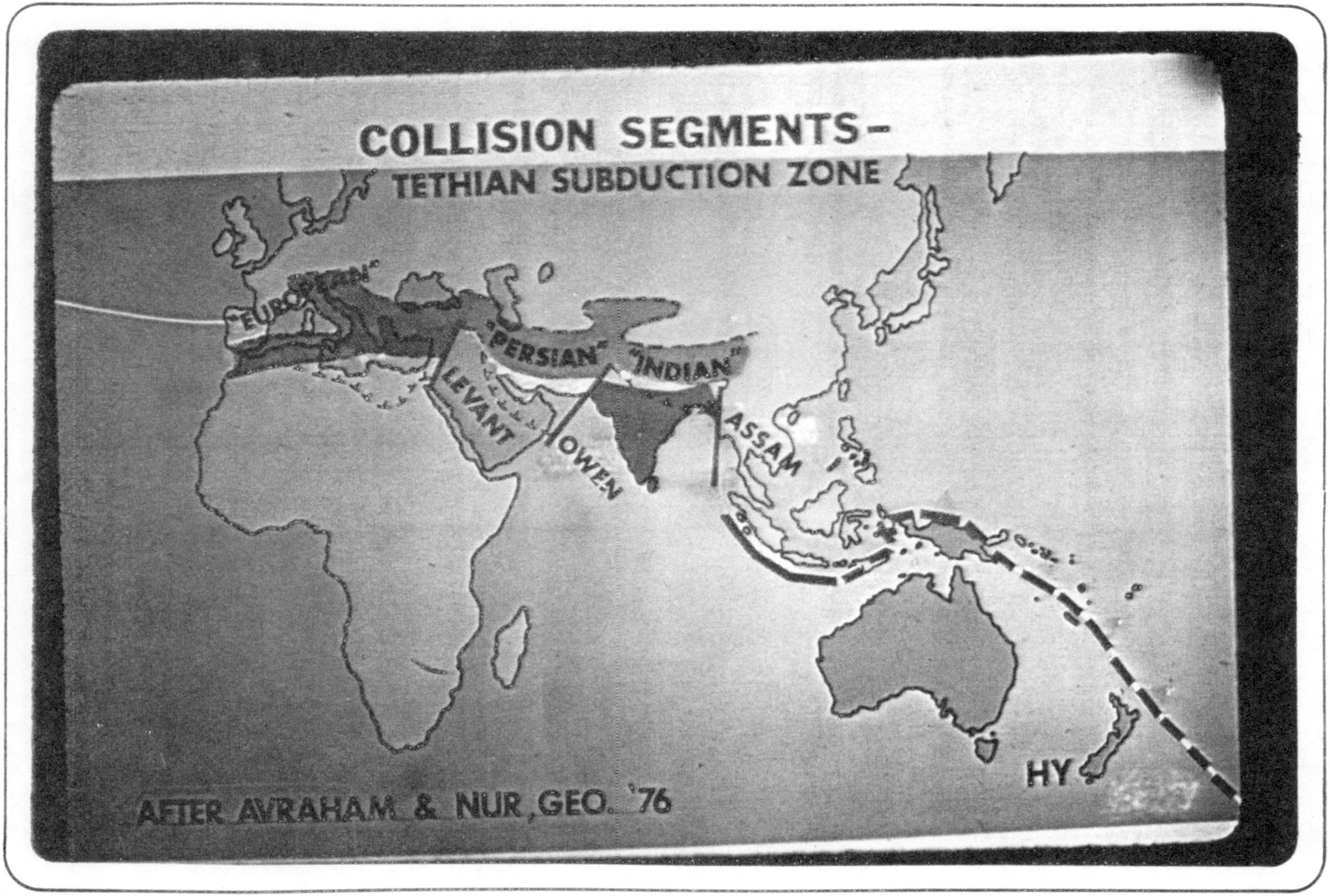

COLLISION SEGMENTS —
TETHIAN SUBDUCTION ZONE

AFTER AVRAHAM & NUR, GEO. '76

FIGURE 38

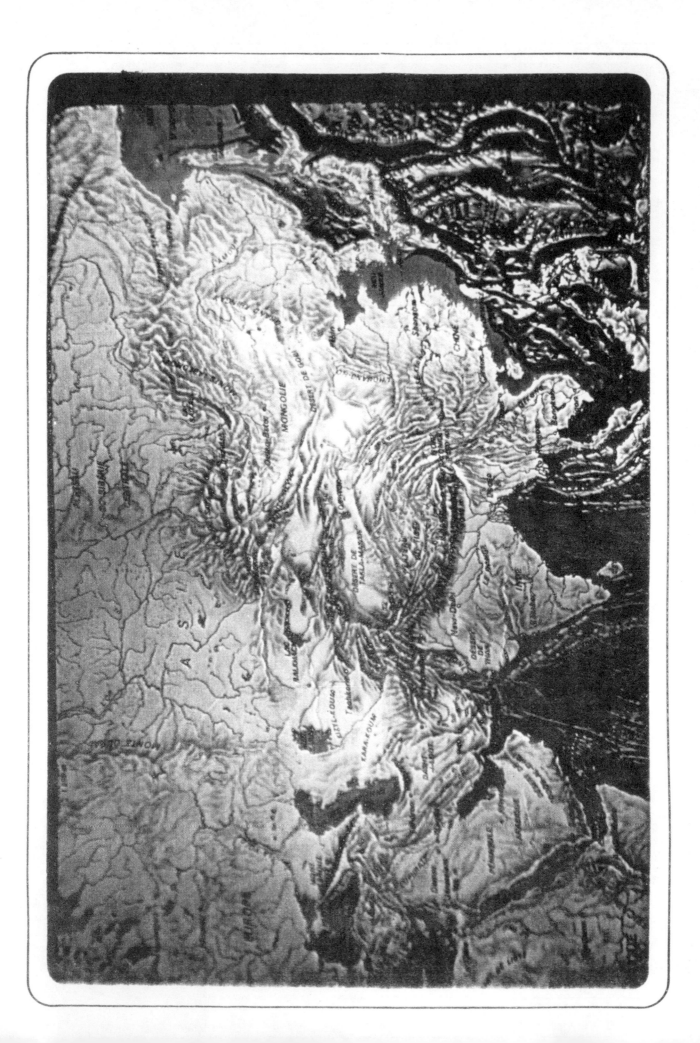

FIGURE 39

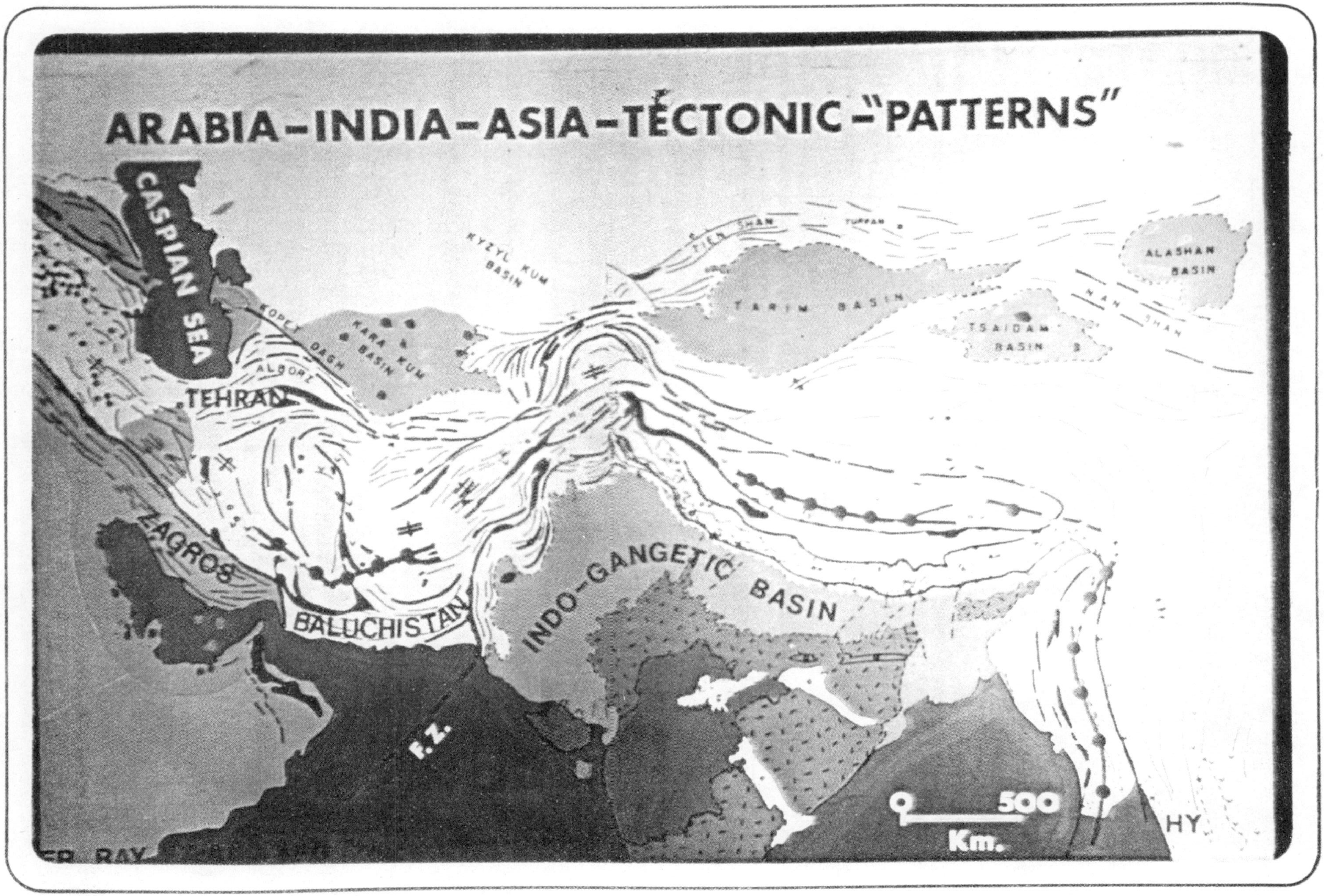
ARABIA-INDIA-ASIA-TECTONIC-"PATTERNS"
CASPIAN SEA
TEHRAN
ALBORZ
KOPET DAGH
KARA KUM BASIN
KYZYL KUM BASIN
TIEN SHAN
TURFAN
TARIM BASIN
TSAIDAM BASIN
NAN SHAN
ALASHAN BASIN
ZAGROS
BALUCHISTAN
INDO-GANGETIC BASIN
F.Z.
0
500
Km.
HY

FIGURE 40

EURASIA–INDIA "COLLISION"

EARLY CENOZOIC

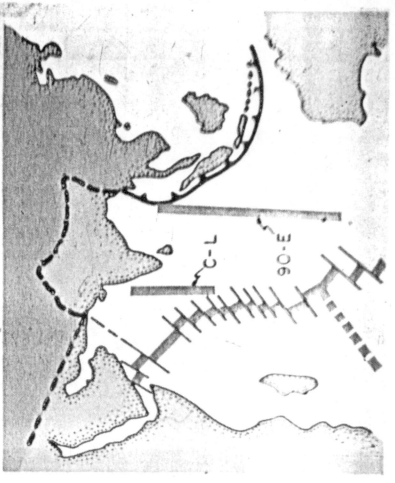

LATE CENOZOIC

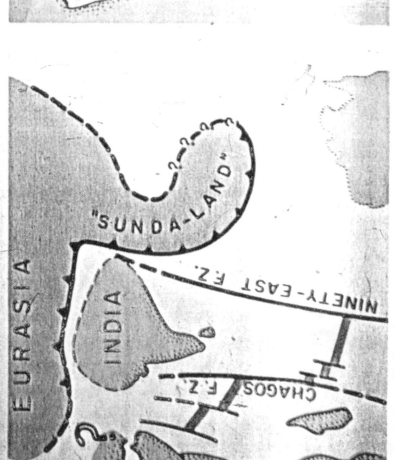

FIGURE 40-A

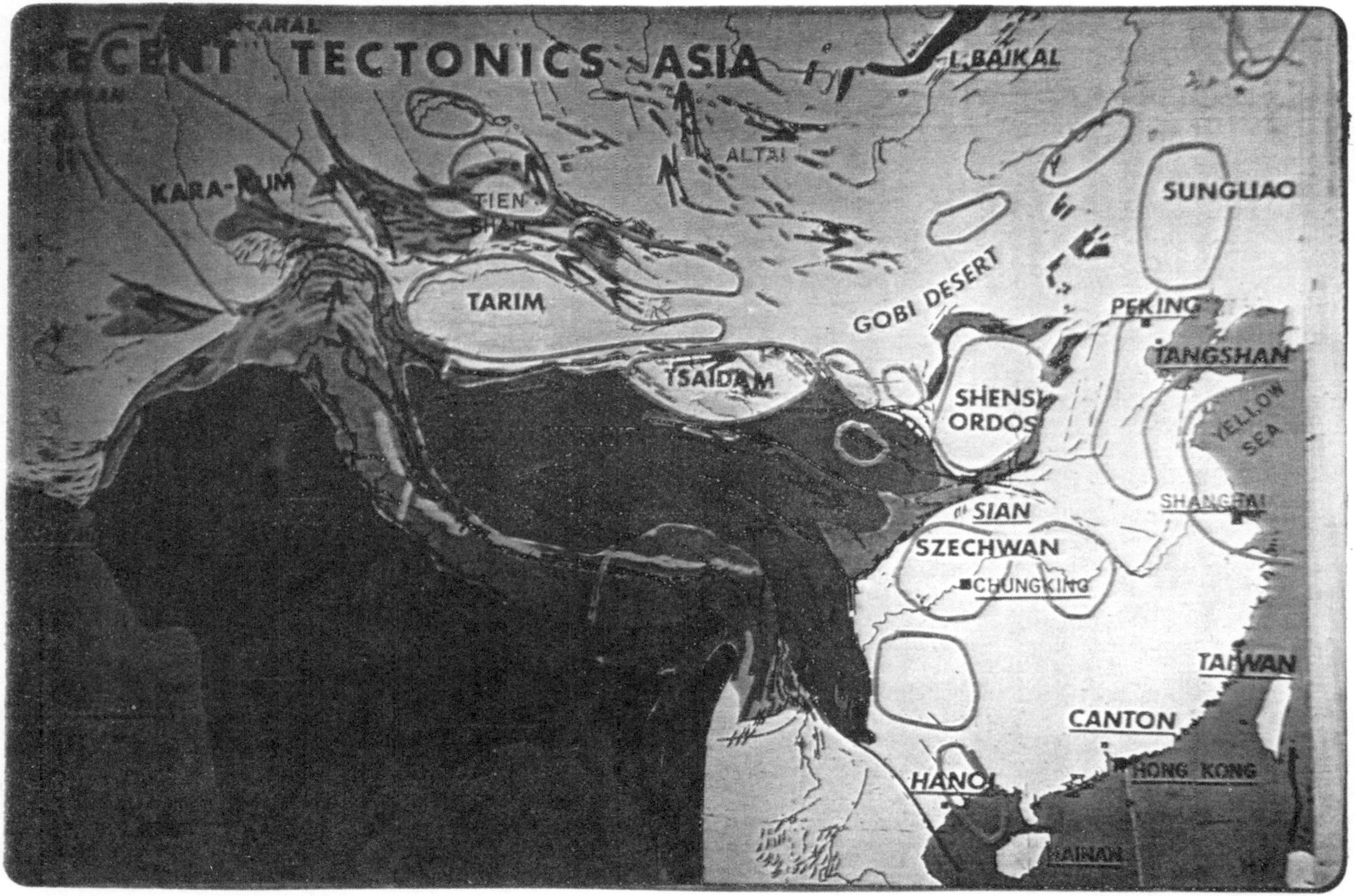

RECENT TECTONICS-ASIA

FIGURE 41

TECTONIC STYLES—ASIA

"EXTENSION"

"SHEAR"

CRUSTAL THICKENING

MOLNAR ET AL '77

HY

FIGURE 42

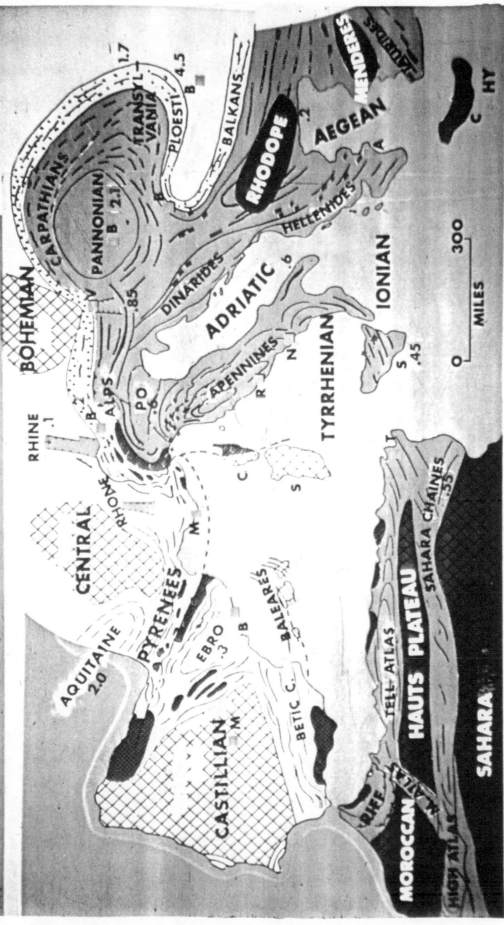

WESTERN MEDITERRANEAN-ALPINE OROGENIC BELT

AFTER DESITTER '64; BIJU-DUVAL '77; BOURBON ET AL '77; DEWEY '73

FIGURE 42-A

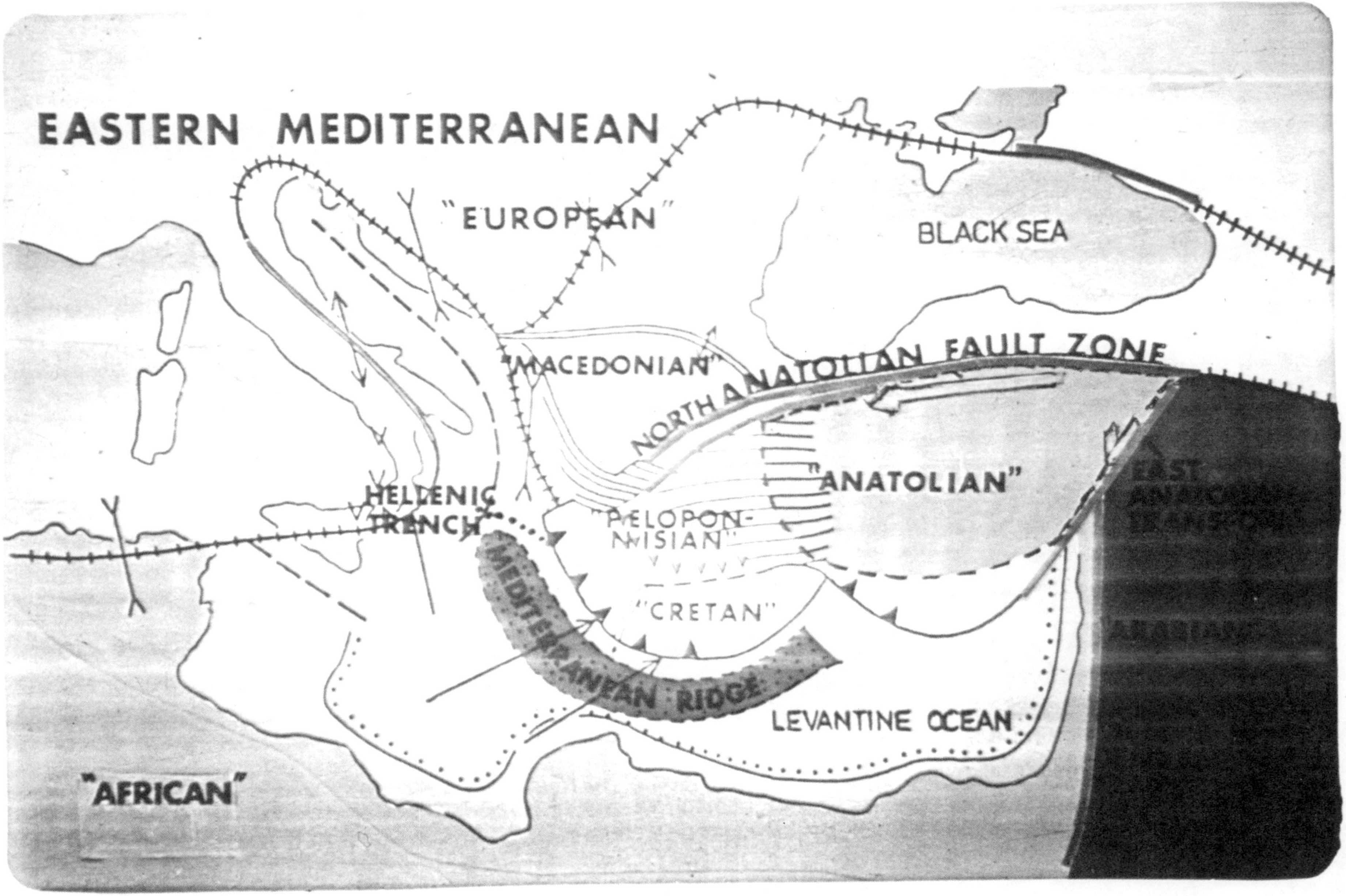

EASTERN MEDITERRANEAN

BLACK SEA

NORTH ANATOLIAN FAULT ZONE

"EUROPEAN"

"MACEDONIAN"

"ANATOLIAN"

EAST ANATOLIAN FAULT ZONE

"PELOPON-NISIAN"

"CRETAN"

LEVANTINE OCEAN

MEDITERRANEAN RIDGE

HELENIC TRENCH

"AFRICAN"

FIGURE 42-B

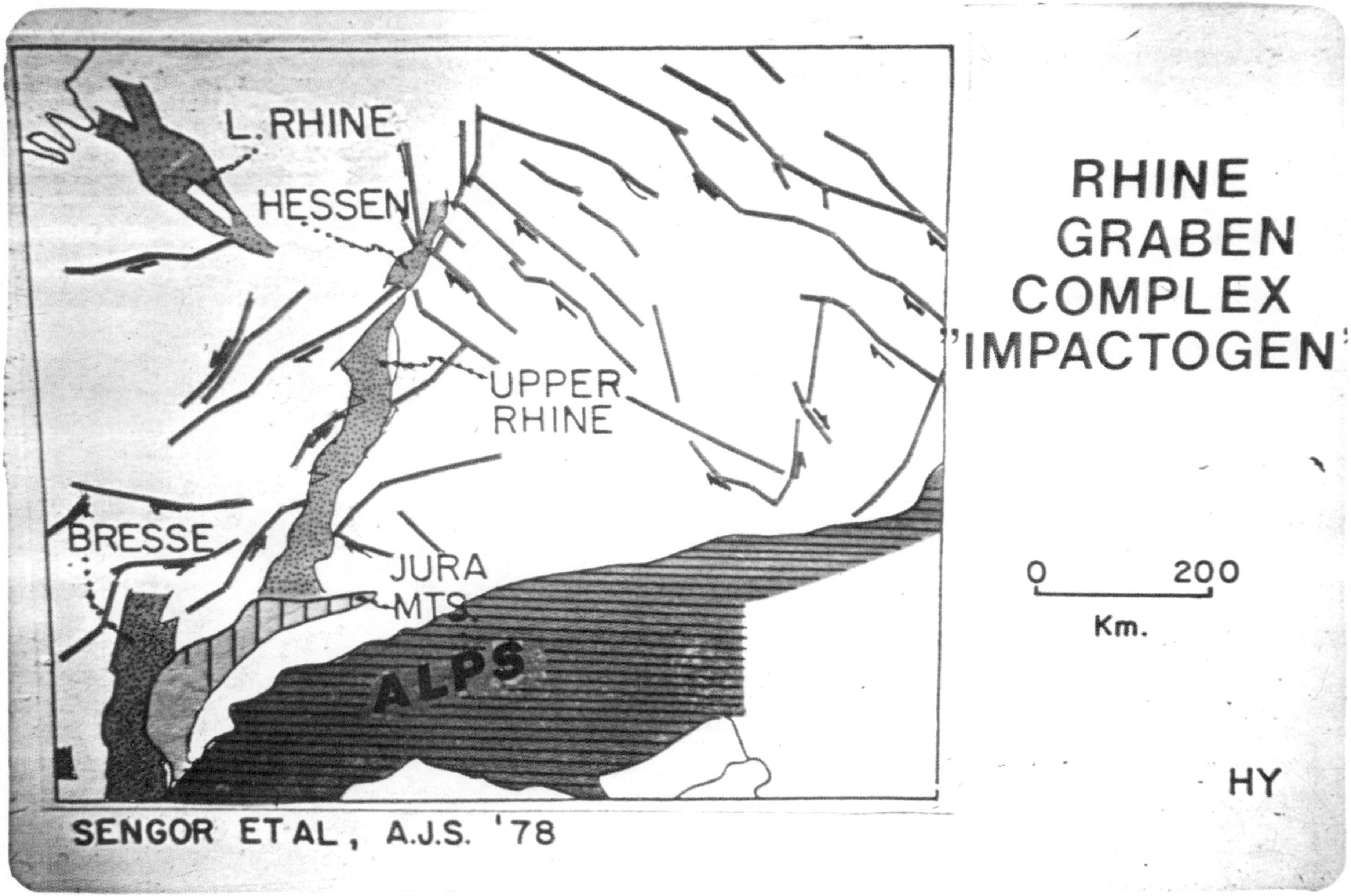

RHINE
GRABEN
COMPLEX
"IMPACTOGEN"

HY

200

Km.

0

L. RHINE

HESSEN

UPPER
RHINE

BRESSE

JURA
MTS.

ALPS

SENGOR ET AL., A.J.S. '78

FIGURE 42-C

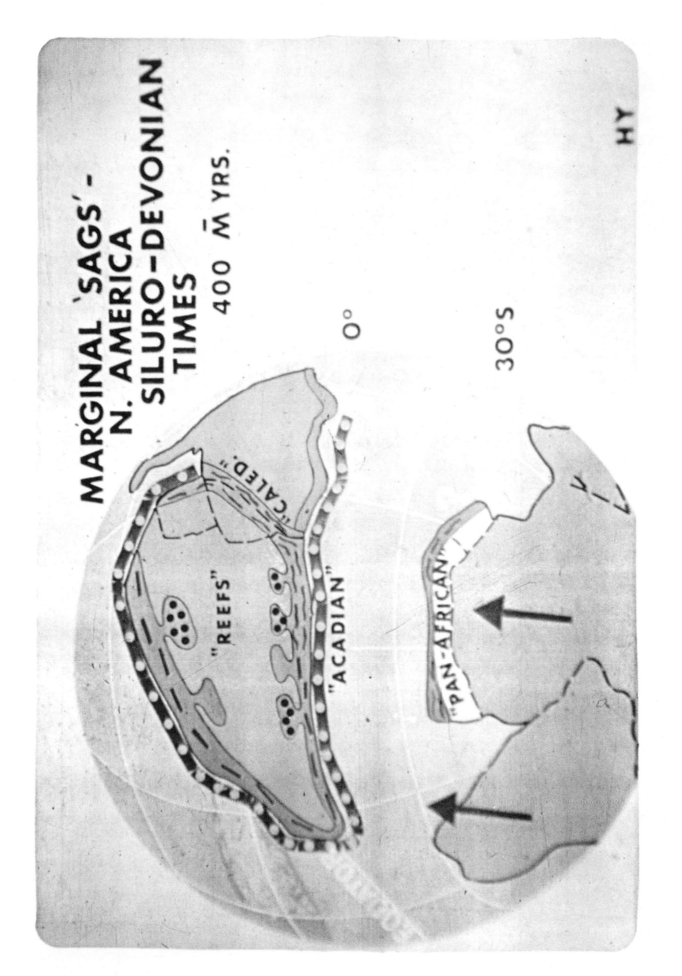

MARGINAL 'SAGS' -
N. AMERICA
SILURO-DEVONIAN
TIMES
400 M̄ YRS.

0°

30°S

"CALED."

"REEFS"

"ACADIAN"

"PAN-AFRICAN"

FIGURE 43

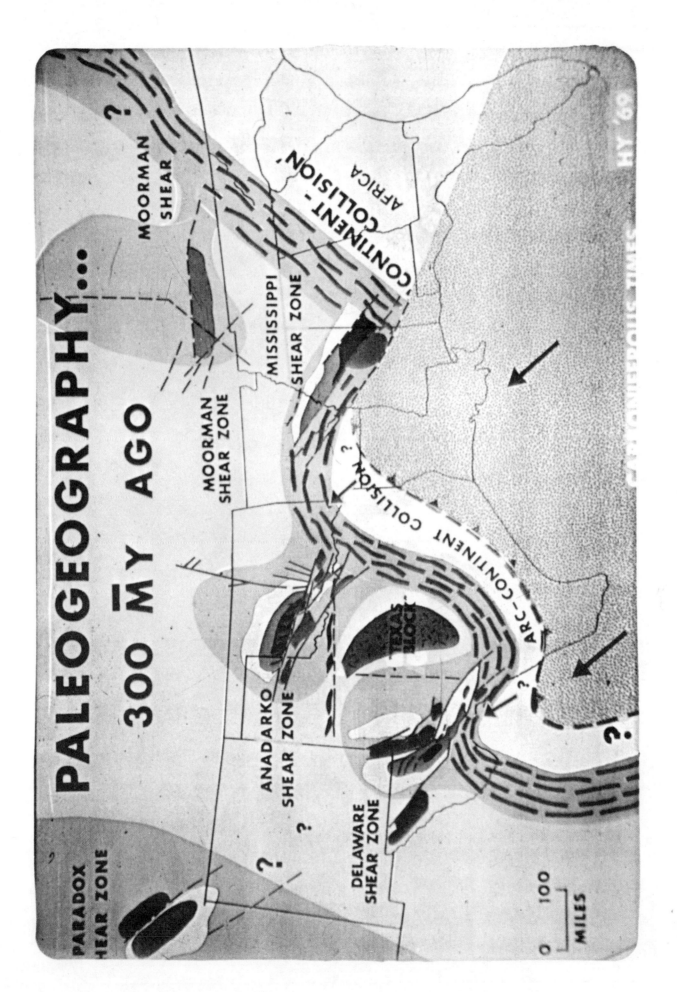

FIGURE 43-A

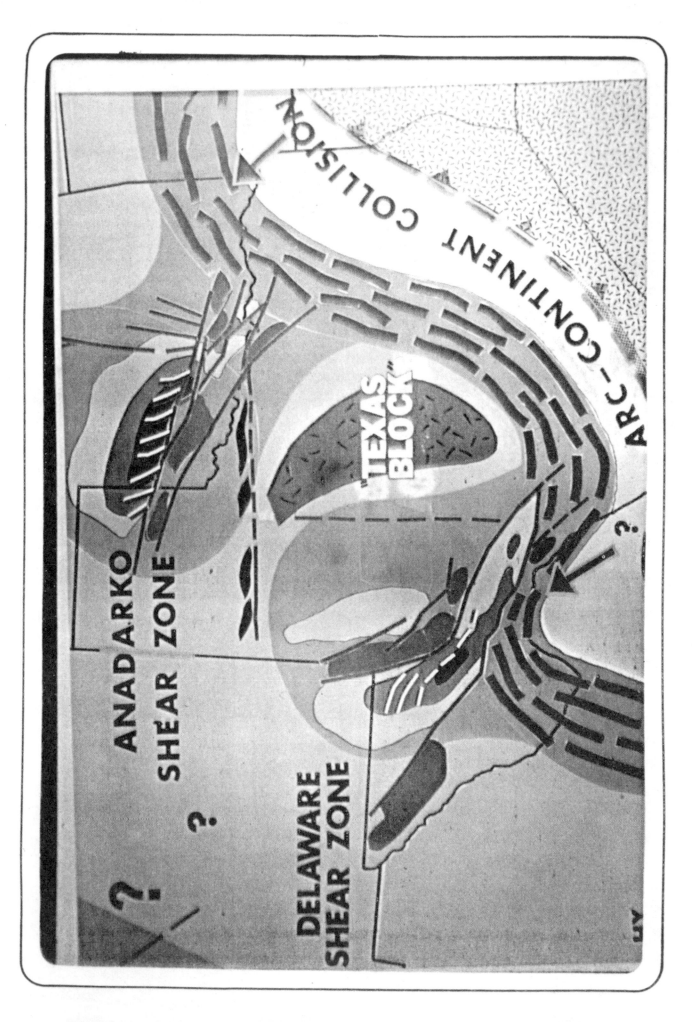

FIGURE 43-B

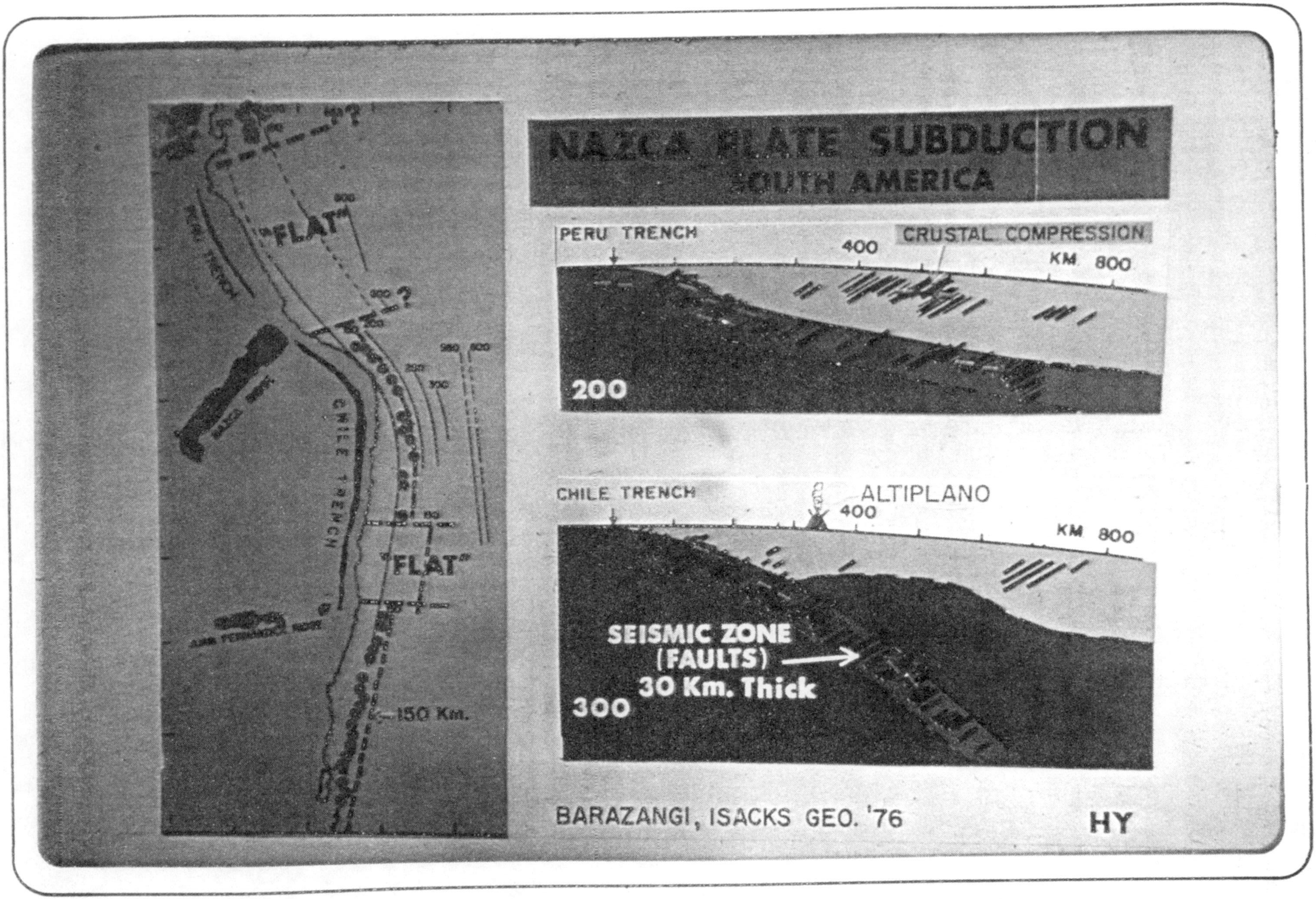
NAZCA PLATE SUBDUCTION
SOUTH AMERICA
"FLAT"
PERU TRENCH
CHILE TRENCH
"FLAT"
150 Km.
PERU TRENCH
400
CRUSTAL COMPRESSION
KM 800
200
CHILE TRENCH
ALTIPLANO
400
KM 800
SEISMIC ZONE
(FAULTS)
30 Km. Thick
300
BARAZANGI, ISACKS GEO. '76
HY

FIGURE 44

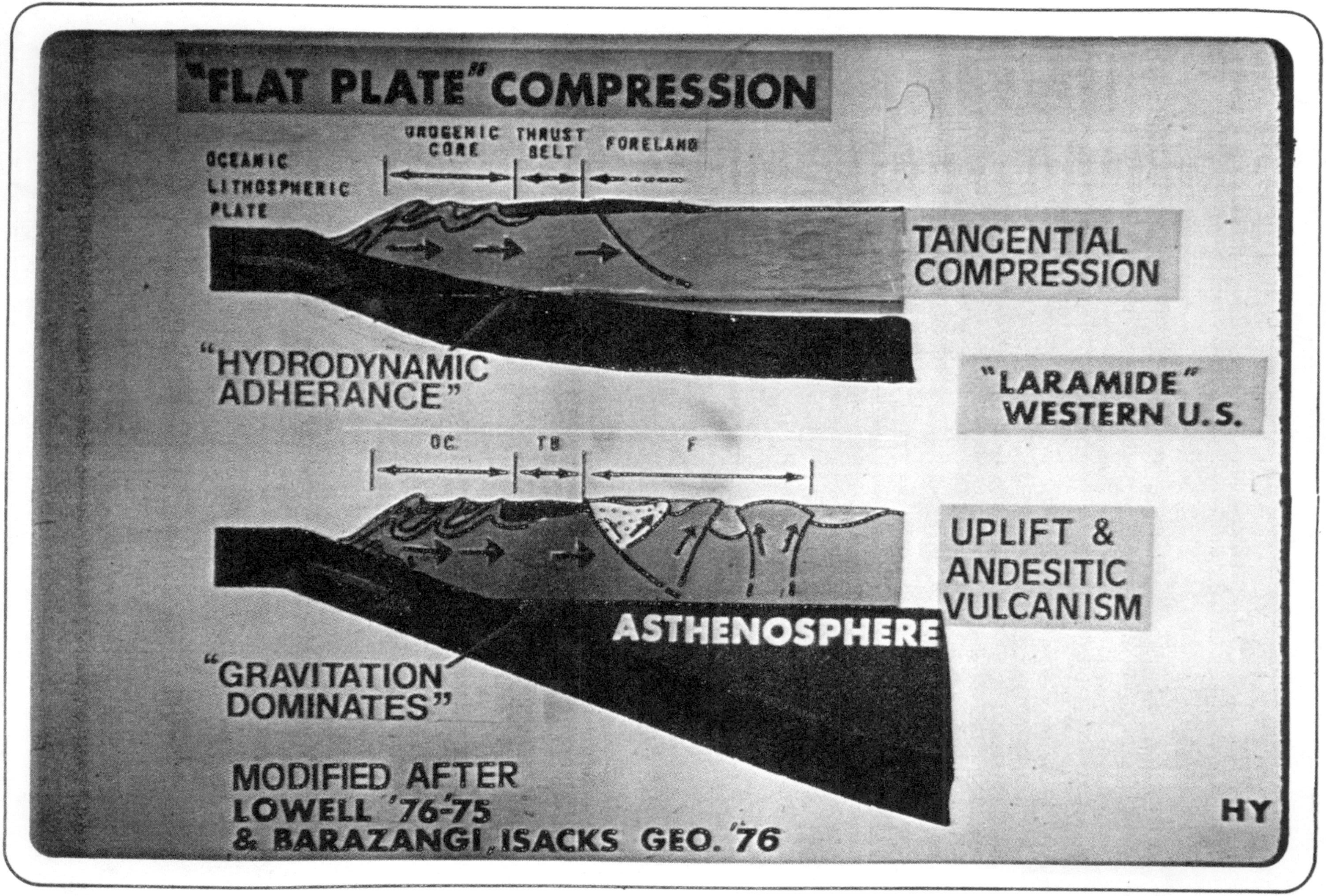
"FLAT PLATE" COMPRESSION
OROGENIC CORE
THRUST BELT
FORELAND
OCEANIC LITHOSPHERIC PLATE
TANGENTIAL COMPRESSION
"HYDRODYNAMIC ADHERANCE"
"LARAMIDE" WESTERN U.S.
OC
TB
F
UPLIFT & ANDESITIC VULCANISM
ASTHENOSPHERE
"GRAVITATION DOMINATES"
MODIFIED AFTER
LOWELL '76-'75
& BARAZANGI, ISACKS GEO. '76
HY

FIGURE 45

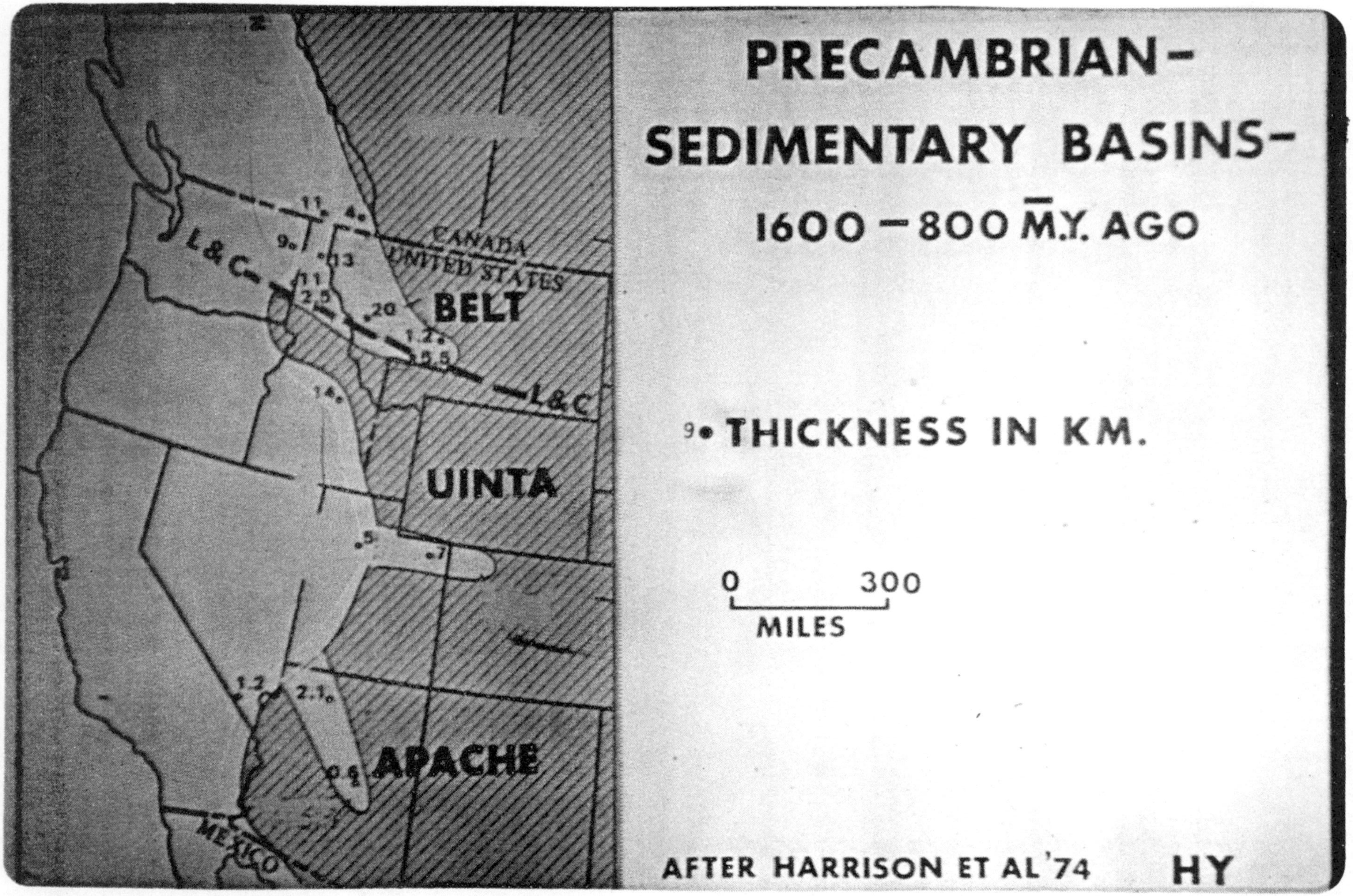

PRECAMBRIAN—
SEDIMENTARY BASINS—
1600–800 M.Y. AGO

9• THICKNESS IN KM.

300

0   MILES

BELT
UINTA
APACHE

L&C
L&C

CANADA
UNITED STATES
MEXICO

AFTER HARRISON ET AL '74   HY

FIGURE 46

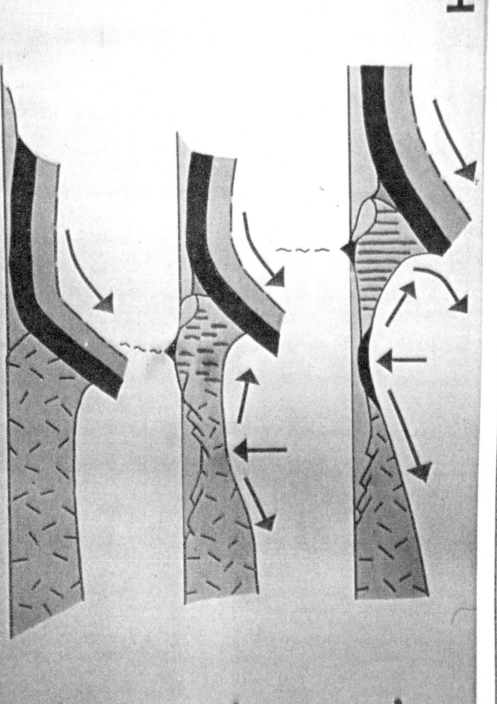

MARGINAL & FRONTAL BASINS
(BACK-ARC) (FORE-ARC, ARC-TRENCH)

A.

B.

C.

HY

FIGURE 47

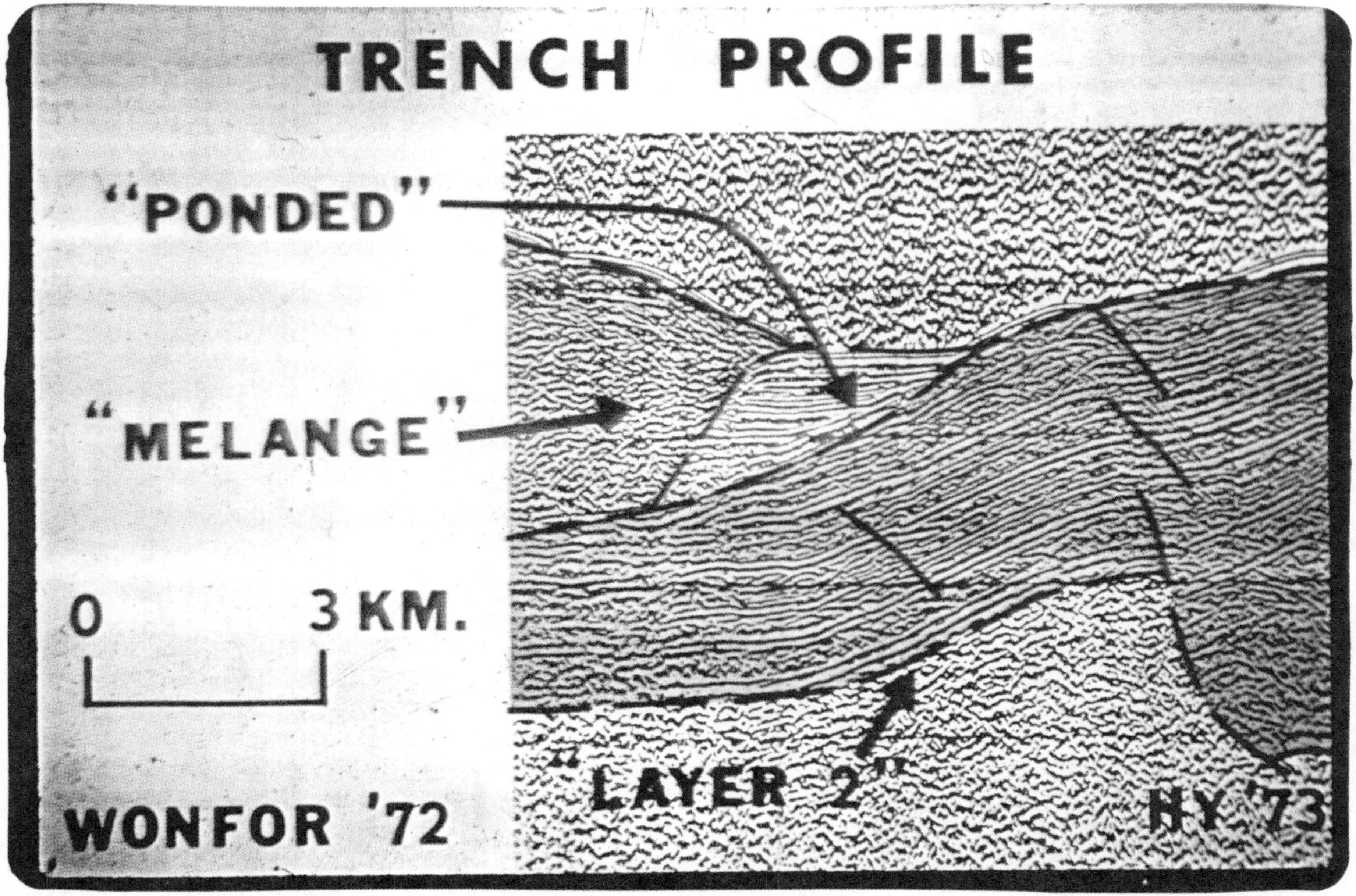

TRENCH PROFILE

"PONDED"

"MELANGE"

LAYER '2''

0   3 KM.

WONFOR '72   RY '73

FIGURE 47-A

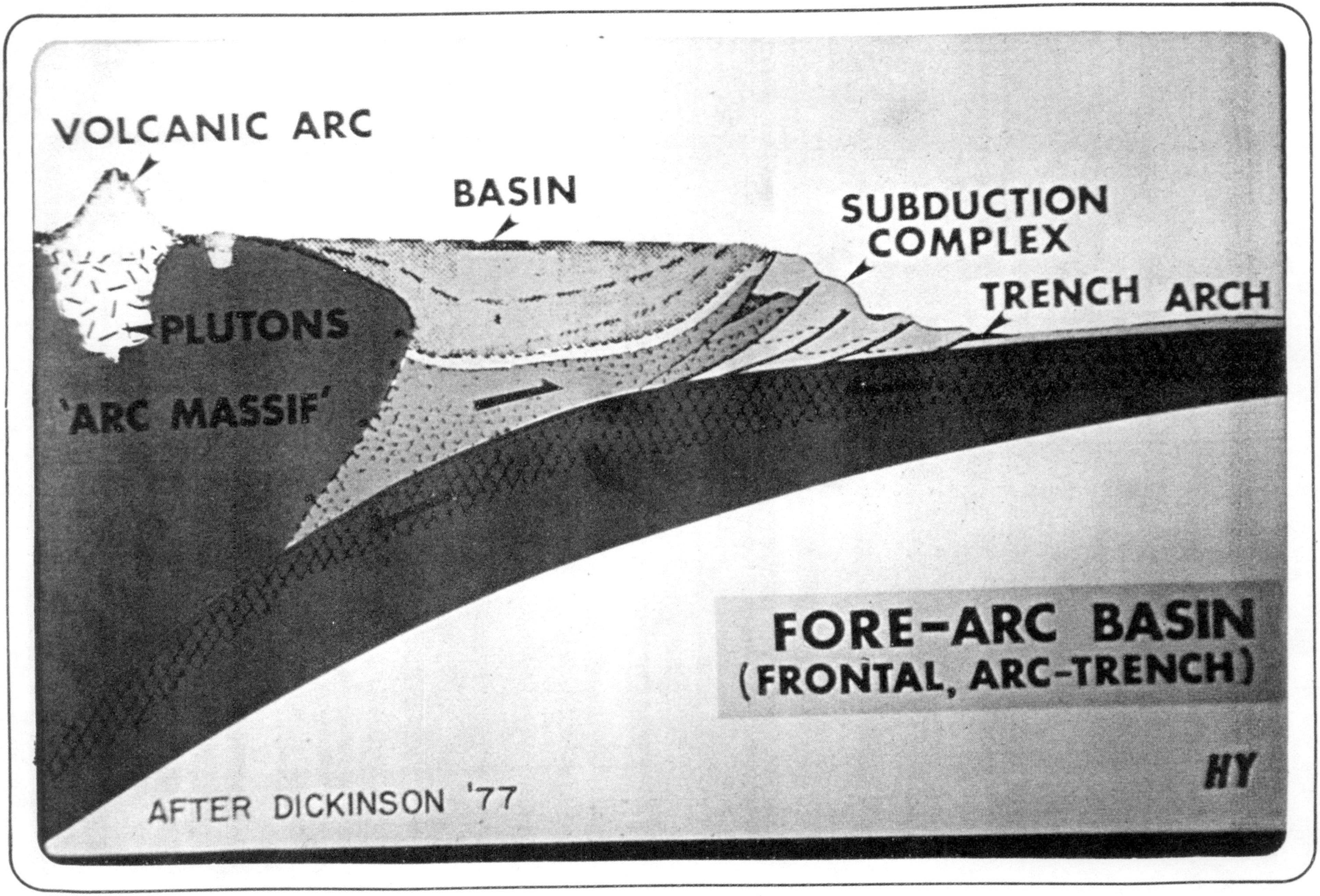

FORE-ARC BASIN
(FRONTAL, ARC-TRENCH)

VOLCANIC ARC

BASIN

SUBDUCTION COMPLEX

TRENCH ARCH

PLUTONS

'ARC MASSIF'

HY

AFTER DICKINSON '77

FIGURE 48

MAJOR STRUCTURAL
FEATURES

WESTERN PACIFIC

BASINS:

MAJOR

ACTIVE MARGINAL

INACTIVE MARGINAL
HHF μcal./cm^2 sec.

INACTIVE MARGINAL
NHF

REMNANT ARC

KOESOEMADINATA & PULUNGGONO '72

SCLATER GSA '72   KARIG GSA '72   HY '73

FIGURE 48-A

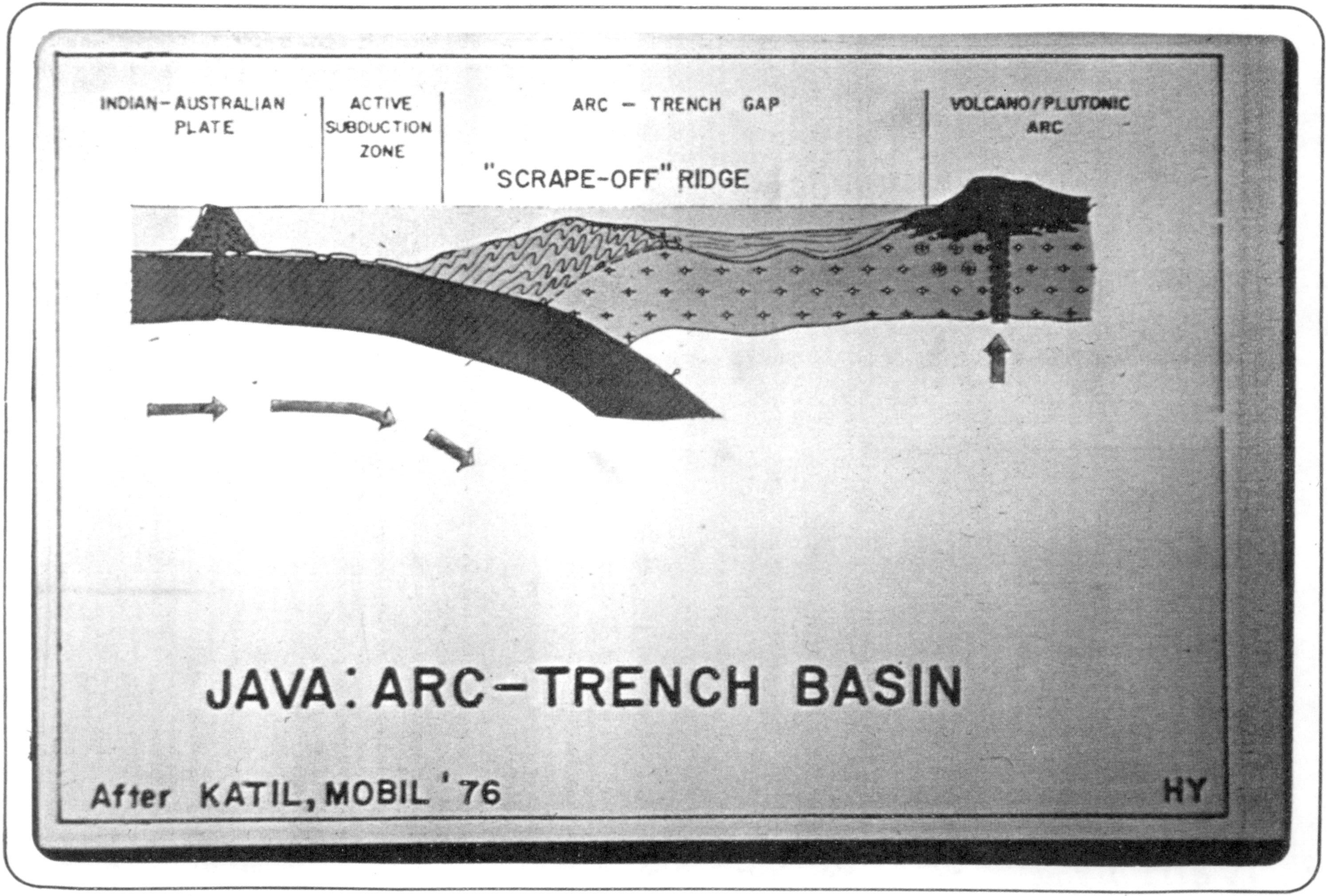
INDIAN-AUSTRALIAN PLATE
ACTIVE SUBDUCTION ZONE
ARC - TRENCH GAP
VOLCANO/PLUTONIC ARC
"SCRAPE-OFF" RIDGE
JAVA: ARC-TRENCH BASIN
After KATIL, MOBIL '76
HY

FIGURE 49

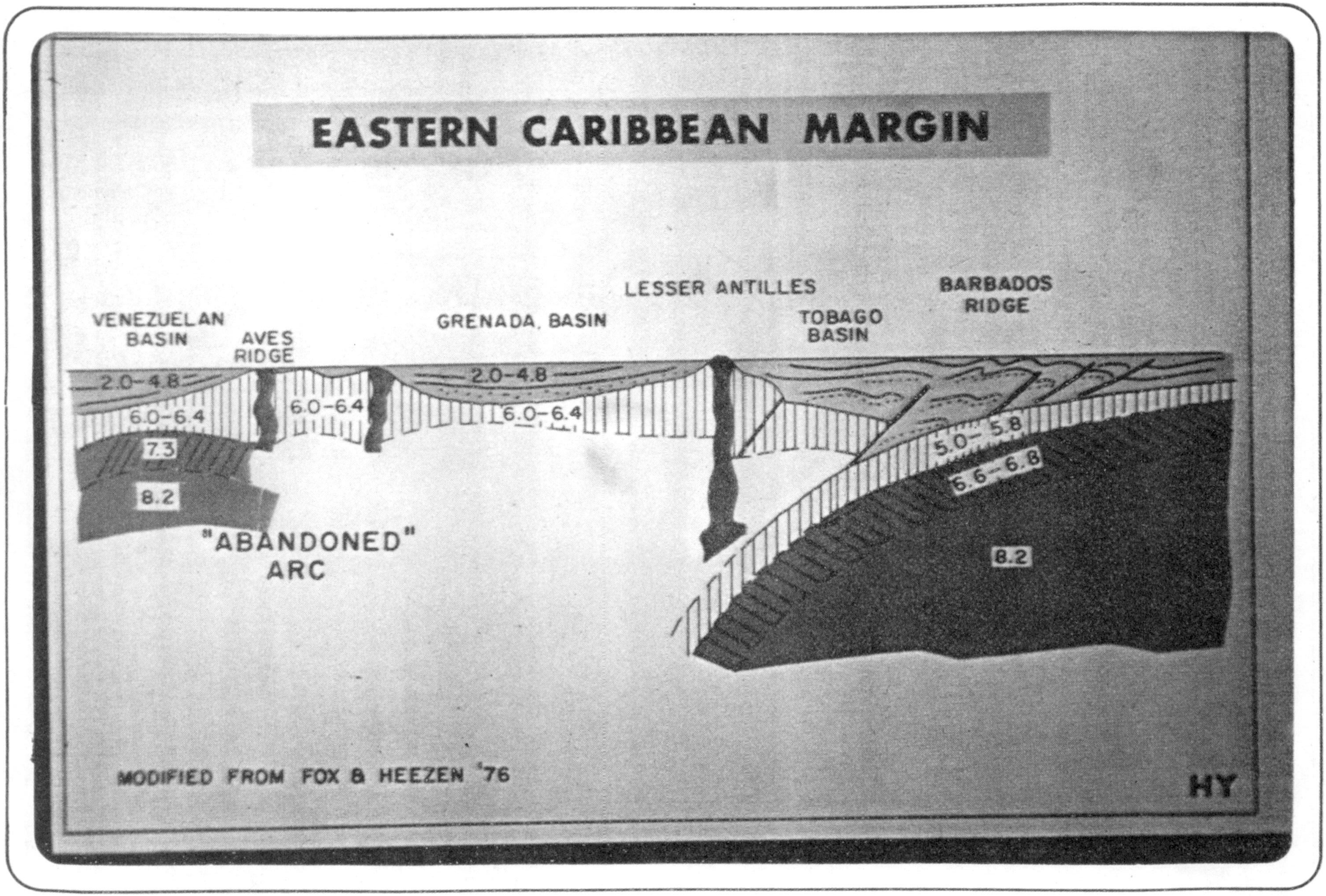

EASTERN CARIBBEAN MARGIN

BARBADOS RIDGE
LESSER ANTILLES
TOBAGO BASIN
GRENADA, BASIN
AVES RIDGE
VENEZUELAN BASIN
"ABANDONED" ARC

2.0-4.8
6.0-6.4
7.3
8.2
6.0-6.4
6.0-6.4
2.0-4.8
6.0-6.4
5.0-5.8
6.6-6.8
8.2

HY

MODIFIED FROM FOX & HEEZEN '76

FIGURE 50

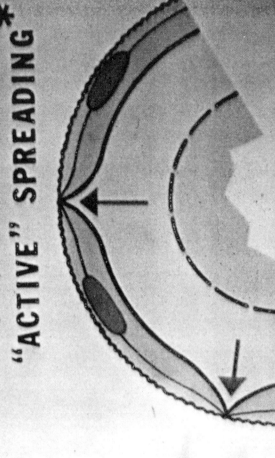

PLATE TECTONICS & SEA LEVEL

"ACTIVE" SPREADING*

"TRANSGRESSION"

*M. & U. CRETACEOUS
 L. & M. PALEOZOIC

"DEAD" SPREADING*

"REGRESSION"

*PERMO-TRIASSIC

HY '67

FIGURE 51

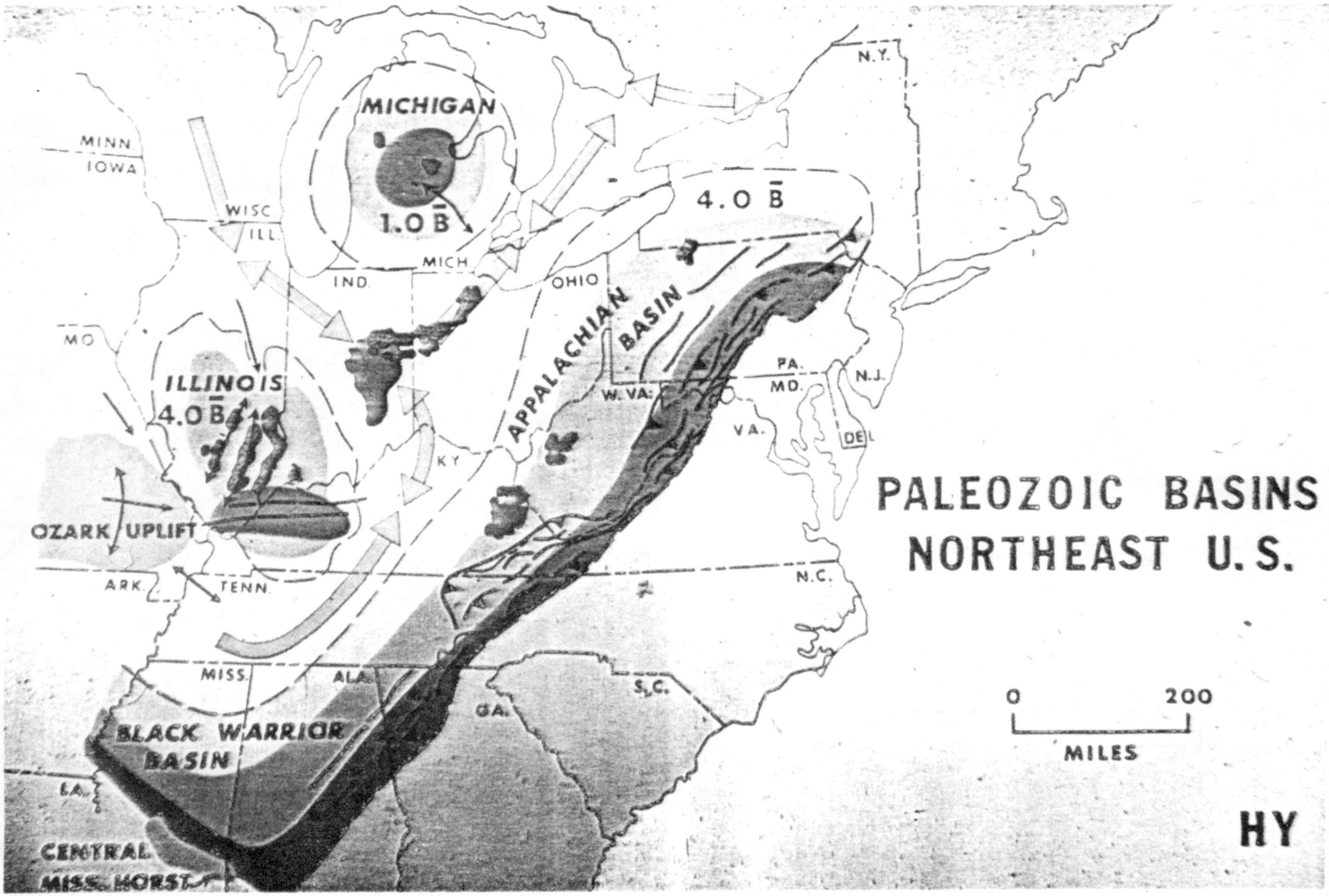
PALEOZOIC BASINS
NORTHEAST U.S.
MICHIGAN
1.0 B̄
4.0 B̄
ILLINOIS
4.0 B̄
OZARK UPLIFT
APPALACHIAN BASIN
BLACK WARRIOR BASIN
CENTRAL MISS. HORST
MINN.
IOWA
WISC.
ILL.
MICH.
IND.
OHIO
MO.
KY.
ARK.
TENN.
MISS.
ALA.
GA.
S.C.
N.C.
VA.
W. VA.
PA.
MD.
N.J.
DEL.
N.Y.
LA.
0
200
MILES
HY

FIGURE 52

PLATE TECTONICS

BASALT-GABBRO 2.95 → ECLOGITE 3.3

EXAG. SCALES

"STAND-STILL" DOMES & BASINS —
ASTHENOSPHERE BUMPS & "SINKS" HY'73

FIGURE 53

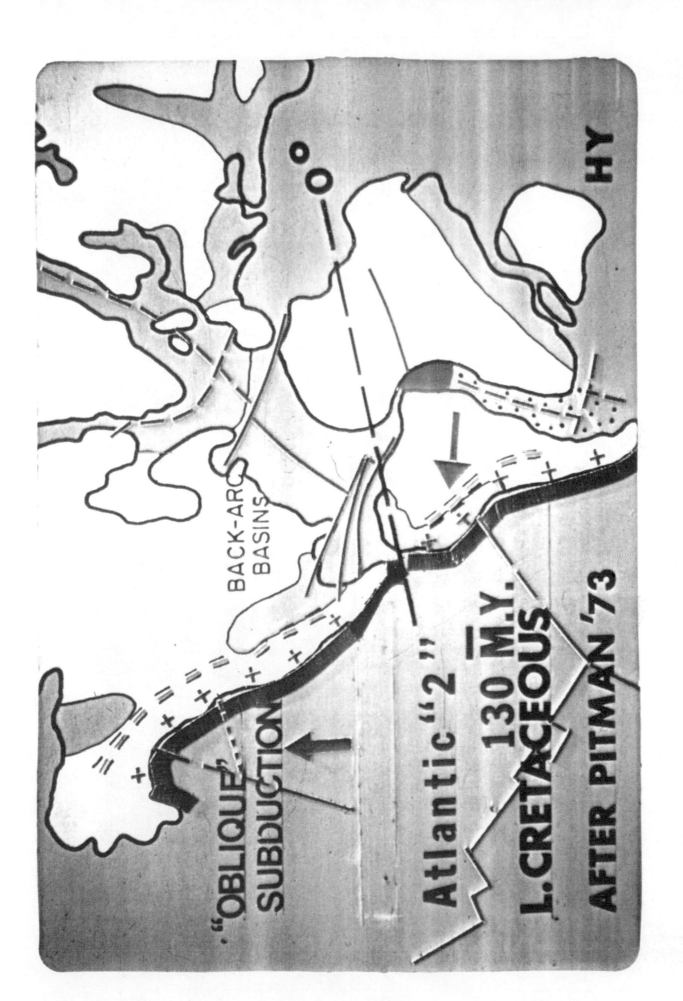

"OBLIQUE" SUBDUCTION

BACK-ARC BASINS

Atlantic "2"
130 M.Y.
L. CRETACEOUS
AFTER PITMAN '73

HY

FIGURE 54

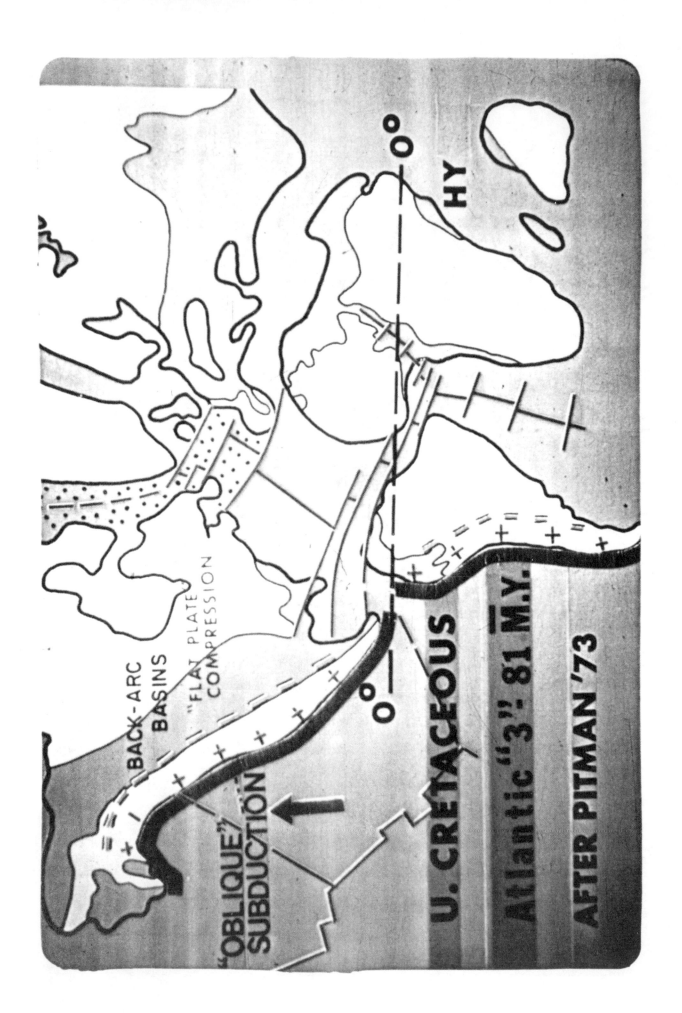

FIGURE 54-A

FIGURE 54-B

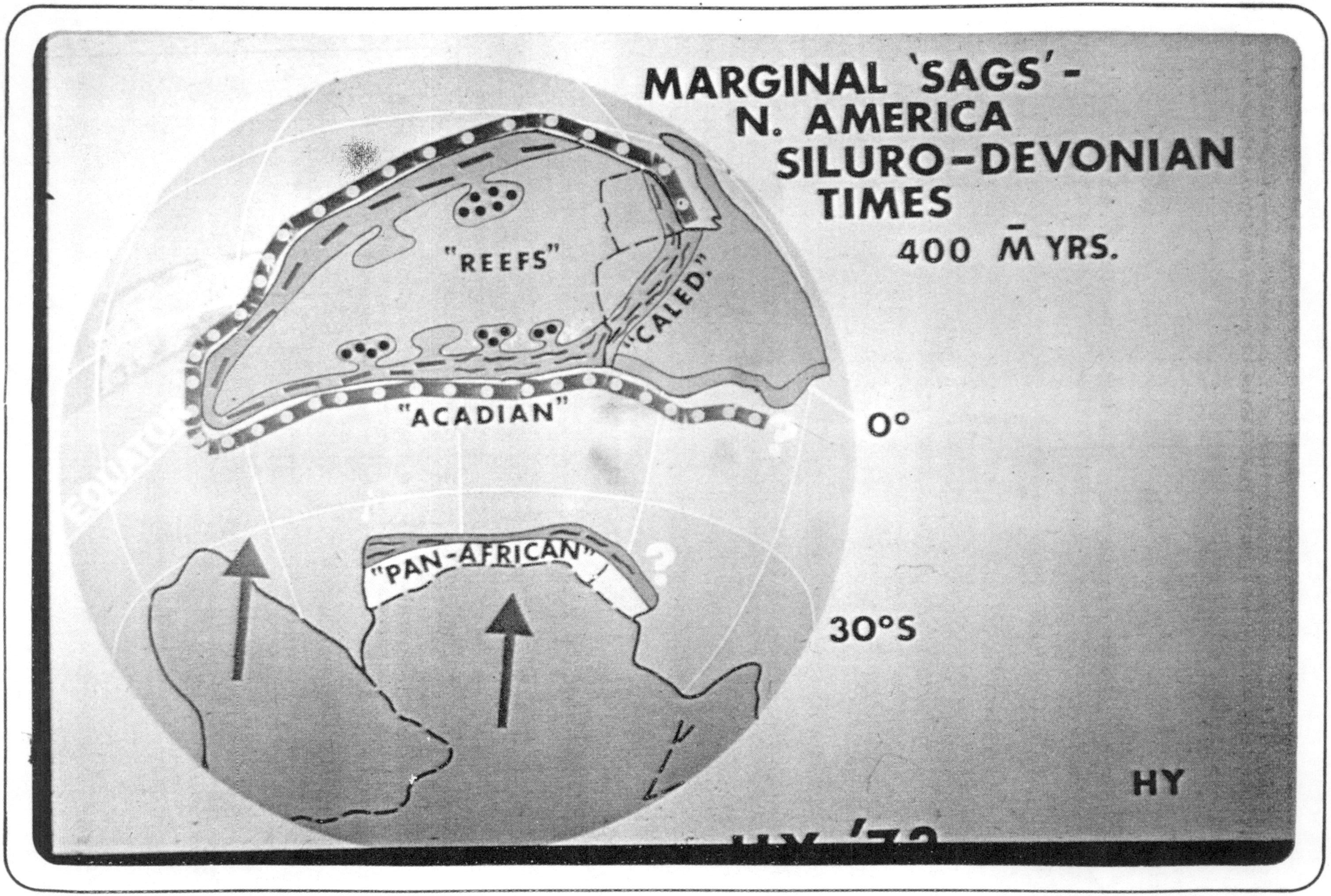

MARGINAL 'SAGS' -
N. AMERICA
SILURO-DEVONIAN
TIMES

400 M̄ YRS.

0°

30°S

HY

"CALED."

"REEFS"

"ACADIAN"

"PAN-AFRICAN"

FIGURE 55

AMERASIAN BASIN — JURASSIC

PARRY IS.

"FOLD BELT"

D-M

PRUDHOE BAY

VERKHOYANSK

"FOLD BELT"

J-K

KOLYMSKI

HERRON ET AL '74

HY '74

FIGURE 55-A

INDIA-BURMA

FIGURE 56

CAMBAY BASIN, INDIA

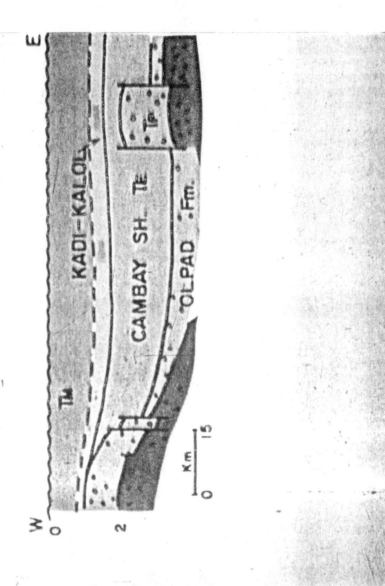

FIGURE 56-A

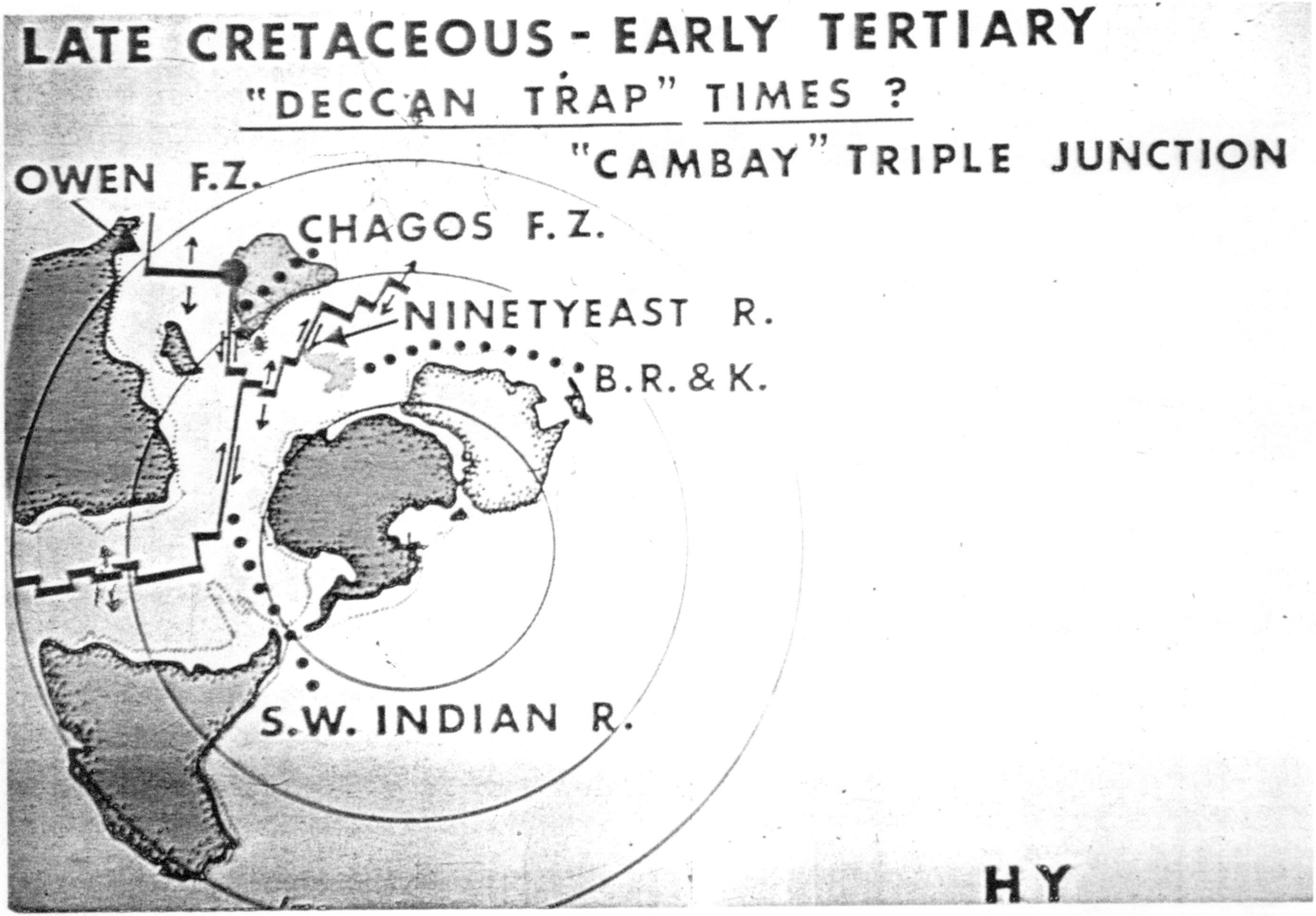

LATE CRETACEOUS - EARLY TERTIARY
"DECCAN TRAP" TIMES ?
"CAMBAY" TRIPLE JUNCTION

OWEN F.Z.
CHAGOS F.Z.
NINETYEAST R.
B.R. & K.
S.W. INDIAN R.

HY

FIGURE 56-B

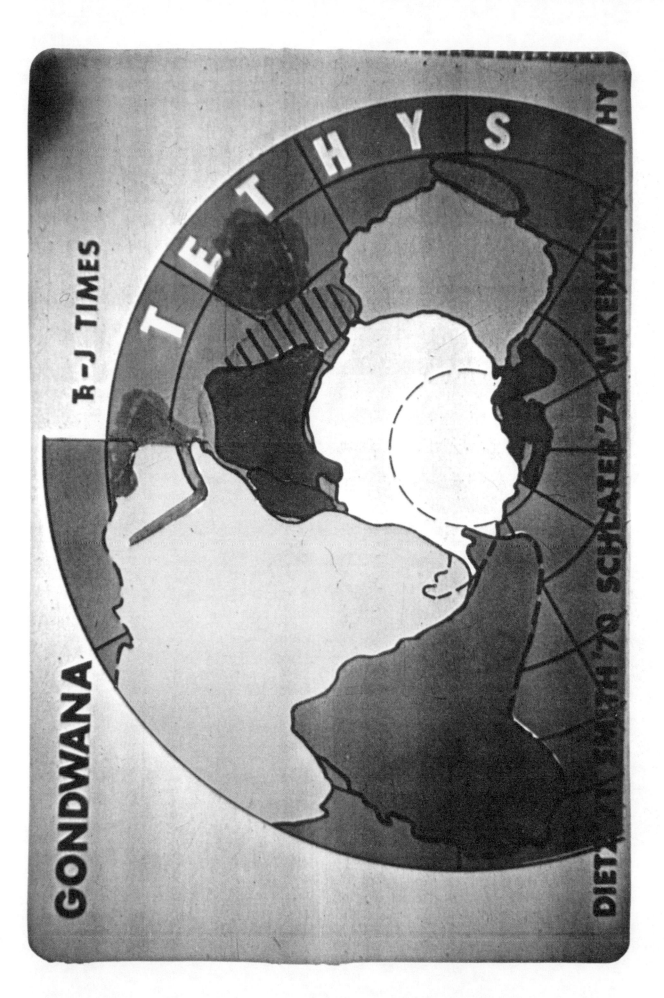

FIGURE 56-C

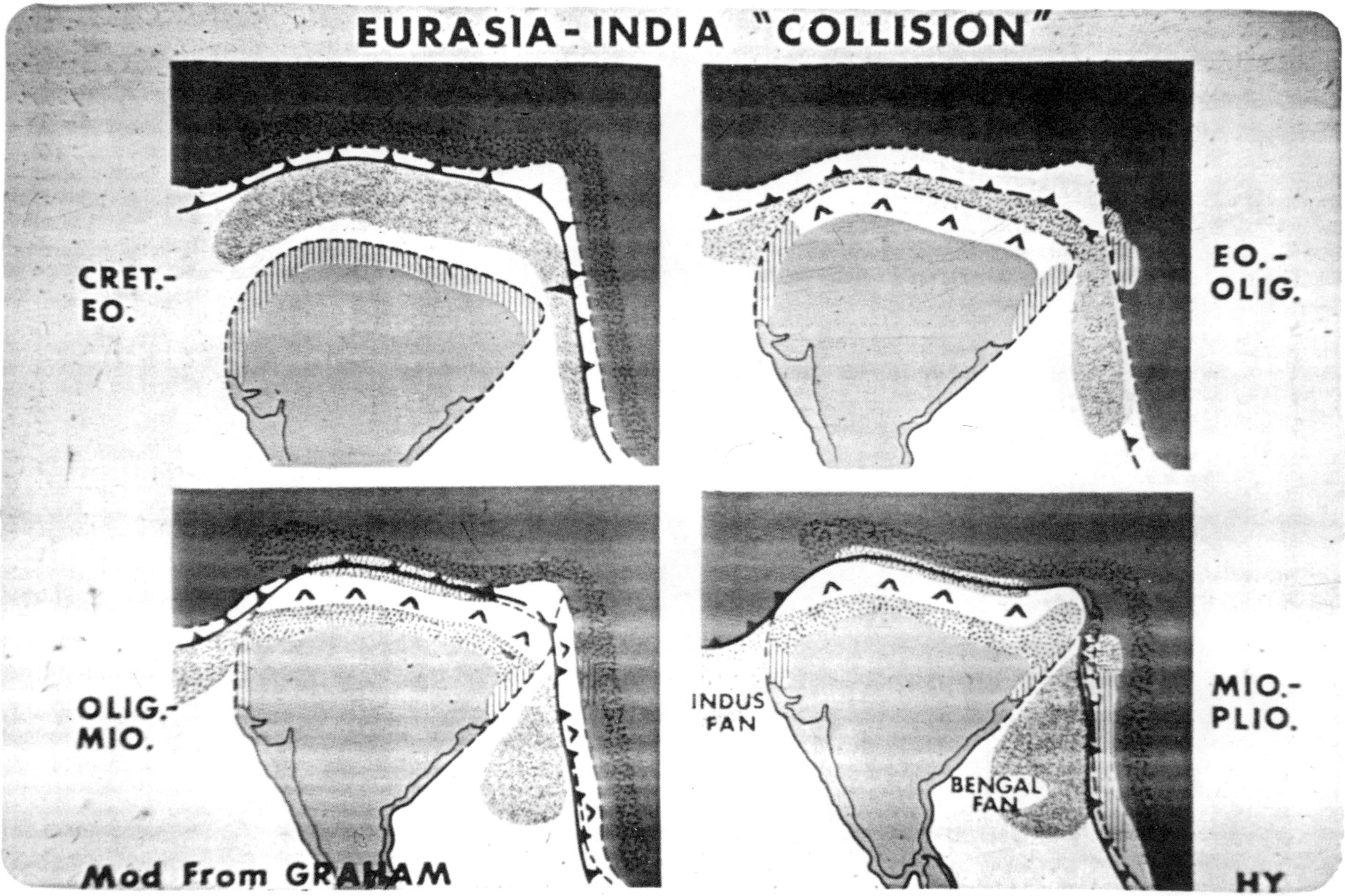

EURASIA-INDIA "COLLISION"

EO.-OLIG.

MIO.-PLIO.

CRET.-EO.

OLIG.-MIO.

BENGAL FAN

INDUS FAN

Mod From GRAHAM

FIGURE 56-D

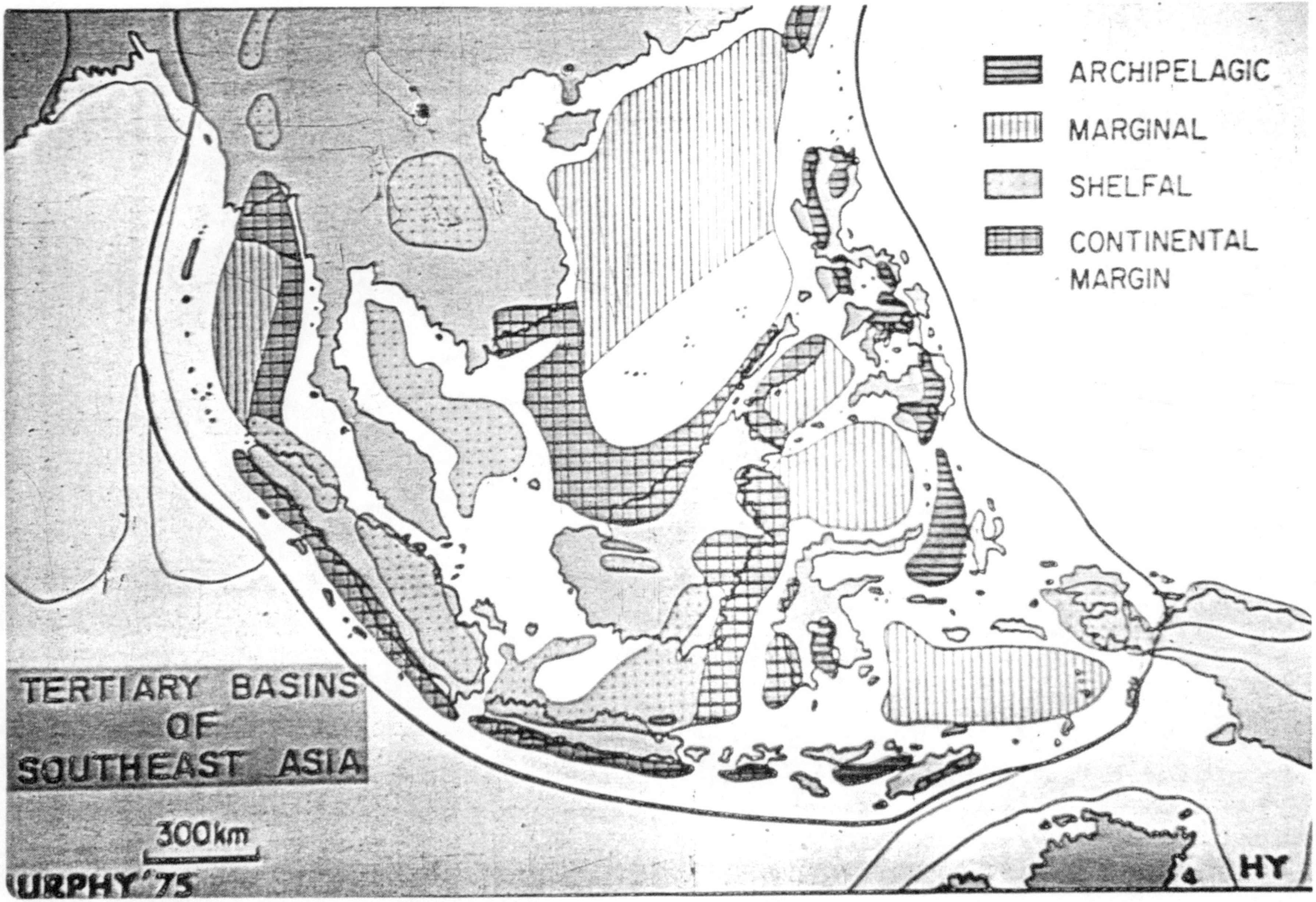

TERTIARY BASINS
OF
SOUTHEAST ASIA

300km

URPHY '75

ARCHIPELAGIC

MARGINAL

SHELFAL

CONTINENTAL
MARGIN

FIGURE 57

CORDILLERAN ("LARAMIDE") OROGENIC BELT

COMPRESSIVE DEFORMATION: LATE CRETACEOUS–EARLY TERTIARY

0 _____ 1000
MILES

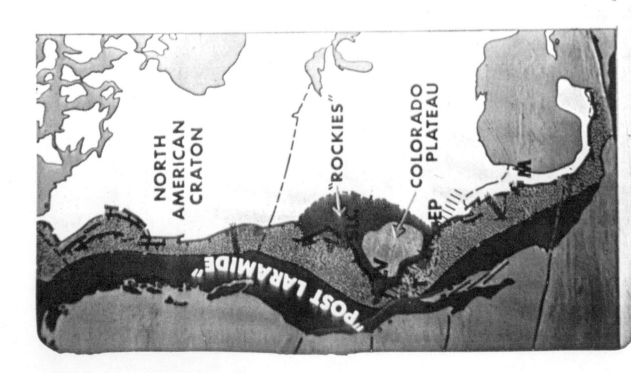

NORTH AMERICAN CRATON

"ROCKIES"

COLORADO PLATEAU

"POST LARAMIDE"

AFTER DREWS, GSA 5-'78

FIGURE 58

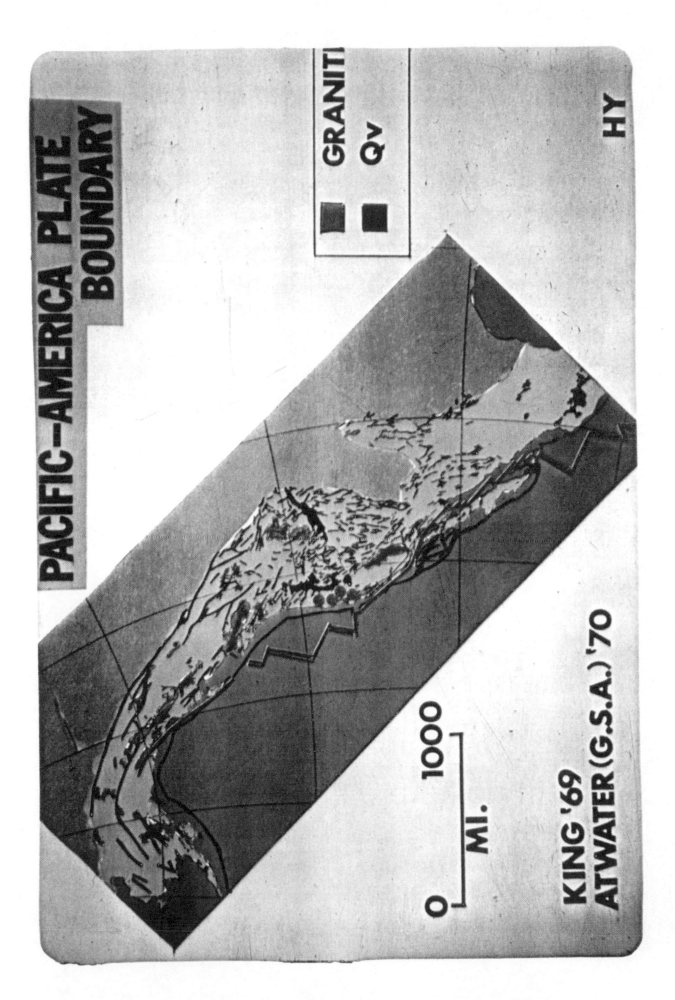

PACIFIC—AMERICA PLATE BOUNDARY

GRANITI

Qv

KING '69
ATWATER (G.S.A.) '70

0   1000
|————|————|
MI.

HY

FIGURE 59

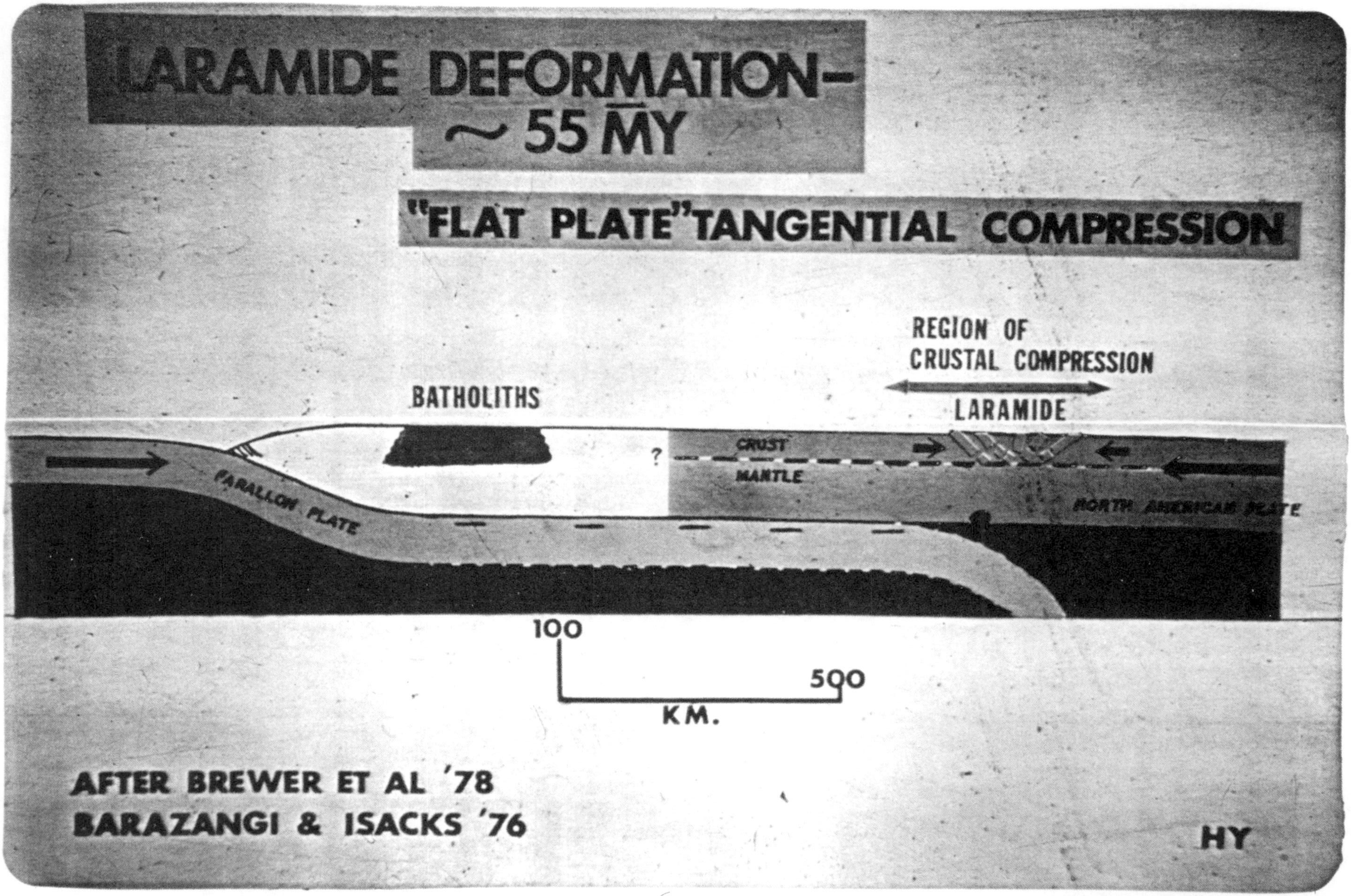

LARAMIDE DEFORMATION– ~55 MY

"FLAT PLATE" TANGENTIAL COMPRESSION

REGION OF CRUSTAL COMPRESSION

LARAMIDE

NORTH AMERICAN PLATE

CRUST

MANTLE

?

BATHOLITHS

FARALLON PLATE

100   K.M.   500

AFTER BREWER ET AL '78
BARAZANGI & ISACKS '76

HY

FIGURE 60

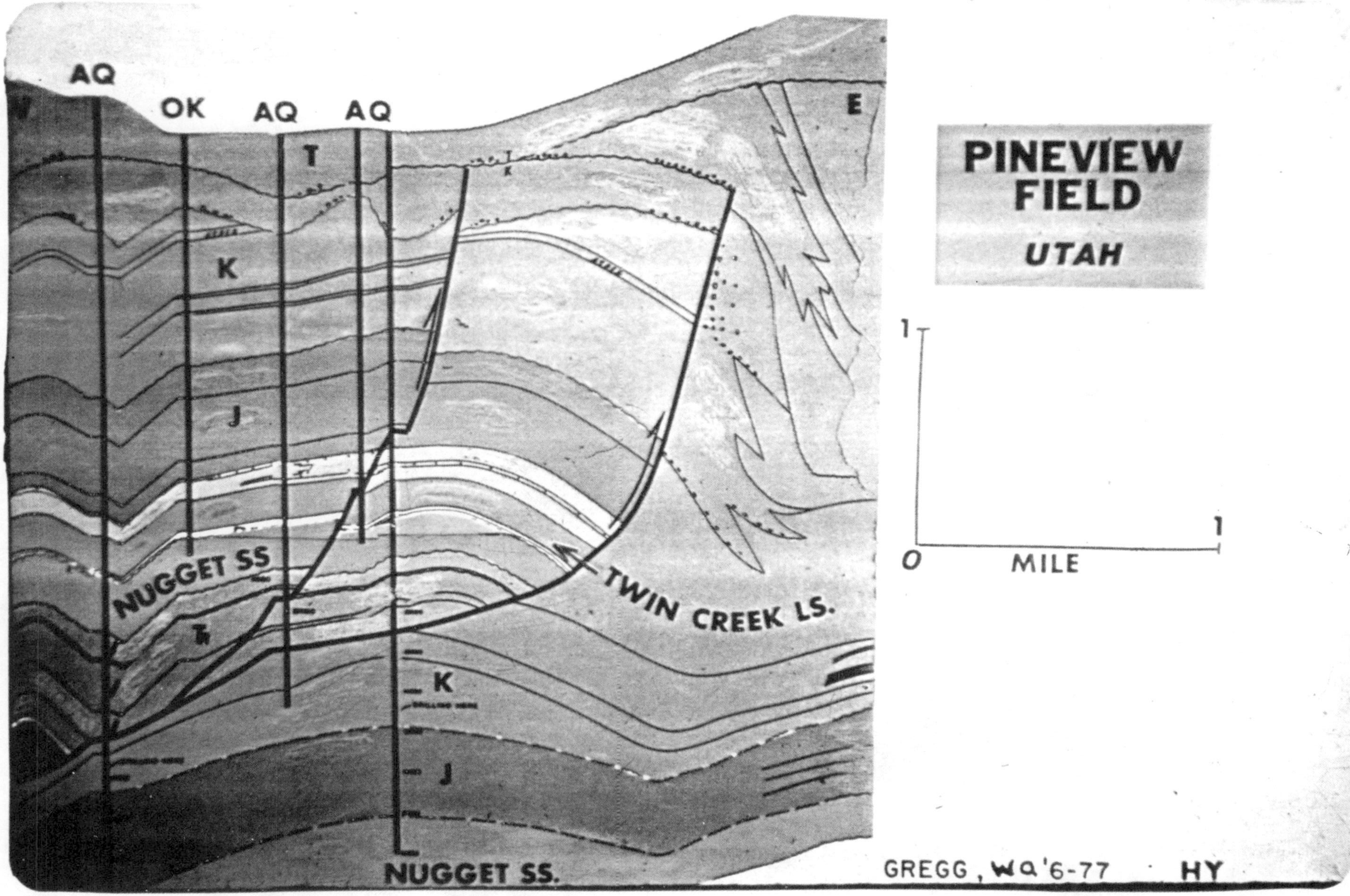

PINEVIEW FIELD
UTAH

FIGURE 61

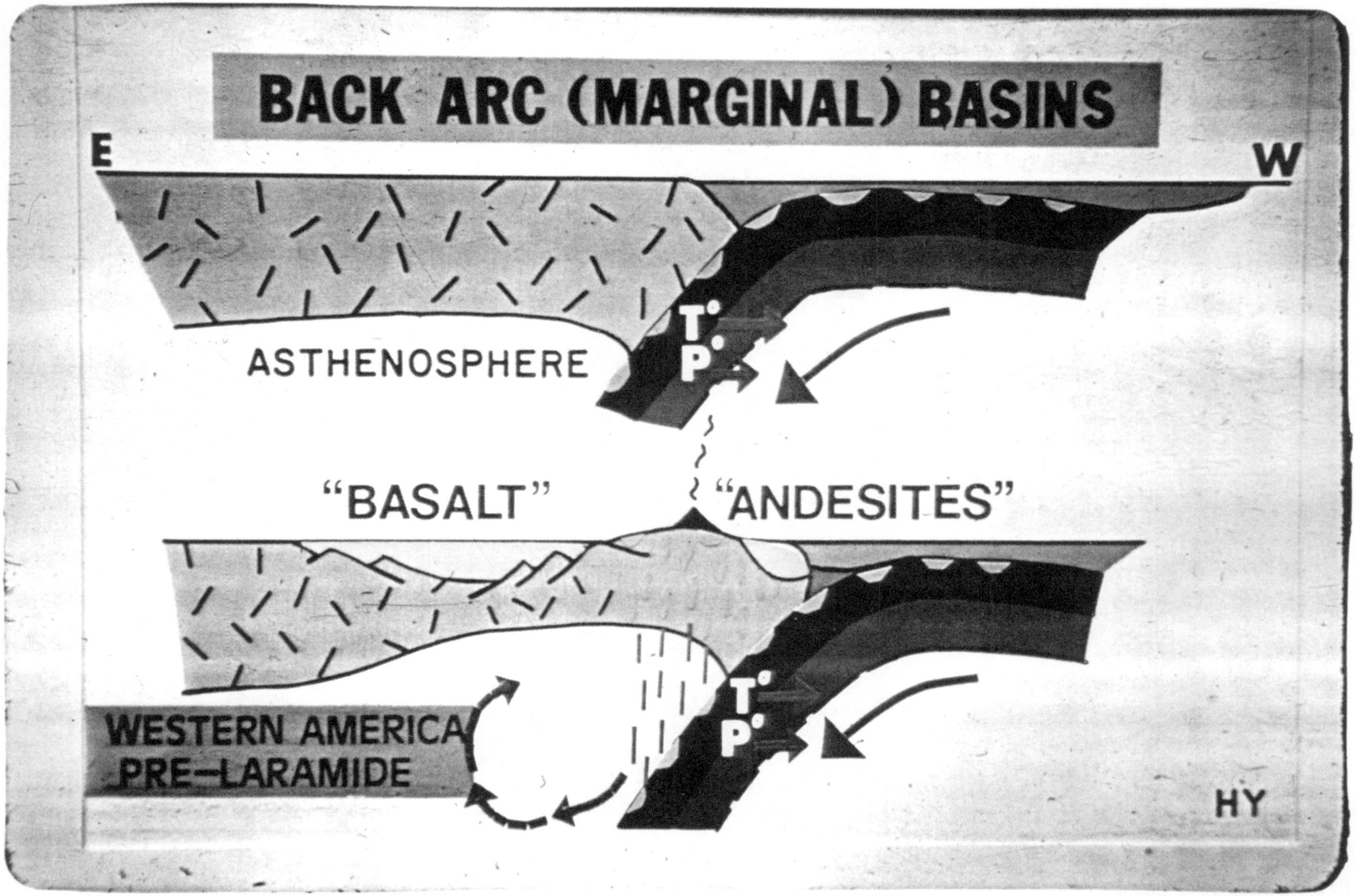

FIGURE 62

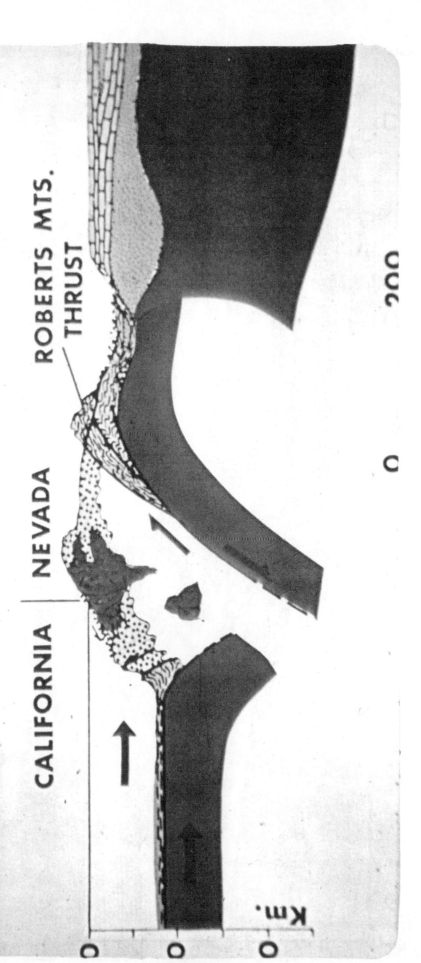

FIGURE 63

FIGURE 64

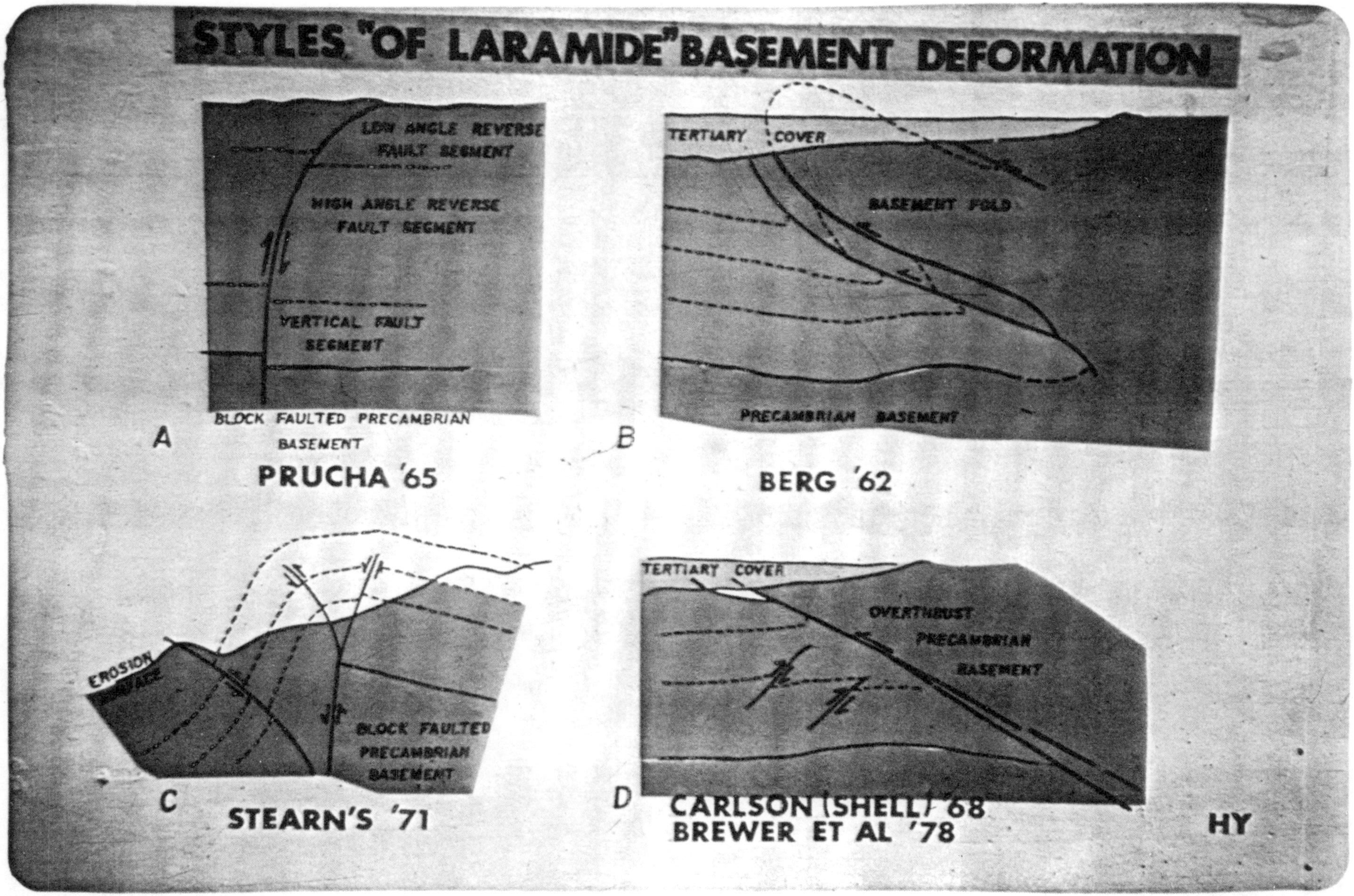

STYLES "OF LARAMIDE" BASEMENT DEFORMATION

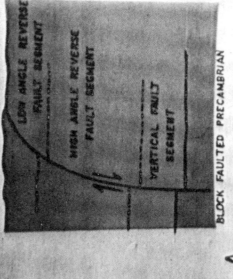

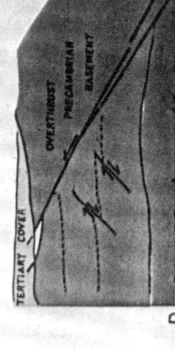

A

LOW ANGLE REVERSE FAULT SEGMENT

HIGH ANGLE REVERSE FAULT SEGMENT

VERTICAL FAULT SEGMENT

BLOCK FAULTED PRECAMBRIAN BASEMENT

PRUCHA '65

B

TERTIARY COVER

BASEMENT FOLD

PRECAMBRIAN BASEMENT

BERG '62

C

EROSION

BLOCK FAULTED PRECAMBRIAN BASEMENT

STEARN'S '71

D

TERTIARY COVER

OVERTHRUST

PRECAMBRIAN BASEMENT

CARLSON (SHELL) '68 BREWER ET AL '78

HY

FIGURE 65

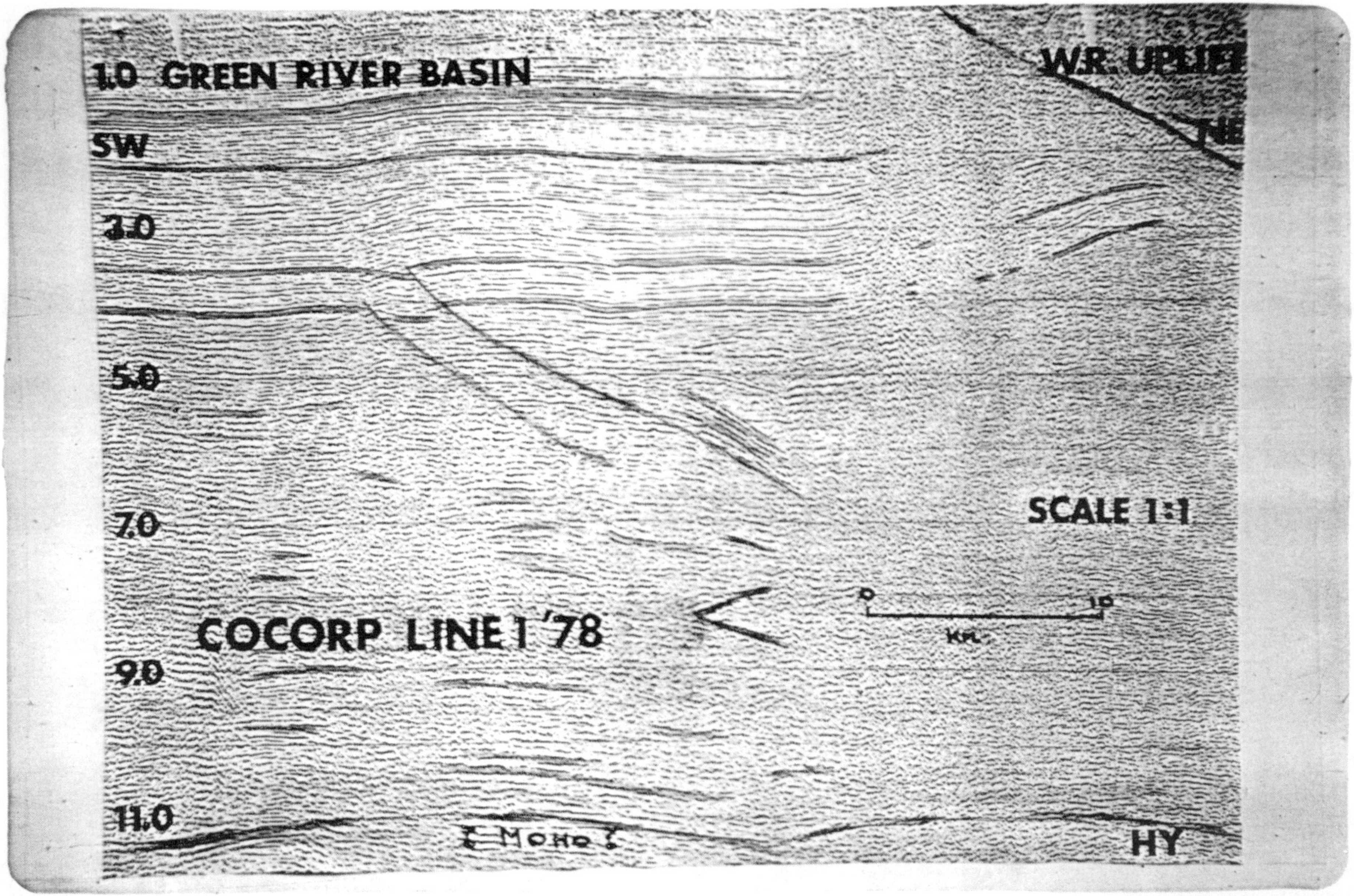

FIGURE 66

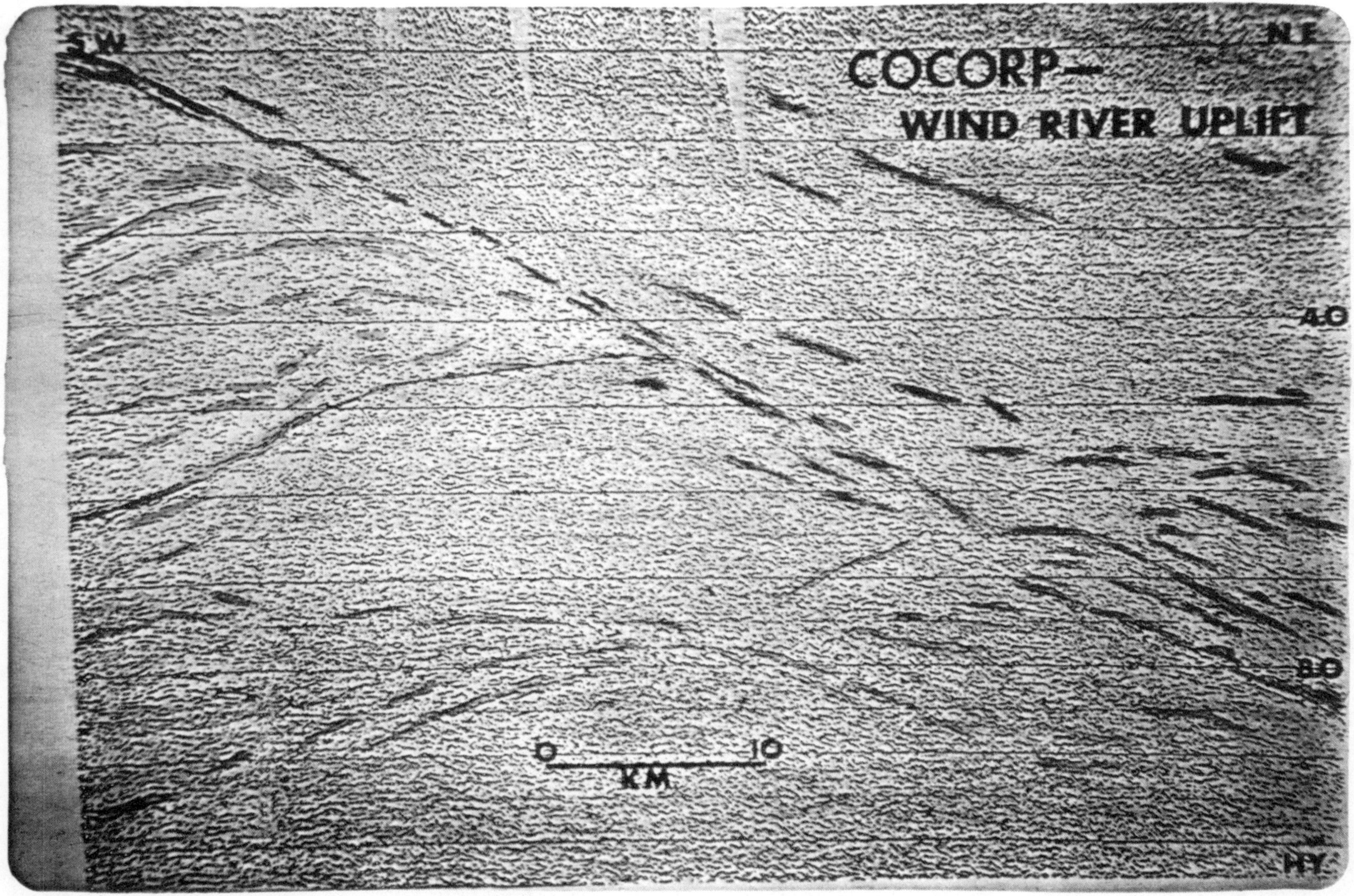

COCORP—
WIND RIVER UPLIFT

FIGURE 67

CRUSTAL "MODEL"

"MOHO"

SUPRA CRUST: METAMORPHICS, GRANITES, MIGMATITES

MIDDLE CRUST: MIGMATITES (MOBILIZED GRANITE, BIOTITE SCHIST AMPHIBOLITE, AUGEN GNEISS)

LOWER CRUST: IGNEOUS—METAMORPHIC—SEDIMENTS ? (GRANITE → GABBRO)

MOD. FROM SMITHSON ET AL '74, '77, '78   HY

FIGURE 68

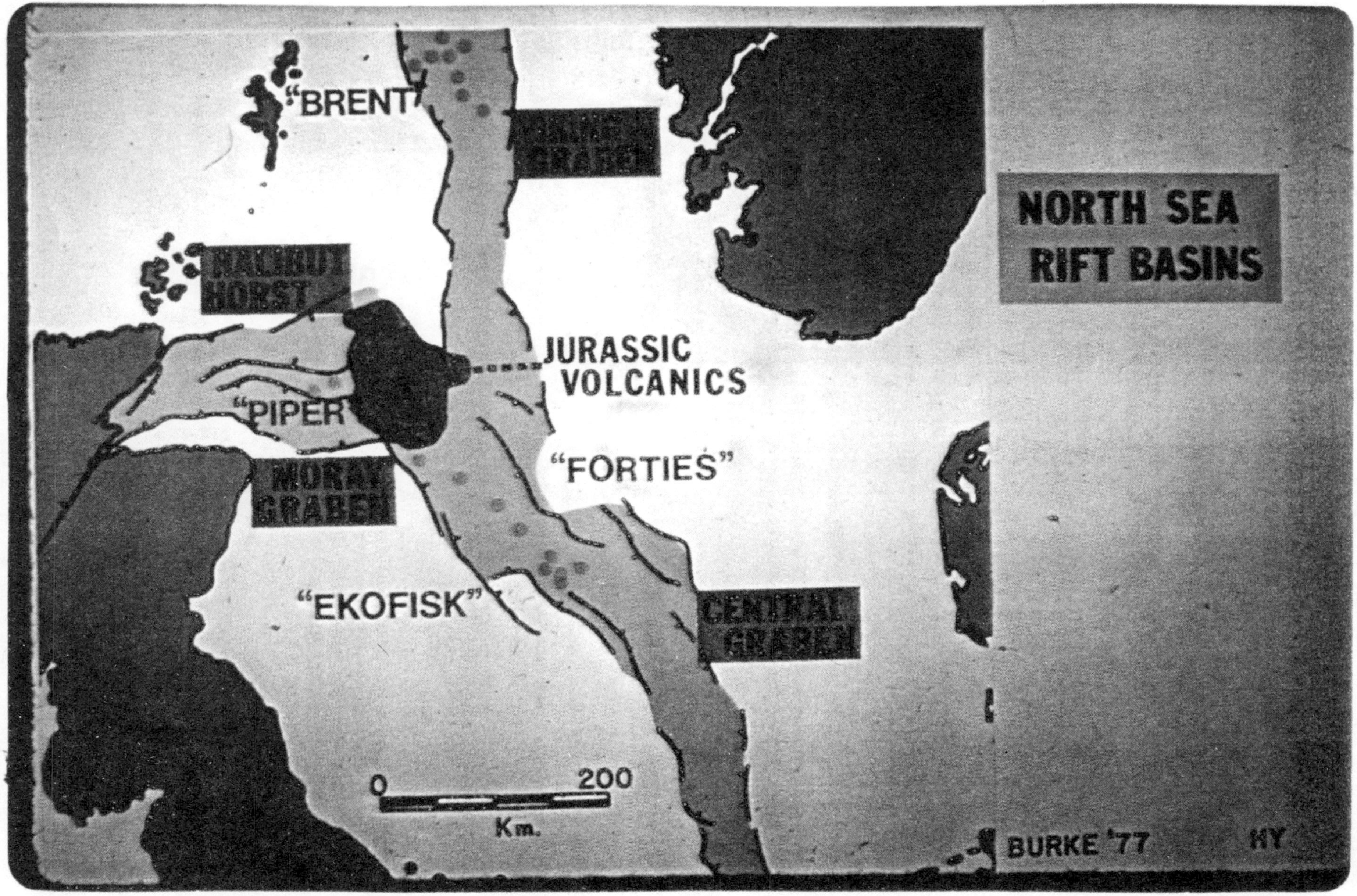

NORTH SEA RIFT BASINS

BURKE '77

FIGURE 69

POTENTIAL PETROLEUM PROVINCES

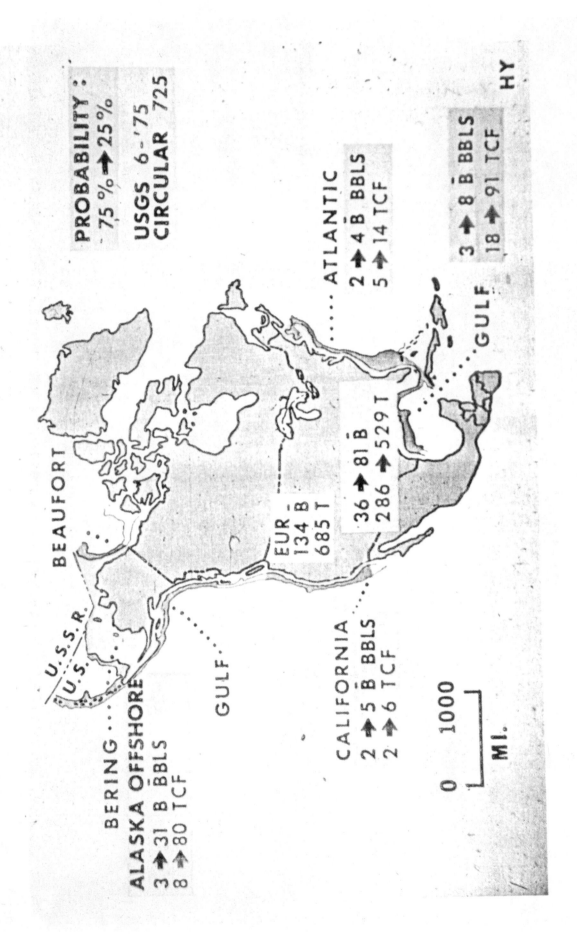

PROBABILITY:
-75% ➔ 25%

USGS 6-'75
CIRCULAR 725

ATLANTIC
2 ➔ 4 B BBLS
5 ➔ 14 TCF

3 ➔ 8 B BBLS
18 ➔ 91 TCF

HY

BEAUFORT

U.S.S.R.
U.S.

BERING
ALASKA OFFSHORE
3 ➔ 31 B BBLS
8 ➔ 80 TCF

GULF

EUR -
134 B
685 T

36 ➔ 81 B
286 ➔ 529 T

GULF

CALIFORNIA
2 ➔ 5 B BBLS
2 ➔ 6 TCF

0   1000
MI.

FIGURE 70

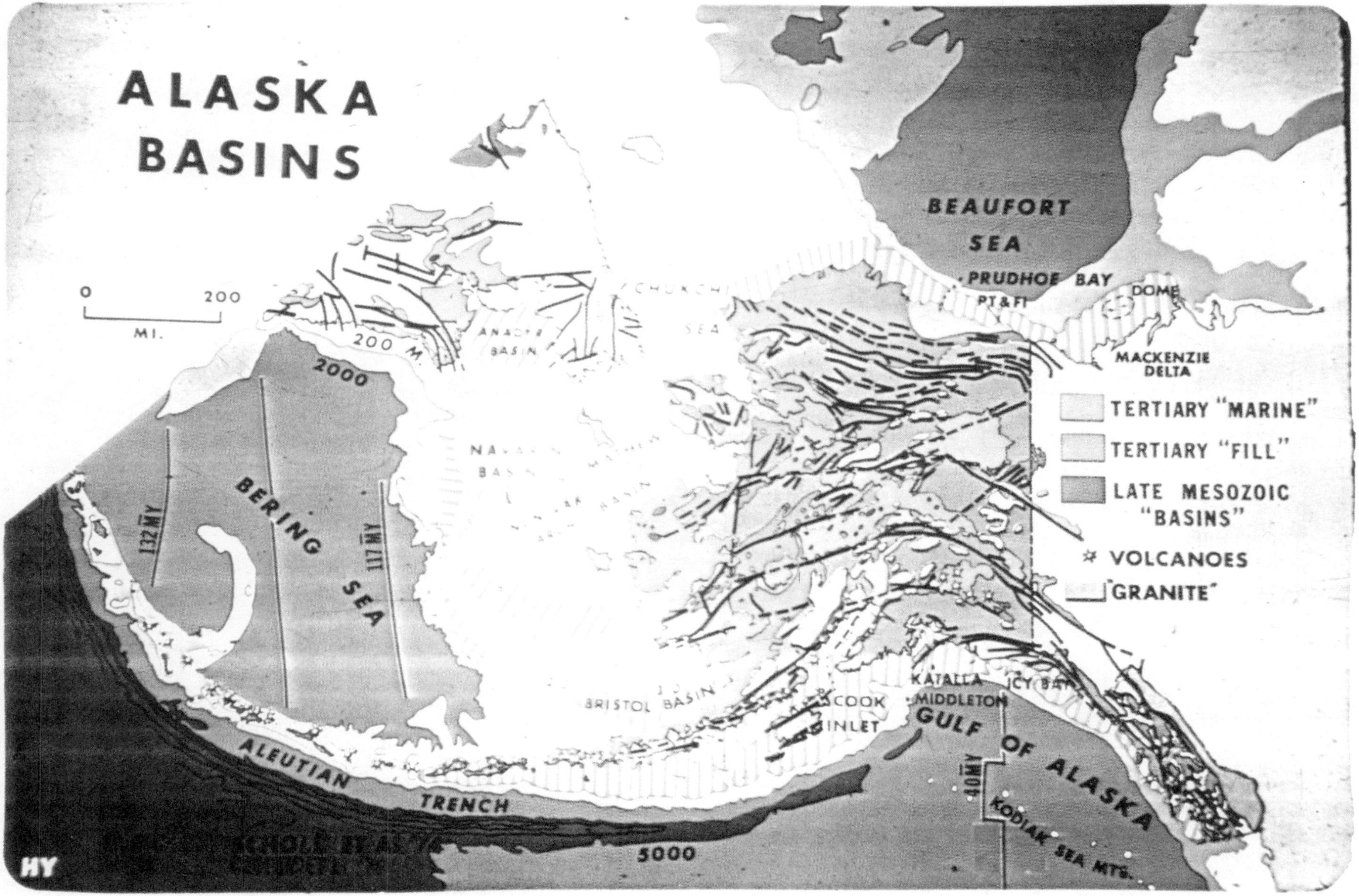

ALASKA BASINS

TERTIARY "MARINE"
TERTIARY "FILL"
LATE MESOZOIC "BASINS"
★ VOLCANOES
"GRANITE"

MACKENZIE DELTA

BEAUFORT SEA

PRUDHOE BAY DOME

PT & FT

CHUKCHI SEA

ANADIR BASIN

NAVARIN BASIN

BERING SEA

200 M.

2000

132 MY

117 MY

ALEUTIAN TRENCH

5000

BRISTOL BASIN

COOK INLET

KATALLA

MIDDLETON

ICY BAY

GULF OF ALASKA

KODIAK SEA MTS.

DOME

200   0   200
|____|____|
MI.

HY

FIGURE 71

-- Notes --

-- Notes --

-- Notes --

-- Notes --